Sucrose Chemicals

Sucrose Chemicals

A critical review of a
quarter-century of research by the
Sugar Research Foundation

by Valerie Kollonitsch
C. H. Kline & Co., Inc.

The International
Sugar Research Foundation, Inc.
1970

Printed in Great Britain by W. S. Cowell Ltd, Ipswich

PUBLISHED IN THE UNITED STATES OF AMERICA

Contents

		Page
	Foreword	7
	A Note on Nomenclature	9
1	Introduction	11
PART I	**Preparation and properties of chemicals**	
2	Ethers	17
3	Fatty Esters	52
4	Other Esters	70
5	Acetals, Thioacetals, and Ketals	94
6	Oxidation Products	106
7	Reduction Products and Unsaturated Derivatives	112
8	Halogen and Sulfur Derivatives	120
9	Metal Derivatives	126
10	Reaction Products of Sucrose with Acids	136
11	Reaction Products of Sucrose and Molasses with Alkalies, Amines, and Azides	138
12	Fermentation of Sucrose and Molasses	144
13	Resins and Polymers	147
14	Miscellaneous Products and Properties	167

			Page
PART II	**Applications**		
	15	Surfactants	173
	16	Surface Coatings	192
	17	Food and Feed Additives	206
	18	Plastics and Polymers	209
	19	Textile Chemicals	216
	20	Pharmaceuticals	218
	21	Pesticides	220
	22	Chelating Agents	224
	23	Analytical Chemistry	229
	24	Selected General References on Sucrose	231
Bibliography			
		Articles, Publications and Patents	235
		Internal Reports	242
Author Index			251
Subject Index			255

Foreword

THE SUGAR RESEARCH FOUNDATION, organized by the American sugar industry in 1943 had, as one of its original purposes, to study the creation of new markets for the commodity sugar. The research program in that first year and in each year since that time has included some studies of the chemical transformation of sugar into products that might be of commercial value. The metamorphosis of the Foundation in 1968 into The International Sugar Research Foundation, Inc., has not diminished the drive toward this goal.

Sugar indeed is a cheap and ubiquitous commodity. Sugar indeed has a purity matched by hardly any other commercial product of the technology of the middle of the twentieth century. Yet, it is a comparatively intractable substance as demonstrated by the fact that relatively few of its derivatives have found commercial markets. This is a vivid attestation of the problems met in trying to convert sugar to a product with some specific set of properties.

After two and a half decades of study, it seems appropriate for Foundation's Executive Committee to step back, survey the research scene, and review each of the chemical endeavors independently to see if there could be some useful correlations of the results to date. It seems also a good time to make a listing of what really has been done.

The Committee was pleased to engage the services of Charles H. Kline & Co., Inc. to make this survey. The present volume attempts to display each item in appropriate light for the use of students of the chemistry of sucrose, for representatives in research organizations of industry and other institutions; above all, in the hope that results can be useful to mankind.

7

The quarter of century of research programs that have been reviewed were directed for the first third by Dr. Robert C. Hockett, the second by Dr. Henry B. Hass, and in more recent years the programs have been guided by Dr. John L. Hickson.

Copies of the reports and information referred to throughout the text can be obtained by application to Philip Ross, Ph.D., President, The International Sugar Research Foundation, Inc., 7316 Wisconsin Ave., Bethesda, Maryland 20014, U.S.A.

JOHN L. HICKSON
Vice President and
Director of Research

January 25, 1970

A note on nomenclature

The nomenclature of carbohydrates has undergone a number of changes. Agreement was finally reached in the 1950's on a set of 35 recommended rules [Revised Rules of Carbohydrate Nomenclature, *J. Org. Chem.* **28**, 281 (1963)].

Since all substitution reactions of the sucrose molecule that are reported or discussed here involve *only* hydroxyl groups, we have considered the inclusion of *O* and *deoxy* unnecessary. For simplicity, derivatives are described by their old names; for example, 1-methyl sucrose instead of the new 1-*O*-methyl sucrose. Similarly, except in the introduction, we have omitted the *D* prefix for glucose, fructose, and other carbohydrates.

1

Introduction

SUCROSE, commonly known as table sugar, is by far the most abundant carbohydrate found in the sap of land plants. It is one of the few organic compounds available in a state of unexcelled purity, in highly crystalline form, on a very large scale, and at low cost. It has been produced since 2000 BC from the juice of the sugar cane and since the early 1800's from the sugar beet.

The combined annual world production of sucrose from sugar cane and beet was 77 million tons in 1968. Of this total the United States (including Puerto Rico) produces six million tons and consumes ten million tons. Other major producing countries (in approximate order of size) are the USSR, Cuba, Brazil, India, France, Germany, Australia, Mexico and Taiwan.

Beets provide much of the sugar for Europe and central and western United States, and cane the rest. Other limited sources include sorghum and maple.

Sucrose is used almost exclusively by the food and other consumer goods industries for sweetening. Of the ten million tons consumed in the United States each year, 27% is sold directly to home and institutional users. The remainder goes to the baking, confectionery, ice cream, beverage, and other food industries. Pharmaceuticals, cosmetics, and other non-food users consume a hundred thousand or so tons annually.

Structure and properties

Sucrose is a sweet, crystalline (monoclinic) solid which melts at 160–186°C, depending on the solvent of crystallization. It is optically active and has a specific rotation $[\alpha]_D$ of $+66\cdot53°$ (c. 26 in water).

The structure of sucrose is shown in Figure 1-1. Work on structure and configuration up to 1949 has been reviewed by Levi and Purves [*Advances in Carbohydrate Chemistry*, **4**, 1 (1949)]. D-Glucose and D-fructose, the hydrolysis products, are linked through the anomeric atoms. A six-membered "pyranose" ring is present in the D-glucose portion and a five-membered "furanose" ring in the D-fructose portion. Further work with enzymes, chemical reactions, and crystallography assigned the α-configuration to the glucose moiety

11

and the β-configuration to the fructose portion [Koshland et al., *J. Biol. Chem.* **208**, 139 (1954); Lemieux et al., *J. Am. Chem. Soc.* **78**, 4117 (1956); ibid., **80**, 2243 (1958); *Can. J. Chem.* **31**, 949 (1953); ibid., **32**, 340 (1954)]. Part of Lemieux's work was sponsored by the Sugar Research Foundation (see References).

Fig 1-1
Structure of sucrose

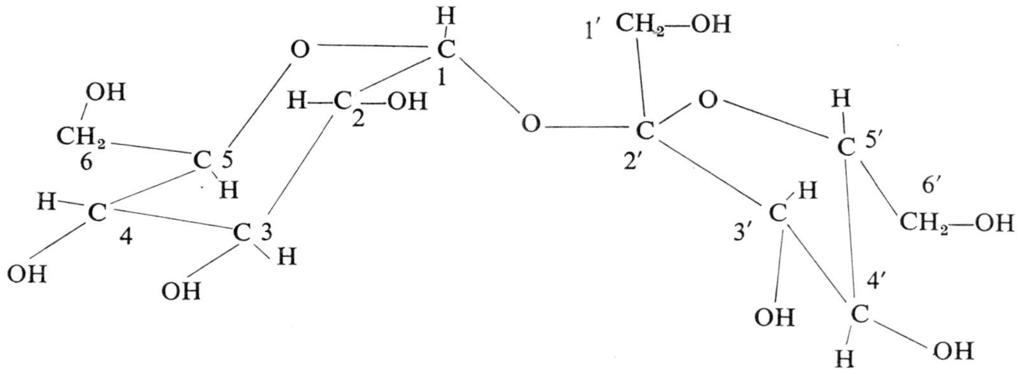

α-D-Glucopyranosyl-β-D-fructofuranoside

The system of numbering the carbon atoms in the sucrose molecule was proposed by Hockett and Zief (72). The carbons in the D-glucose moiety are given simple numerals and those in the D-fructose moiety, prime numerals.

Reactivity

Sucrose has three hydroxyls in primary positions (—CH$_2$OH) and five in the secondary positions (—CHOH—). The reactivity of the hydroxyl groups of the carbohydrates has been reviewed by Sugihara [*Advances in Carbohydrate Chemistry*, **8**, 1 (1953)]. Little is known about the relative reactivities of the hydroxyl groups of sucrose except that the primary hydroxyls at the 6, 1', 6' positions show more reactivity than those at the secondary positions. As will be discussed later under sulfonic acid esters, tosylation and subsequent replacement of the tosyl groups with iodide indicate that the hydroxyls of the 6 and 6' positions are more reactive than that at the 1' position. Monoesterification of sucrose with fatty acids shows a similar priority of the 6 and 6' hydroxyls, and also indicates the preference of 6' to the 6 position by a ratio of about 2:1 (97). A brief recent study of methylation with dimethyl sulfate in 30% aqueous sodium hydroxide concludes that the fructose moiety undergoes methylation about three times more rapidly than the glucose portion (261b).

Although the three primary hydroxyls have greater reactivity in general, attempts to produce exclusively the 6, 1', 6' trisubstituted derivative give complex mixtures, as discussed in the chapter on sulfonic acid esters. However, selective substitution restricted to the three primary hydroxyls has recently been reported with chlorotricyclohexylsilane in excess amounts (11).

The ionization constants of sucrose and some of its derivatives and their change in alkaline medium have also been studied recently. In alkaline media sucrose and other polyhydroxy compounds undergo ionization to different extents (209, 261a).

Derivatives

The presence of five secondary and three primary hydroxyl groups in the sucrose molecule makes possible the synthesis of an enormous number of sucrose derivatives. Substitution with just one type of group could theoretically give some 255 different compounds, and with mixed groups the number becomes astronomical. For example, there are 1.6×10^7 possible octa-substituted derivatives with eight different substituents. However, the preparation of derivatives is hampered by the ease of hydrolysis (inversion) in acidic media of the glycosidic linkage to glucose and fructose. Furthermore, the steric hindrance imposed on some of the hydroxyl groups often makes complete substitution difficult.

Sucrose like other alcohols undergoes a number of reactions. Esters are the most readily prepared products. Other products include ethers, halogen derivatives, and similar compounds produced by displacement. Because of the possibility of several isomers, only the octa-derivatives and some of the partially substituted derivatives are well-defined, chemically uniform products. The number of such derivatives is probably less than 100. A significant percentage of this number have been prepared by chemists whose work was supported by the Sugar Research Foundation, Inc.

Degradation products

Sucrose is readily attacked by acids, oxidizing agents, and also by alkalies and catalytic hydrogenation. Because of the sensitivity of the molecule, sucrose is partially or wholly degraded by these reagents to compounds of lower molecular weight. The products thus formed include acids, glycols, higher polyols, and cyclic compounds. The action of a number of microorganisms—fungi, molds, yeast, and bacteria—also produces these materials. Degradation products of interest include lactic acid, levulinic acid, mannitol, piperazine, and imidazole derivatives.

Commercial significance

The commercial utilization of sucrose chemicals is increasing. Only a handful of compounds are presently used by the chemical and allied industries or other nonfood groups. Sucrose octaacetate and sucrose acetateisobutyrate are manufactured in substantial volume. Both esters are additives for specialty polymers, chiefly in adhesives. The octaacetate is a bitter chemical also used as a denaturant for alcohol. Cyanoethyl sucrose is manufactured on a limited basis for modification of specialty adhesives in the electronics industry. Mannitol is an important product in the food industry.

The Sugar Research Foundation has sponsored work on applications of sucrose chemicals. The most promising results have been obtained with sucrose ester detergents and surface coatings. Sucrose surfactants have been produced by a number of companies in the United States, Germany, Japan, and elsewhere. Although still under test, they show excellent promise as nontoxic, nonionic, highly detersive agents. Sucrose-based surface coatings also exhibit good properties, particularly those made from sucrose linseedate. Various other polymers and plastics have been prepared or modified with sucrose.

Part I

Preparation
and properties
of chemicals

2

Ethers

SEVERAL ethers of sucrose have been prepared and their properties tested. The methyl ethers are particularly important in the determination of the structures of sucrose derivatives. The triphenylmethyl (or trityl) ethers are useful in the synthesis of sucrose derivatives because of their selective reaction with primary hydroxyl groups. The silicone ethers are interesting new products. Some are heat stable and sublime; they find use in analytical chemistry. Allyl ethers show good properties in surface coatings. Other unsaturated ethers are potential monomers in the preparation of polymeric materials; examples are vinyl sucrose and unsaturated silyl ethers. A number of recently prepared long-chain ethers (C_8—C_{18}) show promising surfactant properties.

Other possible industrial applications of sucrose ethers in plastics and polymers are suggested in Reference 212. These include plasticizers for polyvinyl chloride, crosslinking agents in polyester resins, copolymers with acrylics, and modifying agents for alkyds.

Methods of preparation

Alkylation of sucrose to ethers is most simply carried out with the appropriate organic sulfate or halide in alkaline medium. Dimethyl sulfate is the most common agent for the etherification of carbohydrates. The reaction was utilized by Haworth and co-workers in their extensive structural investigations. The process has the advantage of cheapness and solubility of sucrose and other carbohydrates in the reagent. Acetyl derivatives of carbohydrates may also be methylated because they are saponified under the conditions of the reaction and replaced by methoxy groups. The well known reagent of Purdie, alkyl iodide plus silver oxide or barium oxide, is also widely used for alkylation of sucrose. However, the reagent is more expensive than dimethyl sulfate and for complete methylation it is often necessary to repeat the reaction several times.

Several other ethers of sucrose have been made by similar methods. For example, allyl sucrose, with a degree of substitution of six to eight, can be made on a large scale by reacting allyl bromide or chloride with sucrose in aqueous alkali. The organic halide is often reacted with sucrose in water-free conditions in such basic solvents as pyridine or

B   17

dimethyl formamide. Silyl ethers with halosilane and trityl ethers with trityl chloride reagents are made in this manner.

Hydrolysis can be a problem in alkylating with common reagents. For example, methyl iodide hydrolyzes sucrose in the presence of such solvents as liquid ammonia, dimethyl formamide, and dimethyl sulfoxide (17). Methyl iodide and other organic halides react with these solvents to produce acidic products that also cause hydrolysis of sucrose. The use of water-free solvents is very important. Sucrose completely decomposes when heated in aqueous dimethyl formamide at 100°C for two hours (26). The main product is fructose and glucose with a little oligosaccharide and a trace of aldehyde.

The methylation of carbohydrates also results in products containing a carbonyl group. The oxidation is said to be caused by the iodine liberated during the methylation with methyl iodide by the reaction of hydrogen iodide and the solvent [Srivastava et al., *Indian J. Chem.* **1**, 304 (1963)]. The presence of such carbonyl groups in the reaction mixture of methylated sucrose was recently reported (285a, b). Alkylation is therefore often carried out without solvent or in such inert solvents as dimethoxyethane.

The preparation of ethers through the intermediate metal derivative, particularly sodium sucrates, is a newer and increasingly important method of ether synthesis. The metal sucrates can be reacted successfully with a number of organic halides, but not with all (Table 9-2). The reaction is often unsuccessful because of the insolubility of metal sucrates in ammonia or common organic solvents, the reaction of methylating agent with ammonia, and acidic side reactions that may cause hydrolysis of sucrose. Alkylation of the sodium sucrates has been most thoroughly studied with methylating agents, and is discussed under Methyl Ethers, page 19.

It was claimed recently that sodium sucrate could be kept in solution in ammonia in the presence of excess sucrose (196e). In this solution the sodium sucrate reacted fairly rapidly with methyl iodide at −33°C (196d), and with long chain alkyl halides at room temperature and under pressure (196a). However, the yield was very low.

A successful new method has recently been developed for the synthesis of ethers of sucrose and other carbohydrates (90, 196). The sodium sucrate is prepared with sodium hydride and then reacted *in situ* with alkyl, aryl, allyl, and propargyl halides in an aprotic solvent. Sodium hydride reacts vigorously with alcohols. Unlike sodium, it does not react with the solvent or with the organic halide used as alkylating agent unless it contains other reactive groups.

There are few reported applications of sodium hydride to etherification of carbohydrate. The reaction is carried out in dimethyl formamide or N-methyl pyrrolidone because they react only moderately with sodium hydride even at elevated temperatures. For complete etherification, excess sodium hydride is first reacted with sucrose at 25°C, and the resulting sodium alcoholate is further treated with the alkyl halide at 0°C. Octamethyl sucrose and octaallyl sucrose have been prepared in this way in yields of 69% and 90% respectively (90). Partially substituted octyl- and benzylsucrose have also been prepared by the same method (90). It has been suggested that steric hindrance by the long alkyl chain or the benzyl group may preclude further formation of alcoholate or may render the alcoholate unreactive (181).

Solid monoalkyl ethers of C_8—C_{18} fatty alcohols are prepared by reacting one mole of sodium hydride with two moles of sucrose in dimethyl sulfoxide and then *in situ* with one mole of the alkyl bromide at room temperature (196). Lauryl sucrose in 51% yield (196c), octyl sucrose 17%, decyl sucrose 46%, palmityl sucrose 43% and stearyl sucrose 40% have been prepared by this method (196a). However, attempts to prepare benzyl sucrose were unsuccessful (196a).

In general, organic chlorides are less reactive in condensation with sodium sucrates than the bromides and iodides.

A short review of the literature on methods of preparation of sucrose ethers through the metal derivatives is given in Reference 90.

Other methods of preparation include: (a) transetherification with vinyl ethers to obtain vinyl sucrose; (b) addition of sucrose to activated olefinic bonds, such as in acrylonitrile, methyl vinyl ketone and other unsaturated ketones, mesityl oxide, and epoxides. Unsuccessful methods attempted include the direct reaction of sucrose with nonyl phenol (290k). lauryl alcohol (290m) and propylene trimer (290m).

Properties

The ethers are generally very stable compounds. The alkoxy linkage is very resistant to removal. This property makes the sugar ethers, particularly the methyl ethers, an important tool in structural studies. Partially alkylated (tritylated) sucrose can be acylated or halogenated and further converted into sugar derivatives, as described below. An example is the preparation of trimethyl sucrose of well defined structure.

The degree of alkylation may range from one to eight. The fully substituted (peralkylated) compounds can be obtained in pure, homogeneous form. However, it is impossible to alkylate sucrose directly with methyl iodide, dimethyl sulfate, or other agents to obtain a single, well defined ether of only partial substitution. Some studies indicate that selective alkylation could possibly be accomplished through the intermediate metallic sucrate. For example, trisodium sucrate with allyl chloride gives products with a degree of substitution of around three (17). However, the product does not seem to be homogeneous. Also, methylation of trisodium sucrate yields a monomethyl derivative which has the methyl group in four (2, 6, 1', 3') positions (18).

The physical properties of sucrose ethers are given in Tables 2-1 and 2-2. For application properties, see Surfactants, Surface Coatings, and other chapters in the section on uses.

METHYL ETHERS

Although methylation has been widely used in the synthesis and structural determination of carbohydrates, rather surprisingly only a few methyl ethers of sucrose have been reported in the literature. *Hepta-* and *octamethyl sucrose* were prepared during the early constitutional work on sucrose by Haworth [*J. Chem. Soc.* **107**, 8 (1915)], and later more elegantly through sodium sucrate, as described below. Crystalline octamethyl sucrose has been used as starting material in the preparation of vinyl type polymers.

A number of methyl ethers of sucrose and its derivatives have been prepared as intermediates in a sequence of syntheses or as the desired final product. The literature indicates that none of the lower ethers could be obtained in crystalline form.

Preparation by direct methylation

Methylation of sucrose is generally carried out, following Haworth, with dimethyl sulfate in 30% sodium hydroxide (269h) or methyl iodide in the presence of silver oxide (Purdie's method) or barium oxide. The reaction requires careful control, since acidic products formed by the interaction of the methylating agent and the solvent can cause hydrolysis of sucrose (17). The water-free condition may be secured by adding powdered anhydrous calcium sulfate to the reaction (97).

Methylation with methyl iodide is carried out in acetone, dimethyl formamide, or in methyl iodide itself as the solvent.

The relative reactivities of the hydroxyl groups in methylation with dimethyl sulfate in the presence of aqueous sodium hydroxide has been briefly studied. The studies were initiated because of the observation that marked chemical shifts occur in the proton magnetic resonance spectrum of sucrose dissolved in deuterium oxide when sodium deuteride is added (261a). Sucrose was reacted with 0.1 mole equivalent of dimethyl sulfate in 30% aqueous sodium hydroxide (261a). Analysis of the reaction product indicated that the fructose moiety underwent methylation about three times as rapidly as the glucose portion (261b).

The reaction of sucrose with methylene dichloride or methylene disulfate has been attempted, but was unsuccessful (193a). The reaction was intended to provide a bridge between the glucose and fructose moieties of the sucrose molecule. During methylation of acyl derivatives of sucrose with methyl iodide, acyl migration may occur, similar to other carbohydrates.

Methylation of sodium sucrates

Attempts to prepare methyl sucrose through the reaction of sodium sucrate with methyl iodide yield unreacted sucrose and partly methylated products (277, 285a, b). The reaction is carried out *in situ* in liquid ammonia, dimethyl sulfoxide, or with isolated sodium sucrates in dimethyl formamide. Fully substituted octamethyl sucrose has been prepared in two steps by first reacting the ethereal solution of partially methylated sucrose with sodium wire and then reacting the resulting alkoxide with methyl iodide or dimethyl sulfate [Freudenberg et al., *Ber.* **56**, 2119 (1923); Pacsu et al., *J. Am. Chem. Soc.* **61**, 2442 (1939); Bredereck et al., *Ber.* **87**, 35 (1954); Kuhn et al., *Angew. Chem.* **67**, 32 (1955)]. The reaction has been successfully repeated as described by Bredereck (269h).

Thorough studies on methylation of sodium monosucrate with methyl iodide or dimethyl sulfate show that methylation is unsuccessful because (a) the sucrate contains bound ammonia that reacts preferentially with the methylating agent and forms hydrogen iodide or sulfuric acid, and (b) acidic products of this side reaction and that between the methylating agent and the solvent (dimethyl formamide, dimethyl sulfoxide, acetone, or ammonia), causes hydrolysis of sucrose (17). The formation of oxidation compounds containing carbonyl groups has also been reported (285a, b).

However, the bound ammonia may be almost completely removed by extraction of the insoluble sucrate with dimethoxyethane (19). Ammonia-free monosodium sucrate—prepared by desiccation at 100°C *in vacuo* or by extraction with ether and toluene—is reported to have been methylated to the monoether with methyl iodide in dimethyl formamide in up to 60% yield [Prey et al., *Monatsh. Chem.* **91**, 1185 (1960)]. (Prey claims that methylation will also proceed in the presence of ammonia at 20°C, but good yields are obtained only with the ammonia-free products.)

Attempts to repeat the preparation of ammonia-free product by desiccation at 100°C resulted in decomposition of the monosodium sucrate, and only partial removal of ammonia occurred at 50°C (285a, b). The methylation of the heat-treated, ammonia-free products with one mole methyl iodide per mole sucrose in dimethyl formamide gave inhomogeneous oils (285d). In these experiments the methods of Prey could not be repeated successfully.

Trisodium sucrate can be methylated with methyl toluene-*p*-sulfonate in glycerol trimethyl ether as a solvent to yield a mixture of products containing mono-, di-, and higher ethers (17, 18). The higher sucrates contain less bound ammonia than the monosucrate so that they are methylated more easily, although still not quantitatively.

Sucrose has been successfully methylated in one step by the new method with sodium sucrate. The metal sucrate is prepared with sodium hydride in dimethyl formamide and further reacted *in situ* with methyl iodide (90). Octamethyl sucrose is obtained in a yield of 69% by this method. When monosodium sucrate is kept in solution in ammonia with the help of excess sucrose, methyl iodide is reported to react with it fairly rapidly at −33°C (196d).

Monomethyl sucrose

As described above, all attempts to prepare monomethyl sucrose through the monosodium sucrate have been unsuccessful. Even the method given in the literature by Prey could not be repeated (17, 285a, b, d).

Monomethyl sucrose is isolated by chromatography in about 20% yield from the reaction product of the methylation of trisodium sucrate with methyltoluene-*p*-sulfonate (18). The pale yellow, glassy product analyzes as the monoether. Further chromatography reveals that the product is a mixture of isomers, mainly those containing the methyl group on the 2 and 1′ positions. (The monomethyl sucrose, prepared by Prey from the monosucrate, was reported to have substitutions on the three primary hydroxyls, on positions 6, 1′, and 6′ [*Monatsh. Chem.* **92**, 1291 (1961)].)

Trimethyl sucrose

4,1′,6′-Trimethyl sucrose is prepared through a series of intermediates as follows (104):

Sucrose
  ↓ Tritylchloride + Ac₂O
6,1′,6′-Trityl-2,3,4,3′,4′-pentaacetyl sucrose
  ↓ Detritylation
2,3,6,3′,4′-Pentaacetyl sucrose
  ↓ CH₃I
4,1′,6′-Trimethyl-2,3,6,3′,4′-pentaacetyl sucrose
  ↓ Deacetylation
4,1′,6′-Trimethyl sucrose

The preparation and properties of the various intermediates are given under each compound.

To obtain the trimethyl ether of sucrose the trimethylpentaacetyl sucrose is hydrolyzed in 90% aqueous methyl alcohol on a column of strongly basic ion-exchange resin (104). Periodate oxidation and structural studies of the hydrolysis product indicate that the methyl groups are on the 4,1',6' position. The unexpected position of one methyl group on the secondary hydroxyl on carbon *4* is probably the result of the migration of the acetyl group from the secondary hydroxyl in the 4-position to the primary hydroxyl in the 6-position during detritylation in an acidic medium. Otherwise the three methyl groups would be on the three primary hydroxyls (6, 1, 6'), replacing the trityl groups. The possibility of acyl migration during methylation has been rejected (95).

The preparation of the pure compound requires chromatography, since methylation of the pentaacetate gives only 75% triether and also yields 1% mono- and 25% dimethyl sucrose.

Trimethyl sucrose is a colorless viscous syrup.

4,1',6'-TRIMETHYL-2,3,6,3',4'-PENTAACETYL SUCROSE. The compound is made by methylation of the pentaacetate (see Fatty Esters, page 52) with methyl iodide in the presence of silver oxide (104). The methylation must be repeated several times since the reaction is incomplete after one treatment. However, mono- and dimethyl products are present even after repeated methylations. The compound is an intermediate in the preparation of trimethyl sucrose. The pure product is a colorless glass, which does not crystallize on standing for at least six months.

Pentamethyl sucrose

Pentamethyl sucrose is made from tritosylpentamethyl sucrose (35). Removal of the tosyl groups is carried out by hydrolysis with 4% sodium amalgam in aqueous methyl alcohol. The oily product has not been crystallized.

Heptamethyl sucrose

This compound is made by deesterification of heptamethyl sucrose monomyristate in boiling methyl alcohol and potassium methoxide catalyst (97). An oily product is obtained in 92% yield. The product was prepared in the course of identification of the sucrose monomyristate. Chromatography of its hydrolysis product with sulfuric acid indicated that it is almost entirely a mixture of two hepta ethers: the *2,3,4,1',3',4',6'-* and *2,3,4,6,1',3',4'-heptamethyl sucroses*. Heptamethyl sucrose can be converted into derivatives, described below, all of which have been characterized by nuclear magnetic resonance spectra.

HEPTAMETHYLMONOTOSYL SUCROSE. The heptamethyl ether described above is converted to its monotosylate with tosyl chloride in pyridine in quantitative yield (97).

Heptamethylmonoiodosucrose and heptamethyldeoxysucrose

The tosyl derivative is converted into the iodo compound with sodium iodide in acetone (97). The oily iodo derivative is reduced with hydrogen catalytically to the corresponding deoxy derivative (see Reduction Products).

Octamethyl sucrose

Sucrose is reacted with excess sodium hydride (12 moles per mole sucrose) and excess methyl iodide (about 15 moles) in dimethyl formamide at 0°C (90). After standing at room temperature it is further treated with additional methyl iodide. An oily product is obtained with 69%, which shows very little hydroxyl content by infrared analysis and only traces of by-product by chromatography. Bredereck's process (reacting highly methylated sucrose with sodium in ether, and then with methyl iodide) also gives the octa ether in high yield (269h).

The octa ether is hydrolyzed in 0.4% aqueous hydrochloric acid into tetramethyl glucose and tetramethyl fructose (269h). These compounds have been used in the preparation of unsaturated monomers (see Resins and Polymers, page 147).

Other methyl ethers

The following mixed ether-esters are discussed under Fatty and Other Esters, pages 52 and 70:

Heptamethyl sucrose monomyristate and *monotosylate*
Tritosylpentaacetylmethyl sucrose
Tetramesyltetramethyl sucrose

OTHER ALKYL ETHERS

The fatty ethers of sucrose are prepared most successfully through sodium sucrate, which is reacted *in situ* with alkyl bromide in dimethyl formamide or dimethyl sulfoxide.

Propyl sucrose sulfonic acid

Sucrose is reacted with the cyclic ester of 3-hydroxy-propane sulfonic acid, propane sulton, to an ether (285c):

$$ROH + \begin{array}{c} CH_2 \text{---} CH_2 \\ | \qquad | \quad O \\ CH_2 \quad S \\ \diagdown O \diagup \diagdown O \end{array} \longrightarrow ROCH_2CH_2CH_2SO_3H$$

The reaction cannot be carried out in dimethyl sulfoxide or other solvents for sucrose because propane sulton reacts preferentially with these solvents. An intractable black tar is obtained in the absence of solvents.

n-Butyl sucrose

Sucrose is reacted with sodium hydride and then with butyl bromide similarly to n-octyl sucrose (see below). The reaction also yields partially etherified products (181) which contain a number of components, according to chromatographic analysis (256b).

Octyl sucrose

MONOOCTYL (CAPRYLYL) SUCROSE is made by reacting one mole of sodium hydride with two moles of sucrose in dimethylsulfoxide and then with one mole of octylbromide *in situ* (196a). The reaction proceeds by stirring for many hours at ambient temperature under strictly water-free conditions in a nitrogen atmosphere. The ether is separated as the complex with barium hydroxide in a yield of 17%. The excess sucrose can be almost fully recovered. Some alteration in the isolation technique has been reported (196h).

The product is a white, crystalline solid which melts to a sticky glass below room temperature. It has the highest surface activity of the various monoethers of sucrose with fatty alcohols that were tested (Table 15-9).

PENTAOCTYL SUCROSE. Sucrose is reacted with excess sodium hydride (about 14 moles per mole sucrose) in dimethyl formamide and then *in situ* with about 14 moles of n-octyl bromide at room temperature for several hours (90). A syrupy product is obtained in about 70% yield. It contains some octyl bromide and is only a partially etherified sucrose (about penta), as shown by infrared analysis. Chromatography indicates that it contains two compounds.

Decyl sucrose

This compound, also named *monocapryl sucrose*, is made similarly to monooctyl sucrose, with decyl bromide (196a, h). The yield of product is 46%, with 80% of the excess sucrose recovered. It is a white solid, which melts to a sticky glass at room temperature. Together with octyl sucrose, it shows the most promising surface activity among the long-chain fatty alcohol ethers of sucrose (Table 15-9).

Lauryl sucrose and higher substitutes

Attempts to prepare *lauryl (dodecyl) sucrose* have been carried out many times, all unsuccessfully, with the exception of the most recently developed method for the production of long-chain aliphatic monoethers.

Sodium pentasucrate was reacted with the theoretical amount of lauryl chloride in dimethoxyethane at 70°C, without success (17). Mono- or trisodium sucrate reacted similarly, or without a solvent in a sealed tube at 150°C, also did not yield the sucrose ether (54, 55). A similarly unsuccessful reaction has been reported with mono- or disodium sucrate reacted *in situ* with lauryl bromide in N-methyl-2-pyrrolidone (243a). Attempts to prepare the ether by reacting lauryl *p*-toluenesulfonate with the sodium sucrate in liquid ammonia were unsuccessful (196h). The chief product was dilaurylamine.

Some success has been achieved in attempts to carry out the condensation of monosodium sucrate and lauryl bromide in liquid ammonia (196a). The sucrate remains dissolved in ammonia in the presence of sucrose, and reacts with lauryl bromide under pressure. Crude monolauryl sucrose is obtained in 20% yield.

Monolauryl sucrose is made similarly to octyl sucrose with lauryl bromide as the alkylating agent (196c, h). The excess sucrose is completely recovered, and the yield of the pure ether is 51%. It is a crystalline, low melting material with poorer surface activity than the lower fatty ether homologs (Table 15-9). The product is a mixture of isomers with about 64% substitution on the glucose moiety and 36% on the fructose moiety (196h).

Palmityl sucrose

This compound, the hexadecyl ether, is made similarly to octyl sucrose, with palmityl bromide in 43% yield (196a). It is a low melting solid. Though it is very poorly soluble in water, even at low concentrations, the product has some surface activity (Table 15-9).

Stearyl sucrose

Monostearyl (octadecyl) sucrose is made similarly to octyl sucrose with stearyl bromide in

90% yield, based on the converted sucrose (196a). All unreacted sucrose is recovered. The low-melting product is poorly soluble in water, like the palmityl ether.

TRITYL ETHERS

Tritylation, the introduction of triphenylmethyl group, occurs like tosylation chiefly on the primary hydroxyl groups in the 6, 1', 6' positions. This reaction has its greatest value in the preparation of sucrose derivatives that are selectively substituted on the primary and secondary hydroxyls.

The tritylation of sucrose produces a complex mixture of derivatives. Attempts to prepare crystalline *tritrityl sucrose*, as described in the literature, have been unsuccessful (104). The reaction carried out with three moles of tritylchloride per mole sucrose in pyridine at 100°C produced tri- and lower ethers, reducing sugar fragments, and tritanol. However, a well-defined crystalline tritrityl pentaacetyl sucrose has been made by acylation of the trityl compound *in situ* (104). The attempted reaction of pentasodium sucrate with tritylchloride was unsuccessful (17). Mixtures of trityl sucrose have been successfully separated by chromatography on silica (272c). Pure ditrityl and tritrityl sucrose were obtained. The ditrityl compound was crystalline. The tritrityl compound was an oil that could not be crystallized (203b).

The removal of trityl groups is most successful with boiling glacial acetic acid in the presence of water (104). Catalytic hydrogenation with palladium or platinum oxide on charcoal removes only partially the trityl groups of a tritrityl derivative (104). Platinum also catalyzes the saturation of the phenyl groups to cyclohexyl groups. Detritylation with hydrogen bromide in glacial acetic acid or hydrogen chloride causes splitting of the glycosidic linkage of the acid-sensitive sucrose (104). Detritylation in acetic acid may cause migration of acyl groups (see Trimethyl Sucrose, page 21).

6,1',6'-TRITRITYL-2,3,4,3',4'-PENTAACETYL SUCROSE. This compound is simply prepared in 45% yield by tritylation of sucrose in pyridine followed by acetylation with acetic anhydride in the same solution (104). This mixed etherester is an intermediate in the preparation of 4,1',6'-trimethyl sucrose, or possibly vinyl sucrose. The crystalline product is soluble in acetone, chloroform, ethyl ether, and tetrahydrofuran and insoluble in water, ethyl alcohol, methyl alcohol, and petroleum ether. It reduces Fehling's solution only after acid hydrolysis.

TRITRITYL-PENTABENZYLTHIOCARBONYL SUCROSE. Attempts to prepare this compound by methods similar to those used on the tritritylpentaacetate all failed (194c). The reaction was carried out with benzyl thiochloroformate instead of acetic anhydride as the acylating agent.

For a review on trityl ethers, see Helferich, B., *Advances in Carbohydrate Chemistry*, **3**, 79 (1948).

SILYL ETHERS

The field of organosilicon compounds is a rapidly growing branch of chemistry which is attracting increasing industrial and academic attention. (For reviews on organosilicon compounds, see References 55 and 90.)

Recent publications have shown the importance of the reaction of silicon containing compounds with carbohydrates and polyols [Hedgley et al., *Chem. Ind.* 378 (1960); Sprung et al., *J. Org. Chem.* **20**, 1750 (1955); ibid., **23**, 58 (1958); Henglein, *Makromol. Chem.* **21**, 59 (1956); and Schwarz et al., *Angew. Chem.* **68**, 335 (1956)]. However, surprisingly the only silyl ether of sucrose that has been reported prior to the Sugar Research Foundation's work was octatrimethylsilyl sucrose [Henglein et al., *Makromol. Chem.* **24**, 1 (1957)].

The preparation of a number of silyl ethers of sucrose has been investigated under the Foundation's sponsorship. The trimethylsilyl ethers are of interest because of their increased volatility, thermal stability, and the ease with which the silyl groups can be hydrolyzed. Trimethylsilylation thus permits the easy preparation of volatile derivatives from which the parent compound can be recovered readily in a pure condition in high yield (see Analytical Chemistry, page 229).

Selective substitution has been reported on the three primary hydroxyls (6, 1', 6') by reacting sucrose with chlorotricyclohexylsilane (11). This is the only reaction which reportedly produces exclusively a tri-substituted derivative of sucrose. Tosylates, mesylates, and trityl ethers of sucrose, formerly believed to be of uniform nature, may be mixtures (see Sulfonic Acid Esters and Trityl Sucrose).

The reaction of sucrose with di- or trihalosilanes gives directly polymeric materials of promising thermal stability. Silyl ethers of sucrose are also potential monomers that can be crosslinked or copolymerized with other reagents.

A number of silyl ethers have been prepared in excellent yield by reacting a monohalosilane with sucrose in pyridine:

$$R_3'SiCl + ROH \longrightarrow R_3'SiOR + HCl$$

It is necessary to operate in dry conditions because the halosilane is extremely sensitive to moisture, and hydrolysis of the Si—Cl bond occurs.

A second method of preparation of silyl ethers treats sucrose with hexamethyldisilazane in dimethyl formamide in the presence of a trace of chlorotrimethyl silane as catalyst (90):

$$[(CH_3)_3Si]_2NH + ROH \longrightarrow (CH_3)_3SiOR + (CH_3)_3SiNH_2$$

$$(CH_3)_3SiNH_2 + ROH \longrightarrow (CH_3)_3SiOR + NH_3$$

Octa-(trimethylsilyl) sucrose is prepared by this method. This reaction has the advantage that the reagent is much less sensitive to moisture than the chlorosilanes. The only solid formed in the reaction is a small amount of ammonium chloride, which precipitates on addition of the catalyst. The removal of pyridine hydrochloride from the reaction with chlorosilane is more complicated.

Exploratory work has been carried out to prepare silyl ethers by the reaction of organosilicon alkoxides with sucrose with the elimination of alcohol (192). The alkoxides studied include triethoxymethyl silane, triethoxyvinyl silane, triethoxyphenyl silane, diethoxydimethyl silane, and trimethylethoxy silane. The reaction, carried out in pyridine at elevated temperatures, either does not produce well-defined ethers or gives no reaction at all.

Fully or highly substituted silyl ethers of sucrose can be prepared with a number of halosilanes, particularly those with small molecules—for example, chlorotrimethylsilane (41). When the substituent is bulky, as in triphenylsilyl or tricyclohexylsilyl groups, the degree of substitution is lower. Selective substitution on the three primary hydroxyls exclusively is reported with the latter (11).

In general, the number of trialkyl and triaryl silyl groups that can be introduced into the sucrose molecule decreases with increasing size of the alkyl and aryl groups.

The silyl ethers are solid or oily products, which hydrolyze in water at different rates. The trimethyl silyl derivatives decompose more quickly in water at elevated temperatures than the triphenylsilyl and tricyclohexylsilyl ethers under the same conditions. In general, the instability decreases as the size of the organic group increases.

Trimethylsilyl ethers

Octa(trimethylsilyl) sucrose is prepared by treating sucrose with excess trimethyl chlorosilane in pyridine (41, 54, 55) or hexamethyldisilazane in dimethyl formamide (90). The yield is 70% and over.

Hexa(trimethylsilyl) sucrose is made similarly in 85% yield with six moles of halosilane per mole of sucrose (55).

Penta(trimethylsilyl) sucrose is made with five moles of reactant per mole of sucrose in pyridine (238b). The reaction of pentasodium sucrate with trimethyl chlorosilane at 50°C in dimethoxyethane gives in poor yield a product that is insoluble in chloroform (17).

Attempts to prepare *tetratrimethylsilyl sucrose* by similar methods were unsuccessful (238a).

The silyl ethers are oils. None has been crystallized. They are soluble in organic solvents, but insoluble in water, in which they hydrolyze at elevated temperature (41, 238b). The octa-ether is volatile, a property unique among carbohydrates. These silyl ethers are used in the recently developed technique for their determination by gas chromatography (see Analytical Chemistry, page 229).

The ethers can be completely hydrolyzed on refluxing with aqueous methyl alcohol or with a 1:1 mixture of 2-N hydrochloric acid and ethyl alcohol (55).

An attempt to methylate hexatrimethylsilyl sucrose with methyl iodide in dimethyl formamide was unsuccessful. No reaction occurred. The attempted vinylation of the hexa-ether with *n*-butylvinyl ether was also unsuccessful (217c). The vinyl groups, if attached at all, are easily cleaved from the sucrose both by hydrolysis and by heat.

Attempts to prepare the octachloro derivative by reacting the octatrimethylsilyl sucrose with trimethylsilyl chloride in the presence of ferric chloride were unsuccessful (217b). No reaction occurred at atmospheric and elevated pressures or temperatures.

For more details on the hexa- and octa-ethers, see also Reference 55.

Triphenylsilyl ethers

HEXA(TRIPHENYLSILYL) SUCROSE. This compound is made by reacting sucrose with an excess of chlorotriphenylsilane in pyridine (11). Attempts to increase the degree of substitution have been unsuccessful, probably because of the bulky nature of the substituent silicon group.

A solid product is obtained with high yield. It is not readily hydrolyzed in boiling aqueous ethyl alcohol, but can be decomposed with 4-N sodium hydroxide or 4-N hydrochloric acid in a mixture of ethyl alcohol and ether at 65°C (11). The compound is soluble in the common organic solvents except methyl and ethyl alcohol and water (55). An attempt to methylate the hexa-ether with methyl iodide in dimethyl formamide was unsuccessful (55).

Tricyclohexylsilyl ethers

6,1,6'-TRI(TRICYCLOHEXYLSILYL) SUCROSE. The compound is made by reacting sucrose with excess chlorotricyclohexylsilane in pyridine (11). A solid product, obtained in good yield, analyzes as a triether. It is claimed to be the only derivative of sucrose substituted exclusively on the three primary hydroxyls, even though prepared with excess reagent.

The compound is soluble in methyl alcohol, ethyl alcohol, chloroform, benzene, and pyridine and sparingly soluble in ether (55). It is only slightly hydrolyzed when refluxed with aqueous methyl alcohol (1:1) for 24 hours (55).

For more details, including oxidative analysis for the determination of structure, see References 11 and 55.

Reactions with di- and trihalosilanes

The reactions of methylvinyldichlorosilane, dichlorodimethylsilane, dichlorodiphenylsilane, and vinyltrichlorosilane with sucrose in pyridine give polymeric materials (see Resins and Polymers, page 147). Similar reactions with the model compound tetrahydro-2-hydroxy-methylpyran, yield the corresponding ethers (9).

BENZYL ETHERS

Benzyl ethers of sucrose have been reported as made by treating sucrose with benzyl chloride and sodium hydroxide [Gomberg et al., *J. Am. Chem. Soc.* **43**, 1904 (1921)]. The products are mainly *dibenzyl* and *pentabenzyl sucrose*.

No reaction occurs when pentasodium sucrate is reacted with the theoretical amount of benzyl chloride in dimethoxyethane at 70°C (17). Also, benzyl chloride cannot be condensed with monosodium sucrate under conditions successfully employed for the long-chain mono-alkyl ethers of sucrose (196a).

Octabenzyl sucrose is made in good yield by first reacting sucrose with excess sodium hydride (12 moles per mole sucrose) in dimethyl formamide and then reacting the resulting sodium sucrate *in situ* with excess benzyl bromide (17 moles) at 0–25°C (90). The oily product is an almost fully substituted octabenzyl ether, with little free hydroxyl content, according to infrared analysis. After standing in the light for ten months, the product becomes dark brown and now contains a crystalline solid which analyzes as tetrabenzyl glucose. Hydrolysis probably occurs because of the acid released during the decomposition of the unremoved benzyl bromide.

Substituted benzyl ethers of sucrose

Sucrose can be reacted with substituted benzyl alcohols to form the corresponding ethers. The benzyl alcohol derivative can be prepared first from phenol and formaldehyde and then reacted with sucrose, or the condensation can be performed in one step with all reactants combined (199):

$$R'—\langle\ \rangle—OH + HCHO \longrightarrow R'—\langle\ \rangle—OH$$
$$\searrow CH_2OH$$

$$ROH + R'—\langle\ \rangle—OH \longrightarrow R'—\langle\ \rangle—OH$$
Sucrose $\searrow CH_2OH \qquad\qquad \searrow CH_2OR$

The R' substituent on the phenol moiety may be a long-chain alkyl group, which imparts hydrophobic character to the molecule, and the final product may thus become a surfactant. The best approach of synthesis is claimed to be the one-step condensation of sucrose, phenol, and formaldehyde in equimolar proportions. (The reaction of sucrose with phenol and formaldehyde to produce resins is discussed under Resins and Polymers, page 147.) Condensation has been carried out with the following reactants:

p-TERTIARY BUTYL PHENOL. Sucrose is reacted with the formaldehyde adduct of the phenol in boiling ethyl alcohol. The gummy product has a low hydroxyl content.

p-NONYL PHENOL. The phenol is reacted first with formaldehyde. The condensation of the monomethylol-*p*-nonylphenol with sucrose is carried out in water with about one-half mole each of the methylol compound and sodium hydroxide per mole of sucrose. A glassy, very hygroscopic material is isolated in about 10% yield. The raw product can be purified by dissolving it in methyl alcohol and precipitating it with acetone. The reaction is also carried out by direct condensation of sucrose, *p*-nonylphenol and formaldehyde in alkaline water solution. A somewhat purer product is obtained in similar yield.

Direct condensation of the reactants in dimethyl formamide in the presence of potassium carbonate yields a white or tan solid of good analysis, in up to 30% yield. The reaction has been studied to determine and eliminate such side reactions as the polymerization of phenol-formaldehyde adducts, also known as resoles. All products exhibit good foaming power.

p-DODECYLBENZYL SUCROSE. Preparation of *p*-dodecylbenzyl sucrose has been attempted by reacting sodium sucrate with dodecylbenzyl chloride (236). The sodium sucrate for this work was made from sodium amide and sucrose in liquid ammonia, or from sucrose and sodium hydroxide by azeotropic distillation with butyl alcohol, as claimed in U.S. Patent 2,572,923. However, further investigations showed that sodium sucrate cannot be made by this method (see Metal Derivatives, page 126). No well defined uniform product was isolated in any of the several runs. They were probably mixtures of mono- and higher alkylates and polymers.

ALLYL AND RELATED UNSATURATED ETHERS

HEXA-, HEPTA-, AND OCTAALLYL SUCROSE. The preparation, properties, and uses of highly substituted *allyl sucrose*, its mixed ethers and esters was extensively studied by the Foundation in the 1950's and briefly in the 1960's. The products were evaluated primarily as coating compositions, adhesives, and additives for upgrading drying oils. The commercial production of allyl sucrose has been also thoroughly studied. Mixed ethers and some ester mixtures of allyl sucrose have also been described, as shown in Table 2-2. In all cases the aim was to obtain a highly substituted (preferably octa-) derivative, so as to eliminate as much as possible the reactive and often sensitive hydroxyl groups.

$$R(OH)_8 + 8CH_2 = CHCH_2X \longrightarrow R(OCH_2CH = CH_2)_8 + 8HX$$

The reaction is most simply and economically carried out in an aqueous alkaline medium. The recently developed method of preparation through sodium sucrate in an aprotic solvent is more expensive, but it provides the desired highly substituted sucrose ether in one step. A high degree of substitution can also be achieved in two steps by reacting the lower ethers obtained in the first step with sodium and then reacting the sodium sucrate formed with the additional alkyl halide.

The rheological and other related properties of interest in polymer chemistry have also been thoroughly studied. A detailed final summary of the work on the preparation, properties, and uses was issued in 1952 (310).

Research was also carried out in the early 1960's on improved and more economical methods of production of highly substituted allyl sucrose compounds in aqueous alkali solutions (248). On a laboratory scale the ether is prepared by reacting 12 moles of allyl bromide per mole of sucrose in the presence of an equivalent amount of aqueous alkali at slightly elevated temperatures (169). On a larger scale the reaction is most economical when allyl chloride is reacted at about 80°C under slight pressure (up to 30 psi), preferably in a steel autoclave. A detailed description of the method of manufacture and an economic evaluation is given in References 51 and 310.

The product always contains some unreacted or partially reacted sucrose. The overall analysis gives between six and seven allyl groups (of the possible eight) and between one and two hydroxyl groups per sucrose unit. The yield is over 80%.

Octaallyl sucrose can be prepared by further treatment of the heptaallyl sucrose with allyl bromide through the sodium sucrate (114, 305). An elegant one-step method through sodium sucrate has recently been developed (90). Sucrose is reacted with excess sodium hydride (17 moles per mole sucrose) in dimethylformamide at room temperature for several hours. Excess allyl bromide (17 moles) is then added to the suspension and reacted for several hours. The resulting octaallyl sucrose is fully substituted. Reaction with only 4 to 6 moles of allyl bromide per mole of sucrose gives complex mixtures of partially allylated products (181). Similar condensations with allyl chloride fail, as mentioned below.

Partial polymerization can occur during preparation when the autoclave is made of Monel® metal. Poorer quality and lower yield are obtained in glass-lined autoclaves (169, 310).

OTHER METHODS. Several experiments indicate that the reaction of sodium sucrates with allyl chloride needs fairly drastic conditions to be successful. Trisodium sucrate reacts with excess allyl chloride without a solvent in a sealed tube at 100–135°C and a reaction time of one to 45 hours (17). The reaction is incomplete at 100°C, but at 135°C in 3.5 hours gives a syrupy allyl sucrose with a degree of substitution of about three in 83% yield. However, the product has the low specific rotation of +16° vs. +50.5° for the hepta ether indicating decomposition. A tetra-ether with high rotation ($+45°$) is obtained in 50% yield at lower temperature (122°C). Hexasodium sucrate similarly reacted with allyl chloride also gives a product with good rotation ($+35.8°$) in 65% yield (17).

Unsuccessful experiments to prepare allyl sucrose have been attempted by (a) the careful addition of aqueous alkali to a mixture of sucrose and allyl chloride in water at room or elevated temperatures; (b) the reaction of sucrose with sodium (or lithium) and allyl chloride in liquid ammonia or dimethyl formamide and (c) the reaction of octasodium sucrate and allyl chloride without solvent or in dimethyl formamide (186a).

Properties

The properties discussed below are those of the polyallyl sucrose with a degree of substitution between six and seven. The term "allyl sucrose" is used to refer to such poly substituted products.

STABILITY. Pure allyl sucrose is stable at room temperature and can be stored unchanged for long periods. The partially polymerized products are less stable and may gel in 10 to 32 weeks (169). No gelling of any of these products occurs when they are dissolved in an organic solvent such as toluene or turpentine (169). Solutions containing driers can be stored if the container is completely filled. Such solutions have relatively low viscosity (2–3 stokes) at 80% solids content (170).

Allyl sucrose is the only sucrose ether among the simple carbohydrates, such as hexaallyl mannitol or sorbitol, that cannot be distilled in vacuum at 1 mm (305).

POLYMERIZATION AND GELATION. Allyl sucrose polymerizes under thermal and oxidative conditions. The oxidative method gives better results.

THERMAL POLYMERIZATION. The extent of polymerization depends on the temperature, type of catalyst, and nature of the monomer (310). The optimal temperature range lies between 80°C and 135°C. The most effective catalysts are cumene hydroperoxide at 135°C, benzoyl peroxide at 80–100°C, and various butyl peroxides. One to two percent catalyst is employed, and the catalyst is predissolved in benzene, if it does not readily dissolve in allyl sucrose.

Numerous tests show that the extent of polymerization depends on the method of preparation of the allyl sucrose. For example, a product made from allyl chloride in a stainless steel autoclave gels in 65 minutes in the presence of 2% cumene hydroperoxide at 135°C. Under similar conditions the monomer made from allyl bromide in glass produces only a very viscous mass (641 centistokes at 75°C after two hours) (310).

OXIDATIVE POLYMERIZATION AND GELATION. When allyl sucrose is blown with air or oxygen, particularly at elevated temperatures, there is an increase in viscosity, refractive index, and peroxide number (170). During this blowing such common paint driers as 0.1–0.2% cobalt octoate or naphthenate and ultraviolet radiation are effective catalysts. Organic peroxides, however, do not catalyze these reactions (144, 310). Alkalies or organic bases inhibit the polymerization (114). Blowing at 100°C can increase the viscosity from under 20 to 250 centistokes in two hours (169, 170). Polymerization probably proceeds through the formation of epoxy compounds (114). [The mechanism of oxidation originally proposed has been discounted (248a).]

Table 2-2 shows that the formation of saturated acyl or various ether derivatives of allyl sucrose does not improve gelation time. Gelation of such products generally occurs in about 3 to 35 hours (114, 169). The less highly allylated products have a longer gelling time (169).

The gelation time of the allyl sucrose is considerably shortened when the unreacted hydroxyl groups are transformed into unsaturated esters with additional polymerizable groups such as the methacrylyl derivative (169, 174). Such products or their mixtures with allyl sucrose gel in 8 to 146 minutes at 100°C (174). Addition of equal parts of esters of acrylic and methacrylic acids to allyl sucrose can also reduce its gelation time to as low as 19 minutes at 100°C (168, 169, 170). The shortest gelation times are found with mixtures of allyl sucrose with tetrahydrofurfuryl methacrylate (19 minutes) and cyclohexyl acrylate (37 minutes).

SOLUBILITY. Both the blown and unblown materials are soluble in dilute concentrations (around 10%) in most common organic solvents (170). However, they are not soluble in *n*-butyl ether, ethylene, and diethylene glycols and hexane. In many such solvents the monomers can be dissolved in up to 50% concentration (169). Acylation of the unreacted hydroxyl group is claimed to improve solubility (131).

COMPATIBILITY WITH DRYING OILS. Since allyl sucrose has been found to be a useful additive for drying oils, its compatibility with such oils is of importance. At room temperature allyl sucrose is miscible with such drying oils as oiticica oil, but incompatible with most other common drying oils. However, mixtures at elevated temperatures, particularly in the presence of oxygen, becomes increasingly miscible (170).

WATER EMULSIONS. The most successful emulsions are prepared from 80% blown allyl sucrose in toluene (310). Formulations containing cobalt driers exhibit temporary stability, which generally can be repeatedly restored for intervals of 48 hours by shaking. Effective emulsifiers include Triton 770®, Tween 60® and 85®, and Span 60®. Poor results are obtained when other techniques are employed, such as emulsion polymerization and emulsification of plasticized, blown allyl sucrose. A detailed summary of the preparation and properties of baked films obtained from these emulsions is given in Reference 310.

COMPARISON WITH OTHER ALLYL CARBOHYDRATES. The preparation and properties of allyl sucrose are compared with those of allyl derivatives of such polyhydroxy compounds as glycol, glycerol, mannitol, sorbitol, inositol, and pentaerythrol in Reference 305.

GENERAL PROPERTIES. The properties of allyl sucrose and its modified derivatives are given in Table 2-2. The properties of the product prepared by the improved method are given in Reference 248. For applied properties, see Surface Coatings, page 192.

Mono- to pentaallyl sucroses

Allyl ethers of sucrose with a lower degree of substitution have also been prepared. Successful partial allylation can be carried out by the reaction of sucrose with sodium hydride and then with less than eight moles of allyl bromide per mole of sucrose in dimethyl formamide at room temperature (256a). However, such reactions are said to give complex product mixtures (181).

Some lower allyl sucrose can be isolated during the course of preparation of the highly substituted sucrose ethers with allyl halide in aqueous alkali. Some success is also reported when trisodium sucrate is reacted with allyl chloride at over 100°C. Depending on the length of reaction time and the temperature, the product has varying optical rotation, substitution, and also yield (25–70%) (17).

Partially allylated sucroses are of interest because they may be used in copolymerizations or as modifying agents for polymers. Mixed ethers made from allyl sucrose are potential plasticizers for polyvinyl chloride or other resins. Such uses are recommended in Reference 212.

MONOALLYL SUCROSE. Some monoallyl sucrose is probably obtained when monosodium sucrate is shaken with allyl chloride in dimethyl formamide (186a). The mixture also contains sucrose.

DIALLYL SUCROSE. This compound and its blends with allyl starch have been tested in copolymerization with styrene. Their compatibility with plasticizers has also been investigated (304).

TRIALLYL SUCROSE. Triallyl sucrose cannot be prepared by simple allylation of sucrose with three moles of allyl chloride in aqueous alkali (170). This reaction gives low yields of hexaallyl sucrose. An allyl sucrose with only three polymerizable allyl groups can be prepared in the form of a mixed benzyl allyl ether (170). Trisodium sucrate reacted with allyl chloride at 122°C in a sealed tube gives products with three allyl groups per mole sucrose in 30–80% yield (17). However, their specific rotation is low for a true allyl sucrose (+16° to +34° in methyl alcohol) and indicates decomposition.

TETRAALLYL SUCROSE. A product with four allyl groups per mole sucrose is made in 50% yield by reacting trisodium sucrate with allyl chloride at 122°C for three hours in a sealed tube. Its specific rotation $[\alpha]_D$ is +45.3° in methyl alcohol (17).

A product with similar rotation (43°, c. 0.62 in methyl alcohol) is made by reacting tetrasodium sucrate with allyl chloride in dimethyl formamide at elevated temperatures (186a). The reaction product also contains sucrose and hydrolysis products, caused by the acidic by-product of the reaction of allyl chloride with dimethyl formamide.

Tetra-, hexa, and heptaallyl sucrose can also be made by the reaction of the sodium sucrates with allyl chloride in dimethyl sulfoxide (183e).

PENTAALLYL SUCROSE. The penta-derivative is an oil with similar gelation time to the higher ethers (see Table 2-2).

Mixed ethers and esters of allyl sucrose

Allyl butyl and allyl benzyl sucrose are made by first reacting sucrose with a butyl or benzyl halide and then allylating in aqueous alkaline medium (169).

The *allyl esters* of sucrose are made by acylating allyl sucrose in pyridine (131). The products have better solubility in solvents than allyl sucrose itself.

As shown in Table 2-2, these compounds contain few or no free hydroxyl groups, so as to increase the water resistance of the polymerized product. These allyl derivatives have gelation times comparable to or lower than those of allyl sucrose. Only allyl methacrylyl sucrose has improved gelation time.

Crotyl sucrose

Crotyl sucrose is made by reacting crotyl bromide with sucrose in 50% aqueous sodium

C

hydroxide (169). The reaction is carried out following Nichols et al., as described in *J. Am. Chem. Soc.* **68**, 2020 (1946). Crotyl sucrose is also obtained by reacting pentasodium sucrate with the theoretical amount of crotyl chloride in boiling dimethoxyethane (17).

Methallyl sucrose

β-Methylallyl sucrose, the isomer of crotyl sucrose, is made similarly to crotyl sucrose (169). The product is a hexaether. Total or nearly total substitution can be achieved by reacting the hexaether with sodium and the resulting sodium sucrate with additional allyl bromide (305). Reaction of pentasodium sucrate with methallyl chloride in boiling dimethoxyethane gives a product in very low yield (17).

VINYL ETHERS

Vinyl sucrose is a monomer that could polymerize into a linear chain of disaccharide units crosslinked through the third vinyl group (if present) of the units in adjacent chains. The vinylation of sucrose has therefore been explored rather thoroughly by a number of methods successfully applied to simpler alcohols and other carbohydrates. Transetherification with butylvinyl ether is the most successful:

$$ROH + R'OCH = CH_2 \rightleftharpoons ROCH = CH_2 + R'OH$$

The reaction of acetylene with sucrose in dimethyl formamide at 140°C in the presence of potassium hydroxide degrades the solvent and does not vinylate the sucrose (54, 55). Vinylation of sucrose in ethylene glycol under similar conditions is also unsuccessful (54, 55). The vinylation of sucrose by reaction of sodium sucrates with vinyl bromide in dimethyl formamide has also been studied (256a). Vinyl bromide has low reactivity both in this displacement reaction and in reaction with the sodium hydride used to prepare the sodium sucrate.

The successful preparation of vinyl sucrose by transetherification has previously been prevented by lack of a suitable solvent. The use of a basic solvent such as pyridine or dimethylformamide would inactivate the mercuric acetate catalyst used in such reactions. Dimethyl sulfoxide, a good solvent for sucrose, decomposes at the temperatures required for transetherification. Although some vinylation of sucrose occurs, the product cannot be separated from the high-boiling decomposition products of dimethyl sulfoxide (55, 82).

However, tetrahydrothiophene dioxide has been found to be a good, stable solvent at the required transetherification temperatures of over 100°C (11). With this solvent a mixture of partially etherified derivatives can be prepared from which relatively pure amorphous trivinyl sucrose is separated. The transetherification is carried out with *n*-butyl vinyl ether. Attempts to use the lower-boiling ethyl vinyl ether have had little success (54).

When sucrose and a vinyl ether are reacted at temperatures below 50°C in the presence of an acid catalyst, addition takes place with the formation of an acetal (see Acetals and Ketals, page 94).

For more details on the unsuccessful attempts at synthesis, see References 54 and 55. The mechanism of the interchange between sucrose and the vinyl ether is discussed in References 55 and 82.

TRIVINYL SUCROSE. When sucrose is heated in tetrahydrothiophene dioxide with a large excess of *n*-butyl vinyl ether in the presence of catalytic amount of mercuric acetate at 115°C for 70 hours, a thick, amber, gummy product is obtained (11). Chromatographic analysis shows that it contains several compounds. Those soluble in ether are mixtures of vinyl ethers with an average degree of substitution of 4.5. The ether-insoluble portion dissolves in chloroform, and is a relatively pure trivinyl sucrose. The ether extract is a heavy, immobile, dark brown liquid; the insoluble fraction is a hard, brown, glassy product. For more details on the products and analyses (including infrared spectra) see Reference 82.

The preparation of *trivinyl sucrose* was attempted through a sequence of reactions (221b): Sucrose $\longrightarrow$ Tritritylpentaacetyl sucrose $\longrightarrow$ Pentaacetyl sucrose $\longrightarrow$ Trivinylpentaacetyl sucrose $\longrightarrow$ Trivinyl sucrose.

The first two intermediates are prepared as described above in the synthesis of 4,1',6'-trimethyl sucrose. Vinylation of pentaacetyl sucrose has been attempted by Adelman's method with vinyl acetate in the presence of mercuric acetate and sulfuric acid as catalyst at −20°C to −30°C (221b). No uniform, well defined compound can be isolated. In some experiments a colorless syrup is obtained that shows an acetyl content, degree of unsaturation, and molecular weight that correspond approximately to those of trivinylpentaacetyl sucrose. Attempts to hydrolyze the substance yield a dark, insoluble residue.

Further research is needed on vinylation using both the vinyl acetate and the transesterification technique, and on the removal of acetyl groups.

CYANOETHYL ETHERS

Alcohols add to acrylonitrile to form 2-cyanoethyl ethers. The addition takes place in the opposite manner to that shown by a routine Markownikoff addition:

$$ROH + CH_2 = CHCN \longrightarrow ROCH_2CH_2CN$$

This nucleophilic addition is initiated by reagents capable of donating an electron pair to a carbon atom, such as hydroxyl or iodide ions or the water or ammonia molecules. The addition is well catalyzed by acids or bases.

Cyanoethylation of sucrose is successfully achieved by treating sucrose with acrylonitrile in aqueous alkali. The reaction cannot be carried out in solvent-free acrylonitrile because sucrose is not soluble in the reagent. When the reaction is attempted in pyridine, sucrose remains unchanged after three hours at 35°C (82). The degree of substitution can reportedly be controlled by the amount of acrylonitrile so that the desired derivative is obtained (232). The reaction catalyzed by 2% sodium hydroxide gives products in up to 90% yield. The water-free product is obtained by the elimination of the water by azeotropic distillation and a final freeze-drying (232).

A two-stage process for full substitution follows that used for the cyanoethylation of starch and cellulose (11, 82). The first stage involves partial substitution with acrylonitrile in 2-N aqueous alkali to products containing one or two cyanoethyl groups per sucrose molecule. The product is then refluxed with excess solvent-free acrylonitrile in the presence of traces of alkali. Tetracyanoethyl sucrose is obtained, but it is contaminated with di-2-

cyanoethyl ether. Further substitution of the tetraether is achieved by additional reflux with excess acrylonitrile. The final product is a mixture of the octaether and copolymers of sucrose with acrylonitrile.

The *mono-* and *dicyanoethyl sucroses* are somewhat solid. Both are hygroscopic and easily soluble in water. Compounds with higher degrees of substitution are viscous oils, insoluble in water, but soluble in acetone, methyl ethyl ketone, dimethyl formamide, and some other organic solvents (232). The product obtained by treatment of one mole of sucrose with 2 moles of acrylonitrile gives a white, gummy solid (82).

Tetracyanoethyl sucrose is a yellow oil. It is not the pure compound, but a mixture with the by-product di-2-cyanoethyl ether (82).

Octacyanoethyl sucrose is solid. It is prepared in pure form by fractionation of the chloroform-soluble product obtained by exhaustive cyanoethylation, as discussed above (11, 82). Saponification with sodium hydroxide gives the corresponding acid derivative (see Carboxyethyl Sucrose, page 37). Efforts to hydrogenate the nitrile groups to primary amines in the presence of platinum catalyst have been unsuccessful (272b).

For more details on the preparation, elemental and infrared analyses, chromatography, and properties of the ethers and the copolymer, see Reference 82.

CARBOXYALKYL ETHERS

Carboxymethyl sucrose

The most successful method developed for the carboxymethylation of sucrose consists of treating sucrose under mild conditions with methyl bromoacetate and silver oxide in dimethyl formamide (277). The reaction is based on Kuhn's method for the methylation of carbohydrates [*Angew. Chem.* **67**, 32 (1955)]. Many other known methods where the intermediate metal compound is not isolated have also been tested, but without success. Among these are the reaction of sucrose by (a) Haworth's method, monochloroacetic acid plus aqueous sodium hydroxide (237a, c); (b) Williamson's method, sodium in toluene plus methyl bromoacetate (277); (c) the Freudenberg-Muskat method, sodium in liquid ammonia plus alkyl halide (277).

Carboxymethyl sucrose can be made by reacting the appropriate sodium sucrose with monochloroacetate or its ester. However, such products consist of mixtures of ethers, unreacted sucrose, and its hydrolysis products (277).

Pentacarboxymethyl sucrose

Pentacarboxymethyl sucrose is made by reacting sucrose with excess methyl bromoacetate and silver oxide in dimethyl formamide (277). The product is a well-defined and carefully analyzed material that is the dihydrate of its trimethyl ester dilactone:

$$C_{12}H_{15}O_4(OCH_2COOCH_3)_3 \left(\begin{array}{c} -OCH_2 \\ | \\ CO \\ -O \end{array} \right)_2 \cdot 2H_2O$$

The ester is a colorless crystalline product (Table 2-1). It is very soluble in acetone, chloroform, pyridine, and dimethyl formamide; slightly soluble in methyl alcohol and ethyl acetate; and insoluble in water, ether, benzene, or petroleum ether. It does not reduce Fehling's solution. It decomposes in dilute aqueous solutions of sulfuric acid (alone or mixed with acetic acid) and in boron trichloride. The ester can be converted to a crystalline dipotassium salt (277).

Other carboxymethyl products

When sucrose is treated with only four equivalents of methyl bromoacetate, according to Kuhn's method, fewer than four carboxymethyl groups are introduced (277).

Tetracarboxymethyl sucrose is made by reacting tetrasodium sucrate with sodium monochloroacetate at 100°C in dimethylsulfoxide (237a, c). Analysis indicates that the product contains at least four different acidic sugar derivatives (277). Reaction in other solvents, such as dimethyl formamide and Dimethyl Cellosolve®, is equally unsuccessful (277). Attempts to prepare monocarboxymethyl sucrose under similar conditions have also failed (277).

Carboxyethyl sucrose

Carboxyethyl sucrose is made by the addition of stoichiometric amounts of acrylonitrile to sucrose in the presence of 2% aqueous sodium hydroxide (see Cyanoethyl Ethers, page 35). The cyanoethylated sucrose is then hydrolyzed with concentrated sodium hydroxide to the corresponding acid:

$$ROCH_2CH_2CN \xrightarrow[\text{NaOH}]{} ROCH_2CH_2COOH$$

By this method all possible derivatives can be made in degrees of substitution from one to eight.

Tetracarboxyethyl sucrose is the most important derivative that can be made simply by this method (237b). Preparation from β-propiolactone and sucrose is unsuccessful (237c). A viscous oil is separated after the removal of inorganic compounds by ion exchange (237h).

Di-, tri-, penta-, hexa-, and *octacarboxyethyl sucrose* are prepared similarly (237f, g).

EPOXIDE REACTION PRODUCTS

The many important commercial products derived from ethylene glycol, glycerol, and sorbitol with such epoxides as ethylene oxide suggested the preparation of similar sucrose adducts. For example, sorbitol or mannitol, the reduction products of sucrose, are reacted with fatty acids and ethylene oxide to produce surfactants marketed under the trade name Spans® and Tweens®. Solvents such as Cellosolves® and humectants such as Carbowax® are other examples.

The addition of ethylene oxide to starch and cellulose has been reported in the literature (94). Some work on sucrose-ethylene oxide adducts has also been disclosed (German Patent 737,352).

The initial reaction of sucrose with ethylene oxide or other epoxides probably forms mono- and higher 2-hydroxyalkyl ethers. When sucrose is reacted with more than eight moles of the epoxide per mole of sucrose, the product is a polyoxyalkylene adduct:

$$
\begin{array}{c}
CH_2-CH-R' \\
\diagdown\ \diagup \\
O
\end{array}
$$

$$
ROH \xrightarrow{\hspace{3cm}} ROCH_2CHOHR'
$$

$$
\begin{array}{c}
CH_2-CH-R' \\
\diagdown\ \diagup \\
O
\end{array}
$$

$$
\downarrow
$$

$$
ROCH_2CHR'(OCH_2CHR')_nOH
$$

The reaction product is often a complex mixture that cannot be fractionated with much success. Many attempts, particularly with higher epoxides, have been unsuccessful or have resulted in the formation of polymeric materials (Table 13-1). Alkylene oxide adducts of sucrose esters of fatty acids have also been prepared (see Fatty Esters, page 52).

Ethylene oxide adducts

Ethylene oxide adducts of sucrose are made by reacting sucrose with ethylene oxide at room temperature (94, 288). The reaction is carried out in aqueous sodium hydroxide solution with molar ratios of ethylene oxide to sucrose of 1:1 to 4:1 and 11:1. In all cases gummy or glassy mixtures are obtained. Their sweetness decreases with increasing ethylene oxide content. Attempts to separate these mixtures into their components have had little success. One crystalline substance, probably the *di(β-hydroxylethyl) sucrose*, has been isolated (Table 2-1).

The gummy products are soluble in water, methyl alcohol, and pyridine and insoluble in ether, chloroform, and acetone. The solubility in ethyl alcohol and dioxane increases with the proportion of ethylene oxide. The material is about as hygroscopic as glycerol. Except for the tetra-adduct, none of these products shows surface activity in water.

The adducts can be successfully acylated with acetic anhydride or phthalic anhydride. Reaction with benzoylchloride in pyridine gives black tars. Reaction with phenyl hydrazine indicates that the adducts, with ratios of ethylene oxide to sucrose of 1:1 and 2:1, probably contain some sucrose.

For more details on the preparation and properties of these adducts see Reference 288.

Attempts to react ethylene oxide with the saccharates of aluminum, lead, sodium, potassium, and other metals have been unsuccessful (306).

Propylene oxide adducts

Polyoxypropylene adducts of sucrose are made by reacting sucrose with propylene oxide in a concentrated aqueous solution in the presence of sodium hydroxide as catalyst (227). The mole ratio of propylene oxide to sucrose varies from 8:1 to 48:1.

The reaction products are mixtures of adducts of various molecular weights. Purification is carried out by fractional precipitation in toluene with petroleum ether. Properties of selected fractions have been studied. All fractions are oils, most often viscous and of pale yellow color.

The solubility in toluene increases with increased molecular weight. The product becomes miscible with toluene when the ratio of propylene oxide to sucrose is 24:1. Fractional purification of an adduct (48:1 mole ratio) shows the presence of compounds with molecular weights from 400 to 1400. All fractions have about equal surface activity (45–47 dynes per cm).

A polymeric adduct of propylene oxide of unknown structure has also been prepared by other workers (183k).

Butadiene monoxide adducts

When 3,4-epoxy-1-butene reacts with sucrose under conditions similar to those for ethylene oxide, a soft, gummy product is obtained (288). The adduct contains three moles of the epoxy compound per mole of sucrose.

Lauryl glycidic ether adducts

Lauryl (dodecyl) glycidic ether has been unsuccessfully reacted with sucrose in an acetone-water solution or in dimethyl formamide containing sodium hydroxide (290f). The reaction could produce a derivative of possible good surface activity:

$$ROH + CH_2CH_2CH_2OC_{12}H_{25} \xrightarrow{\qquad} ROCH_2CHOHCH_2OC_{12}H_{25}$$
$$\overset{\diagdown\;\diagup}{O}$$

Octylene oxide adducts

The attempted reaction between sucrose and octylene oxide in alkaline media has not been successful (246b). (The reactant epoxide was somewhat decomposed in this work.) Further experiments with an octylene oxide consisting of 15% 1,2-isomer and 85% 2,3-isomer also failed (199). The reaction was carried out with one mole of epoxide per mole sucrose in water containing 0.15 mole sodium hydroxide at 97°C. Considerable caramelization of sucrose occurred.

Adducts with mesityl oxide epoxide

The reaction of sucrose with the epoxide of mesityl oxide has been briefly investigated (191). The reaction was carried out at room temperature under various conditions including the aqueous sodium hydroxide medium successfully used for the preparation of hydroxyethyl sucroses. A crystalline compound, probably the monoether [$RO(CH_3)_2CCH_2COCH_3$], has been obtained (Table 2-1). Other catalysts tested included calcium hydroxide, basic ion-exchange resins, and solvents such as pyridine and piperidine. The reactions had little success.

Dodecylene oxide adducts

Sucrose has been reacted with one mole of dodecylene oxide per mole sucrose in dimethyl formamide in the presence of 12 g potassium carbonate per mole of sucrose (199). The mixture was kept at 99°C for ten hours. The use of a solvent was thought to eliminate caramelization formerly observed in aqueous media. A light tan, waxy solid was separated in a yield of 20%, but exhaustive acetylation indicated that the material is mostly unreacted sucrose.

Adducts with mixed C_{16}—C_{18} olefin oxides

Reactions similar to that of dodecylene oxide have been conducted with epoxides of higher olefins, but also without success (199). The epoxide mixture consisted of 60% C_{16} olefin and 40% C_{18} olefin. The epoxide was reacted with excess sucrose (0.33 moles per mole of sucrose). The solid product isolated was the 1-2 glycol of the mixed paraffins.

Other adducts

The reaction of sucrose with other epoxy compounds has been tried under conditions similar to those used with ethylene oxide. Phenylethylene oxide does not react at room temperature (288). Epichlorohydrin is apparently hydrolyzed rapidly by the alkali (288). A water-sensitive resin is formed with epichlorohydrin (183a, k) and a water-resistant polymer with trisodium sucrate and epichlorohydrin (272c).

Reactions of epoxides to polymers

A few exploratory attempts have been made to condense sucrose with styrene, butylene, and propylene epoxides and with epoxides of more complex structure to give polymeric materials (see Resins and Polymers, page 147).

OTHER ETHERS

Cinnamyl sucrose

An attempted preparation by reacting pentasodium sucrate with cinnamyl chloride was unsuccessful (17).

Triazine sucroses

The reaction between sodium sucrate and cyanuric chloride (2,4,6-trichlorotriazine) gives no well-defined derivative (19). Condensations have been carried out with disubstituted triazines in which only one chlorine atom is available for replacement, such as 2-chloro-4,6-bis(2'-chloro-4'-nitrophenoxy)-*s*-triazine (19). Products made from deammoniated trisodium sucrate in boiling dimethyoxyethane give a derivative with the highest specific rotation, $+10.0°$ (Table 2-1). Penta- and trisodium sucrate containing bound ammonia yield products with low rotation, suggesting that very little sucrose is present.

The sucrose derivative is a pale yellow, glassy product. It is soluble in chloroform, acetone, and ethyl acetate, and insoluble in water, ethyl alcohol, ether, benzene, carbon tetrachloride and light petroleum.

Pentaerythritol sucrose

Experiments have been carried out to prepare *pentaerythritol sucrose* (191). This derivative of sucrose should have unusual chemical properties and could be used like dipentaerythritol as an intermediate in alkyd resins.

Pentaerythritol itself is obtained by reacting acetaldehyde and formaldehyde in the presence of calcium oxide in water. When the reaction is carried out in the presence of alcohol, some ether is also formed:

$$\begin{array}{c} CH_2OH \\ | \\ ROCH_2-C-CH_2OH \\ | \\ CH_2OH \end{array}$$

Sucrose should react preferentially at the primary hydroxyl groups. Since the formation of pentaerythritol proceeds through acrolein, the reaction of sucrose and acrolein has been studied, as well as the reaction of their condensation product with formaldehyde to give the desired pentaerythritol sucrose (191).

None of the reactions has been successful under the conditions studied. The condensation of sucrose and acrolein has been attempted in dimethyl formamide, pyridine, and other basic solvents in the presence of copper, peroxide, and hydroquinone as catalysts. Also, the procedure has been attempted in aqueous medium with calcium hydroxide as catalyst followed by reaction *in situ* with formaldehyde. In all cases unreacted sucrose was detected by paper chromatography.

The attempted reaction of sucrose with acrolein through the alkali sucrose saccharate addition compound has also proved unsuccessful. Other routes of synthesis have been proposed, but not investigated (191). However, further work could lead to a successful method of preparation.

Trichloromethyl thiolsucrates

Attempts to react disodium sucrate (233) or sucrose (229) with perchloromethyl mercaptan show some indications of reaction to produce *bis* (*trichloromethyl*) *thiol sucrate*. A viscous syrup is obtained, which turns dark brown on standing.

2-Chloroethyl sucroses

Tetra-2-chloroethyl sucrose is said to be made by reacting tetrasodium sucrose with ethylene dichloride (183d). The product also contains tri- or lower substituted derivatives.

Trisodium sucrate reacts with ethylene dichloride at 130°C, but sucrose is the main product formed (17). Ethylene dichloride probably loses hydrogen chloride under the alkaline conditions employed. The liberated acid then reacts with the sodium sucrate to give sucrose and sodium chloride.

Unsaturated ketone adducts

Exploratory experiments have been carried out to react sucrose with α,β-unsaturated ketones to give the corresponding ethers. The catalytic addition of alcohols to such ketones is used extensively for the synthesis of β-alkoxy ketones otherwise difficult to obtain:

$$ROH + -COCH = CH- \longrightarrow COCH_2CHOR-$$

The reaction is catalyzed by both acids and bases. Several of these additions have been reported in the literature, but none with sucrose as the alcohol component.

Sucrose has been tested in this reaction with methylvinyl ketone and mesityl oxide. The addition of sucrose on mesityl oxide was studied more thoroughly. The results indicate that the reaction proceeds with a very poor yield. Only one product, the crystalline mesityl oxide-sucrose adduct (1:1) has been isolated, and the yield was only a few percent.

METHYLVINYL KETONE. The reaction of sucrose with methylvinyl ketone was attempted in the presence of calcium hydroxide in water (191). All reagents were used in equimolar amounts. Paper chromatography revealed the presence of sucrose and an unidentified product which gave a positive reaction with reagents specific to ketoses and reducing sugars.

MESITYL OXIDE. The possibility of the addition of mesityl oxide to sucrose was also examined (191, 229):

$$ROH + (CH_3)_2C = CHCOCH_3 \longrightarrow ROC(CH_3)_2CH_2COCH_3$$

Since mesityl oxide is sparsely soluble in water, the reaction was carried out in water-free organic solvents or in solvent mixtures with water. The catalysts tested included acidic and basic ion-exchange resins, calcium hydroxide, and sodium hydroxide. Dimethyl formamide, pyridine, and piperidine were used as solvents. Although in all cases excess mesityl oxide was used, chromatography indicated that only one compound, the mono adduct, was always formed, with possibly a trace of a second material. The formation of higher adducts is said to be blocked by steric or other hindrance. The mono-adduct was isolated as a crystalline material in less than 5% yield. For details on the many experiments run, see Reference 191.

Miscellaneous ethers of poorly characterized structure

Several ether derivatives of sucrose have been prepared solely to evaluate their activity as agricultural chemicals. They are listed in Table 21-1. None has been characterized by melting point or other physical properties.

Ethers of other carbohydrates

Among the ether derivatives of other carbohydrates that have been prepared or tested are:

Compound	Reference
1,6-Divinyltetraacetyl mannitol	221a
Allyl mannitol and allyl pentaerythritol	310
Methacrylyl ester of allyl mannitol	174
Allyl mannitol	168
Acylated allyl starch and allyl mannitol	131
1,6-Ditrityltetraacetyl mannitol	221a
1,6-Ditrityl mannitol	221a
2,3,4,5-Tetraacetyl mannitol	221a
1,6-Dimethyl-2,3,4,5-tetraacetyl mannitol	221a
1,6-Dimethyl mannitol	221a
1,6-Ditrityl-2,3,4,5-tetraacetyl sorbitol	287
Methyl-2,6-dimesyl-3,4-dimethylglucoside	108
Methyl-3,4-dimethylglucopyranoside	108
Methyl-3,4,6-trimethylglucopyranoside	108
Methyl-2-mesyl-3,4,6-trimethylglucoside	108
3,4-Dimethyl and 3,4,6-trimethyl glucose	108

Unsuccessful attempts have also been made to reduce the cyanoethyl glucose to the amine (86). Tetramethylglucopyranoside, and its acetate, propionate, or bromide have been prepared. Unsuccessful attempts were made to react these products with ketene (125).

INTERNAL ETHERS OF ANHYDRO DERIVATIVES

The ethers discussed above are called external ethers. Internal ethers or anhydrides are stable cyclic compounds formed by internal etherification between hydroxyl groups.

Anhydrides are prepared by alkaline hydrolysis of tosylates, mesylates, or halogen derivatives that undergo a displacement reaction instead of normal hydrolysis as carboxylic esters do:

$$RCH_2 \text{---------} OSO_2C_6H_4CH_3 \qquad RCH_2O \text{---------} COR$$

In the presence of free hydroxyl groups, in sterically favorable positions the split occurs with an intramolecular action, namely a nucleophilic attack on the esterified carbon by the oxygen:

$$Tosyl\text{---}OC$$
$$O$$
$$OH$$

The result is the displacement of the ester function with the concomitant closure of the anhydro ring. The ring formation can also proceed with the inversion of the configuration (Figure 2-1, compound II). The oxygen atom may bridge two to five carbons.

Sucrose can form *mono-*, *di-*, or *trianhydrides*. The structure of the two presently known trianhydrides is given in Figure 2-1. Both are prepared by alkaline alcoholysis of tritosylates. Compound I is the only presently known sucrose derivative where a bridge links the fructose and the glucose moiety of the molecule. It is also the only such crosslinked compound among the di- and polysaccharides.

The kinetics of oxide-ring formation in monosaccharides have been briefly studied (209). Previous work has shown that the relative rates of formation of internal ethers from isomeric hexoside tosylates can give information about some of the steric and electronic effects which control the reactivity of carbohydrates. The work has been extended to additional carbohydrates, which may serve as models in understanding the behavior of sucrose.

The formation of *anhydrosucrose* has also been reported by heating sucrose in a vacuum at 195°C for three hours (290k). The product failed to give an amine with ammonia or lauryl amine or an ether with nonyl phenol.

Concentrated hydrochloric acid or simple heat treatment show a strong dehydrating action on carbohydrates. Several anhydrites of fructose have been prepared by these methods, as discussed below.

None of the possible *monoanhydro ethers* of sucrose have been prepared.

Dianhydro ethers

Dianhydro ethers contain two cyclic rings. The dianhydro ether, like the trianhydro, has

Figure 2-1   Internal ethers made from sucrose

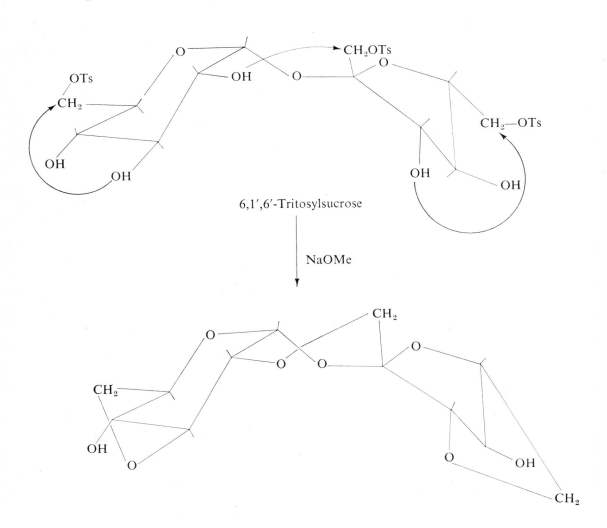

6,1′,6′-Tritosylsucrose

NaOMe

1′,2:3,6:3′,6′-Trianhydrosucrose (101)

I

Figure 2-1 continued

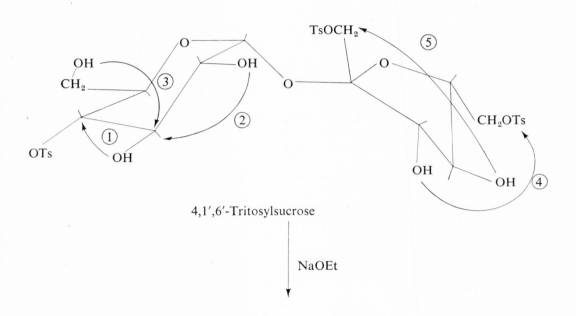

4,1′,6′-Tritosylsucrose

NaOEt

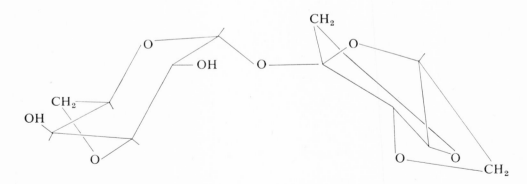

3,6-Anhydro-α-D-galactosyl-1′,4′:3′,6′-dianhydro-β-D-fructoside (95)

II

been prepared by alkaline treatment of the tosyl derivative. The structure of the 3,6:3'6'-dianhydride is similar to that of Compound I in Figure 2-1 except for the missing ring on the 1',2 carbons.

3,6:3',6'-DIANHYDRO SUCROSE. This crystalline derivative has been made by treatment of 6,6'-ditosyl sucrose with sodium methoxide (194d, e). The compound has been acylated with benzoyl chloride and acetic anhydride to the crystalline tetraesters *3,6:3'6'-dianhydro-2,4,1',4'-tetrabenzoyl sucrose* (194h) and *3,6:3',6'-dianhydro-2,4,1',4'-tetraacetyl sucrose* (194e). The latter was obtained in 73% yield (194j). It is soluble in chloroform and ether (194j).

Trianhydro ethers

Two such derivatives have been made from sucrose, both by alkaline hydrolysis of two isomers of tritosyl sucrose (Figure 2-1). Compound II is a galactose derivative, which indicates that the reaction in one case proceeded with Walden inversion on the *4*-position in the glucose moiety. None of the anhydro ethers contain an epoxide ring, but rather rings with three or four carbons. Compound I is the only bridged sucrose derivative of well-established structure with the bridge between the glucose and fructose moieties.

Both compounds are nonreducing. They are extremely sensitive to acids, but stable to strong alkalies. Their structures have been determined by thorough investigation both of derivatives and of hydrolysis products by chemical and physical methods.

The formation of the 1,4:3,6-dianhydrofructosyl group in Compound II also confirms the absolute configuration of the anomeric center of the fructose moiety of sucrose. Such dianhydro derivative can only be formed from a fructoside with β-configuration (95).

1',2:3,6:3',6'-TRIANHYDROSUCROSE. This compound (Figure 2-1, Compound I) is obtained by the treatment of 6,1',6'-tritosyl sucrose with sodium ethoxide in boiling ethyl alcohol (12, 95, 101). The tritosylate is a component of the tritosyl sucrose obtained by the reaction of sucrose with three moles of tosyl chloride in pyridine (see Sulfonic Esters, page 70). The compound is obtained in low yield (3.5% overall) because of the heterogenous nature of the reaction mixture of tosylation. The compound is crystalline.

Hydrolysis in 0.01-N hydrochloric acid at 25°C was 200 times more rapid than that of sucrose (101). The compound is unchanged by heating in 25% potassium hydroxide for 24 hours as well as in 85% hydrazine at 100°C for 36 hours (101). It is also inert to oxidation by periodate at pH 7 or above (101).

1',2:3,6:3',6'-TRIANHYDRO-4,4'-DITOSYL SUCROSE. This compound is made from trianhydrosucrose by tosylation (101). It is crystalline. It remains unchanged when heated to 100°C with sodium iodide in acetone or with hydrazine in sealed tubes for 24 hours (101).

1'2:3,6:3',6'-TRIANHYDRO-4,4'-DIMETHYL SUCROSE. The trianhydride is methylated with boiling methyl iodide in the presence of silver oxide (12, 101). The product is crystalline. Acetolysis with acetic anhydride in the presence of concentrated sulfuric acid gives a syrupy product (12).

1,2:3,6:3',6'-TRIANHYDRO-4,4'-DIACETYL SUCROSE. The diacetate is made by heating the trianhydrosucrose with acetic anhydride and sodium acetate (12, 95). Its structure has been thoroughly investigated by hydrolysis, reduction with sodium borohydride, and periodate oxidation (12).

3,6 - ANHYDROGALACTOSYL - 1,4:3,6 - DIANHYDROFRUCTOSIDE. This compound (Figure 2-1, Compound II) is obtained by hydrolyzing 4,1′,6′-tritosyl sucrose pentaacetate with sodium ethoxide in boiling ethyl alcohol (12, 95). The pentaacetate is first deacetylated by the alkali. The formation of the 3,6-anhydrogalactose from the glucose moiety proceeds through the formation of 3,4-epoxide ring (Step 1) followed by migration of the epoxide ring to the 2,3-position (Step 2) to make available a route for the closure of the 3,6-anhydro ring (Step 3). The galacto configuration is achieved by the inversion of carbon *4* (Step 1) with the two successive inversions at carbon *3* (Steps 2 and 3) leading to a net retention of configuration at the latter center. Steps 4 and 5 are a well-recognized type of reaction.

Compound II is also obtained by treatment of the tritosylate with a strongly basic ion-exchange resin (255c). The tritosylate is made by direct tosylation of sucrose so that it should yield almost exclusively the 6,1′,6′ derivative. The reported high yield (62%) of the derivative indicates that such tosylation could possibly produce the 1′,4,6′-tritosylate in high proportion (255c).

The substance is unattacked by treatment with 25% aqueous potassium hydroxide at 100°C for 24 hours, or by hydrazine for 12 hours (95). It resists periodates at pH 8, but is decomposed by treatment at pH 5 (95).

DIACETATE. The crystalline diacetate is made by heating the compound with acetic anhydride and sodium acetate (12, 95).

DIMETHYL DERIVATIVE. Treatment with excess methyl iodide and silver oxide gives the crystalline dimethyl ether (12, 95).

DITOSYLATE. This compound is made by conventional tosylation (95). It is crystalline and unchanged by treatment with both sodium iodide in acetone and hydrazine at 100°C.

The chemical properties and structure of the trianhydro derivatives have been thoroughly investigated (12).

Internal ethers of other carbohydrates

ANHYDRIDES OF DIFRUCTOSE. Fructose has a tendency to form bimolecular cyclic anhydrides. [See *Advances in Carbohydrate Chemistry*, **2**, 253 (1946)]. Anhydrides of difructose can be made by treatment of the aqueous solution of fructose with acid or heat, or by acid depolymerization of inulin. The products are mixtures of isomeric pyranose and furanose anhydrides with a central 1,4-dioxane ring.

Difructose anhydride, prepared by acid depolymerization of inulin triacetate, is the 2,1′-anhydro derivative (98). The configuration and conformation of the anhydride have been thoroughly studied.

Treatment of fructose with concentrated hydrochloric acid at −5°C yields several isomers and possibly anomers of difructose-1,2′:2,1′-dianhydrides, (fructopyranose-fructofuranose, difructofuranose, difructopyranose, α- or β-linkage, etc.) (161, 162, 164). Some of the isomers have been previously reported. Similar dianhydrides are formed by heat treatment (161, 163). The reaction also yields 0.1% glucose and 0.6% 5-hydroxymethyl-2-furaldehyde (163).

3,6-ANHYDRO-1,2-ISOPROPYLIDENE GLUCOSE. This anhydride was prepared by the thermal decomposition of 1,2-isopropylidene glucose-5,6-carbonate (53).

DIANHYDROMANNITOL. Two anhydrides, 1,5:3,6-dianhydro—(66, 132) and 1,2:5,6-dianhydromannitol (132) have been prepared and their structures studied.

2,5-MONOANHYDROSORBITOL. The compound prepared from 1,6-dibenzoylmannitol with sodium methoxide is 2,5-monoanhydrosorbitol, and not 2,5-monoanhydromannitol, as previously reported by Brigl and Gruner (67).

Table 2-1
Physical properties of saturated sucrose ethers

METHYL ETHERS

Monomethyl sucrose
Pale yellow glass. $[\alpha]_D$ +60.6° (20°C), c. 2.1, water. It is a mixture of isomers, chiefly the 2- and 1'- ether. (18)
4,1',6'-Trimethyl sucrose
Colorless viscous oil. $[\alpha]_D$ +67.6° (24°C), c. 174, water. (104)
4,1',6'-Trimethyl-2,3,6,3',4'-pentaacetyl sucrose
Colorless glassy product. $[\alpha]_D$ +57.7° (17°C), c. 3.72, CHCl$_3$. (104)
Pentamethyl sucrose
Oil. $[\alpha]_D$ +16° (23°C), c. 0.75, CHCl$_3$. Contains two compounds. (90)
Octamethyl sucrose
Oil. B.p. 162-165°C at 0.4 mm. $[\alpha]_D$ +61.9° (20°C), c. 1.1, CHCl$_3$. n_D^{20} 1.4570. Contains traces of a partially methylated sucrose. (90)
Oil. B.p. 150°C at 0.0008 mm. $[\alpha]_D$ +69.6° (25°C), c. 0.1, MeOH. n_D^{24} 1.4571. (269h)

OTHER ALKYL ETHERS

Monooctyl sucrose
Colorless solid. M.p. <25°C. $[\alpha]_D$ +52.8° (20°C) in ethyl alcohol. $[M]_D^{20}$ 240° (ethyl alcohol). Crystalline at 0°C, melts to a sticky glass below room temperature. (196a)
Monodecyl sucrose
White solid. M.p. 23-25°C. $[\alpha]_D$ +45.7° (20°C) in ethyl alcohol. $[M]_D^{20}$ 221° (ethyl alcohol). (196a)
Monolauryl sucrose
White crystal. M.p. 54-56°C. $[\alpha]_D$ +46° (20°C) in ethyl alcohol. (196c)
Monopalmityl sucrose
White solid. M.p. 48-50°C. $[\alpha]_D$ +36.5° (20°C) in ethyl alcohol. $[M]_D^{20}$ 207° (ethyl alcohol). (196a)
Monostearyl sucrose
White granules. M.p. 55-57°C. $[\alpha]_D$ +30.0° (20°C) in ethyl alcohol. $[M]_D^{20}$ 179° (ethyl alcohol). (196a)

TRITYL ETHERS

Tritrityl sucrose
Colorless glass. M.p. 125-130°C. Not pure compound. (104)
6,1′,6′-Tritrityl-2,3,4,3′,4′-pentaacetyl sucrose
Colorless hexagonal plates. M.p. 236°C. $[\alpha]_D$ +68.9° (17°C), c. 2.45, CHCl₃.
(104, 221b)

SILYL ETHERS

Penta(trimethylsilyl) sucrose
Colorless viscous oil. B.p. 147-150°C at 1 mm. (238b)
Hexa(trimethylsilyl) sucrose
Oil. B.p. 304-306°C at 0.6 mm. $[\alpha]_D$ +39.8° (18°C), c. 2.44, CHCl₃. n_D^{20} 1.4510.
(55)
Octa(trimethylsilyl) sucrose
Colorless viscous oil. B.p. 190-200°C at 0.6 mm. $[\alpha]_D$ +3.47° (20°C), c. 50,
benzene. n_D^{20} 1.4434. The low rotation given is probably inaccurate. (41)
Colorless viscous oil. B.p. 195-196°C at 0.2 mm. $[\alpha]_D$ +36.2° (23°C), c. 1.26,
CHCl₃. $n_D^{19.5}$ 1.4459. (90)
Colorless viscous oil. B.p. 250-260°C at 0.6 mm. $[\alpha]_D$ +31.1° (16°C), c. 2.73,
CHCl₃. n_D^{19} 1.4445. (55)
Hexa(triphenylsilyl) sucrose
White solid, M.p. 105-110°C. $[\alpha]_D$ +22° (20°C), c. 3.5, CHCl₃. (11)
6,1,6′-Tri(tricyclohexylsilyl) sucrose
Solid. M.p. 150-160°C. $[\alpha]_D$ +21° (21°C). c. 1.1, pyridine. (11)

OTHER ETHERS

Octabenzyl sucrose
Pale yellow oil. $[\alpha]_D$ +15° (22°C), c. 4.84, CHCl₃. Contains some dimethyl-
formamide, benzyl bromide, and partially etherified sucrose. (90)
Tetra-2-cyanoethyl sucrose
Pale yellow oil. $[\alpha]_D$ +35.05° (20.8°C), c. 0.505, acetone, Contains 35% di-2-
cyanoethyl ether. (82)
Octa-2-cyanoethyl sucrose
Solid. $[\alpha]_D$ +36.4° (18.8°C), c. 0.08, CHCl₃. (11, 82)
Pentacarboxymethyl sucrose trimethyl ester dilactone of sucrose
Colorless rhombic crystals. M.p. 140°C. $[\alpha]_D$ +35.5° (20°C). c. 3.25, CHCl₃.
Starts to decompose at 80°C. (277)

D

Di(2-hydroxyethyl) sucrose
White needles. M.p. 215°C. [α]$_D$ −38.7° (25°C). c. 2.95, H$_2$O. Structure uncertain. Obtained with small yield as a by-product of the reaction of sucrose with ethylene oxide. (94)

Mesityl oxide ether of sucrose
White crystals. M.p. 72-74°C. Mono derivative. Contains some diether. (191)

4,6-Bis(2′-chloro-4′-nitrophenoxy)triazine ether of sucrose
Yellow glassy product. [α]$_D$ +9.1-10.0°. c. 2.5, dimethoxyethane. Structure not established. (19)

INTERNAL ETHERS

3,6:3′, 6′-Dianhydro-2,4,1′,4′-tetraacetyl sucrose
Crystal M.p. 69-71°C. [α]$_D$ +32.5° (25°C). (194j)

1′,2:3,6:3′,6′-Trianhydro sucrose
Crystal. M.p. 163-164.5°C. [α]$_D$ +117.0°, c. 0.92, CHCl$_3$ (101)

1′,2:3,6:3′,6′-Trianhydro-4,4′-ditosyl
Crystal. M.p. 164.5-166°C. (101)

1′,2:3,6:3′,6′-Trianhydro-4,4′-dimethyl sucrose
Crystal. M.p. 179-181°C. [α]$_D$ +140.0° (24°C), c. 1.9, CHCl$_3$. (101)

1′,2:3,6:3′,6′-Trianhydro-4,4′-diacetyl sucrose
Crystal. M.p. 181.5-182.5°C. [α]$_D$ +128.6°, c. 1.8, CHCl$_3$. (95)

3,6-Anhydro-α-D-galactosyl-1,4:3,6-dianhydro-β-D-fructoside
Crystal. M.p. 191-192.5°C. [α]$_D$ +137.5°, c. 1.6, water.
This compound (and its derivatives) are made from 4,1′,6′-tritosyl sucrose (See text). (95)

2,4-Diacetyl derivative
Crystal. M.p. 137.5-138.5°C. [α]$_D$ +94.3°, c. 2.0, CHCl$_3$. (95)

2,4-Dimethyl derivative
Crystal. M.p. 105-106°C. [α]$_D$ +48.6°, c. 1.45, CHCl$_3$. (95)

2,4-Ditosyl derivative
Crystal. M.p. 158-159°C. (95)

Table 2-2
Properties of allyl sucrose and related unsaturated derivatives

ETHERS

Allyl sucrose
Degree of substitution 5. Viscosity at 100°C, 46.2 centistokes. Light yellow oil. Yield 80-90%. n$_D$ 1.4974. Gelation time at 100°C, 224 min. (308)
Degree of substitution 6-7. Light yellow oil. Yield 80-90%. n$_D$ 1.4846-90.

Allyl sucrose—*continued*

Gelation time at 100°C, 205-210 min. Prepared on pilot-plant scale. The properties of allyl sucrose depend on the degree of polymerization during the reaction. (See text). (170)

Degree of substitution 7, $[\alpha]_D^{25}$ +50.5°. Light yellow oil. n_D 1.4912. (114)

Degree of substitution 8, d_D^{20} 0.9837; molecular refraction 178.0°. Light yellow oil. n_D 1.4822. (305)

Degree of substitution 8, $[\alpha]_D^{19}$ +45.4°, C. 1.4, CHCl₃. Light yellow oil. Yield 90%. n_D 1.4818. (90)

Allylbutyl sucrose

Degree of substitution 6.7 allyl, 0.9 butyl. Brown oil. Yield 35%. n_D 1.4801. Gelation time at 100°C, 300 min. (169)

Allylbenzyl sucrose

Degree of substitution 6.1 allyl, 1.0 benzyl. Light brown oil. Yield 50%. n_D 1.5090. Gelation time at 100°C, 590 min. (169)

β-Methallyl sucrose

Degree of substitution 6. Gelation time at 100°C, 465 min. (169)

Degree of substitution 7.5, $[\alpha]_D$ +42.1°; d_4^{20} 1.0303. n_D 1.4835. (305)

Crotyl sucrose

Degree of substitution 6.2. Gelation time at 100°C, 2175 min. Prepared from sucrose in aqueous alkali. (169)

Degree of substitution probably 5 (not given in reference). Yellow oil. Yield 62%. Prepared from pentasodium sucrate. $[\alpha]_D$ +34° in ethyl alcohol. (17)

ESTERS OF ALLYL SUCROSE

Allyl methacrylyl sucrose

Degree of substitution 6.7 allyl, 1.2 methacrylyl. Yellow oil. n_D 1.4788. Gelation time at 100°C, 78 min. (169, 174)

Allyl acetyl sucrose

Degree of substitution 6.7 allyl, 1.3 acetyl. Light brown oil. n_D 1.4782. Gelation time at 100°C, 226 min. (131)

Allyl propionyl sucrose

Degree of substitution 6.7 allyl, 1.2 propionyl. Light brown oil. n_D 1.4763. Gelation time at 100°C, 258 min. (131)

Allyl lauroyl sucrose

Degree of substitution 6.7 allyl, 1.3 lauroyl. Brown oil. n_D 1.4671. Gelation time at 100°C, 258 min. (131)

Allyl benzoyl sucrose

Degree of substitution 6.7 allyl, 1.3 benzoyl. Light brown oil. n_D 1.5171. Gelation time at 100°C, 229 min. (131)

NOTE: Refractive indices are measured at 19-25°C. Gelation time is determined in the presence of oxygen as described in *J. Am. Chem. Soc.* **68**, 2020 (1946).

3

Fatty esters

S UCROSE ESTERS of fatty acids are generally prepared either by acylation with an acid chloride or anhydride or by transesterification with fatty esters. The degree of substitution ranges from one to eight. Esterification of sucrose was first attempted by Berthelot in 1860 and later reported by many workers. Many of the researchers failed to obtain an ester, probably because sucrose degrades easily under the conditions of heat and acidity normally used in the preparation of fatty acid esters.

The Foundation has sponsored a great deal of research in this field, particularly in the development and scale-up of the transesterification method, since this is probably the only economically feasible process for the production of potentially important monoesters and higher esters. Many of the products, particularly the polyesters, are often mixtures of esters with differing degrees of substitution. However, some monoesters and diesters can be prepared in pure form. A future goal is refinement of the transesterification technique so that any of the desired esters can be obtained in the possible purest form by well-controlled standardized methods of economically competitive prices.

Sucrose esters have many potential uses, particularly as surfactants (Table 15-1) and surface coatings (Table 16-1) but also as humectants, plasticizers, and ingredients of suppositories. Sucrose acetate isobutyrate, SAIB®, is commercially available for use as an additive for lacquers and hot-melt adhesives. Sucrose octaacetate is a widely used denaturant for ethyl alcohol and a modifier for adhesives.

METHODS OF PREPARATION

Acylation in pyridine

Conventional acylation with the acid chloride or anhydride in pyridine is the best, if not the most economical, method for the preparation of sugar esters with a high degree of substitution. (Acid chlorides or anhydrides are generally too expensive.) However, with the exception of sucrose monoacetate (see below), this process is not practical for the preparation of lower esters (143). A detailed study on acylation with myristoyl chloride shows that

52

the product is a mixture of highly substituted sucrose myristates (16). With this method the following compounds were prepared:

— Sucrose monoacetate

— Sucrose linseedates (degree of substitution 6-7)

— Saturated fatty esters (C_2-C_{18}) of sucrose (degree of substitution 7-8)

Transesterification

Since the 1950's many studies on transesterification of sucrose with methyl and other lower alkanol esters of fatty acids have been sponsored by the Sugar Research Foundation. The process basically consists of transesterification in a dry aprotic solvent, preferably dimethyl formamide, at elevated temperatures in the presence of an alkaline catalyst, preferably potassium carbonate, followed by stripping of the methyl alcohol formed under reduced pressure or by simple distillation:

$$\text{Sucrose} + \text{methyl fatty ester} \rightleftharpoons \text{sucrose fatty ester} + \text{methyl alcohol.}$$

With this method a wide range of useful sugar esters can be produced under economically attractive and competitive conditions. The methyl esters of fatty acids are relatively plentiful and inexpensive. They are available as intermediates in a number of processes for recovering fatty acids from agricultural and paper mill wastes.

The process was first developed and patented for the production of mono- and diesters (58, 119). Additional work on improved production methods and the reaction mechanism led to a dependable and well-standardized method summarized in a report available from the Foundation (143).

The first experiments for the preparation of polyesters were rather unsuccessful (198). A successful process was later patented (57) and further developed into a pilot-plant process (23) for the production of higher esters of the drying oil type (linseed and linoleic esters) with a degree of substitution of about six to seven. The engineering and pilot-plant data are available from the Foundation (142) as well as a review on the preparation of the higher fatty esters by similar techniques (141).

In general, it is essential to operate under strictly water-free conditions. Otherwise the rate of transesterification considerably decreases, and side reactions, mainly saponification and hydrolysis, occur (143). Moderate temperatures are also required. Heating sucrose alone in aqueous dimethyl formamide at 100°C for two hours completely destroys the sucrose molecule (26). The reaction products are chiefly fructose and glucose.

The reaction conditions can be set so as to give the ester with the desired degree of substitution. For example, sucrose monostearate is prepared by reacting three moles of sucrose with one mole of methyl stearate in the presence of 3 grams of potassium carbonate per mole of sucrose. The reaction is carried out in about 1.1 liters of dimethyl formamide per mole of sucrose at 90°C and pressures of 70 mm for six hours. The distearate is made in more concentrated solution with the theoretical amounts of reactants in the presence of 12 grams of catalyst per mole of sucrose (143). When excess methyl ester is employed, the degree of substitution increases to six to seven (141, 142).

Other methods

Unsuccessful exploratory tests have been carried out to prepare sugar esters by other methods. Among these reactions are:

Glycerol esters of fatty acids + sucrose (311b)
Stearic acid + sucrose (311b)
Stearic acid + pentaacetyl glucose (311b)
Fatty acid chloride or anhydride + pentasodium sucrate (see Table 9-3)

PROPERTIES

Little is known about the composition of sucrose esters. Except for the fully-substituted octaesters, all other esters are mixtures of isomers, generally with varying degrees of substitution. These mixtures are oils or amorphous solids that are extremely difficult to purify to the individual components. Separation by chromatography is probably the only method of purification, as discussed below under Monoesters.

Of the "crystalline" monoesters, the studies of sucrose monomyristate reveal that it contains about 60% 6'-ester, about 30% 6-ester, and 10% other isomers (97).

The fatty esters are stable compounds that can be stored without deterioration. They tend to decompose in aqueous solution, particularly in alkaline media and hydrolyze easily in acidic solution. None of the esters, except the lower acetates and some monoesters of fatty acids, are soluble in water. They are soluble in many common organic solvents, the lower esters in ketones and alcohols, the higher esters in hydrocarbons and oils.

The properties of sucrose fatty esters are given in Tables 3-1 and 3-2. (See also Surfactants and Surface Coatings, page 192.)

MONOESTERS

The preparation and properties of sucrose monoesters of the fatty acids (C_{12} to C_{22}) have been thoroughly studied because of their promising surfactant and detersive qualities and their nonionic character.

Of the lower homologs, *sucrose monoacetate*, a good humectant, can be prepared in good yield by the conventional method of acylation with acetic anhydride in pyridine. The preparation of sucrose fatty esters by transesterification was first described in the literature by the Foundation in the 1950's (58, 119, 120, 122). Further studies (16, 100, 103, 245, 260e) on the reaction led to the development of well-controlled, standardized methods, summarized in a report available from the Foundation (143).

The recommended laboratory-scale reaction is carried out with 3 moles of sucrose and one mole of methyl ester in the presence of 3 grams of potassium carbonate catalyst in about 1.1 liter of dimethyl formamide per mole of sucrose at 90°C and 70 mm pressure for six hours (143). The conversion of methyl ester is close to 100%, and yields are up to 90%.

The transesterification with sodium methoxide catalyst also gives 100% conversion and high yields. The reaction proceeds under similar conditions, except in more dilute solution and with a somewhat higher level of catalyst per mole of sucrose. The reduction in the amount of solvent used in the former method can reduce the rate of solution of the catalyst, but homogeneous conditions will be attained during the reaction. Less solvent is important in view of the cost of large-scale use of dimethyl formamide.

The esters are claimed to be of very high purity, as determined by their fatty acid content. However, *sucrose monostearate*, the product most widely studied in this preparation, is said to be of 80-90% purity.

The apparatus for the bench-scale reaction and the continuous process is described and details of the process are given in Reference 143.

THEORETICAL STUDIES. The mechanism and kinetics of the esterification reaction have been thoroughly studied by many workers and reviewed in the Foundation report. Investigations have been made on the rate of reaction and the effect of such parameters as type and concentration of catalyst, concentration of reactants, type of solvent, influence of water, chain length of fatty acid, side reactions and equilibrium measurements for the two reactions:

(1) Sucrose + sucrose dimyristate $\rightleftharpoons$ 2 sucrose monomyristate

(2) Sucrose + methyl myristate $\rightleftharpoons$ sucrose myristate + methyl alcohol

For details of these studies, see References 100 and 103.

COMPOSITION AND PURIFICATION. The sucrose monoester prepared by transesterification always contains some diester and higher esters. Attempts to separate the monoester from the diester by recrystallization have been unsuccessful (143). They produced mixtures of the two esters in the original proportion or even enriched in diester because of reversion according to equation (1), especially if heating is prolonged. However, the monoesters can be separated from the higher esters of sucrose by chromatography on paper impregnated with silicic acid with solutions of methyl alcohol and chloroform as the developing phase (16, 100) or by countercurrent distribution (16). This method can also be used for the separation on silica gel columns on a laboratory or larger scale.

STRUCTURE. Earlier investigations concluded that the substitution takes place preferentially at the 6-position of the glucose moiety (166). Thorough examination by chromatography and nuclear magnetic resonance spectroscopy has indicated that the reaction mixture of the diester-free sucrose monomyristate contains 6′-myristate, 6-myristate sucrose and unidentified isomeric esters in the relative proportion of 0.62:0.28:0.10, respectively (97).

ANALYSIS. The method of analysis recommended by the Foundation are given in Reference 143. They include the analyses of the finished product by saponification, fatty acid content, molecular weight of fatty acids, ratio of monoester to diester, moisture, and content of unreacted starting material and solvent.

Properties

The sucrose monoesters of fatty acids are generally soluble in such common organic solvents as lower alcohols, ketones, and chlorinated hydrocarbons but they are only slightly soluble in water. In a two-phase system of water and organic solvent, the esters concentrate at the interface and are oriented toward the solvent layer by their lipophilic fatty chain. The hydroxyl groups of the sucrose molecule turn to the water surface, a phenomenon characteristic of all surface-active agents.

The esters of saturated fatty acids are white solid products and often crystalline. Sucrose monooleate and esters made with mixtures of fatty acids of natural origin, such as castor oil, coconut oil, linseed oil, are mostly pasty semisolids or oils (143).

Of the monoesters prepared, probably only sucrose myristate has been obtained in pure form. All other monoesters are mixtures, although often claimed to be of high purity. However, purification by chromatography (as described for the sucrose myristate (103) could be applied to other esters if desired.

STABILITY. The dry sucrose esters have good shelf life. No changes are observed after standing in glass jars for more than two years. Only very small changes take place in the sucrose ester after standing for nine months either in dimethyl formamide or in water (143). However, some hydrolysis is observed in alkaline media (see Surfactants, page 173). Under acidic conditions the ester is unstable because the sucrose molecule hydrolyzes into glucose and fructose. Similarly, solutions of the monoester, particularly in nonpolar solvents at higher temperature, disproportionate into diester and sucrose, according to the reversion in equation (2) above.

TOXICITY. Tests performed with selected esters indicate that they are generally nontoxic. They are well tolerated by rats. The only ester which had a deleterious effect on rats at the high level of 5% in the ration was the dipalmitate (143). For details, see Surfactants, page 173.

Sucrose monoacetate

Sucrose monoacetate is prepared by acetylation of sucrose with acetic anhydride in pyridine (93, 242). The yield is close to theoretical, based on reacted sucrose. Analysis by paper chromatography shows traces of higher acetates (93). More thorough analysis by partition chromatography reveals that the compound is actually a mixture of sucrose 17%, sucrose monoacetate 70%, sucrose diacetate 14%, and possibly higher esters. The monoacetate itself is a mixture of the various isomers (16, 179).

Attempts to prepare the monoacetate from sucrose and sucrose octaacetate by transesterification has been unsuccessful (245l).

Sucrose monoacetate is a white hygroscopic, crystalline compound with a melting point of 80-82°C. It can be recrystallized from polar organic solvents, such as lower alcohols, acetone, and dioxane. It is very soluble in water, but insoluble in benzene, toluene, and other nonpolar solvents. In alcoholic solution it is stable for more than six months, but in water it disproportionates into sucrose and higher acetates after 30 days (93).

Sucrose monostearate

Among all the fatty esters the preparation and properties of the monostearate have been the most thoroughly studied. This compound has served as the model to determine optimal conditions for the transesterification and the isolation of the final product (143).

The stearate can be obtained as a white crystalline product of 80-90% monoester content in a yield of 80-90%, based on methyl stearate. Acylation with the acid chloride in pyridine gives chiefly di- and higher esters, similar to those obtained in unsuccessful attempts with other acyl chlorides (143).

SOLUBILITY. At room temperature, the monostearate (with 10% diester content) is sparingly soluble in organic solvents, except butyl alcohol (6.8 g per 100 ml). At higher temperature the solubility increases, particularly in methyl ethyl ketone, the best solvent for recrystallization. The monostearate is unusually soluble in water at room temperature (over 3.9 g per 100 ml) and very soluble in hot water, in which it partially gels. Detailed data on solubility are found in Reference 143.

STABILITY. Solutions in water (saturated) and dimethyl formamide (5% and 10%) are not affected on standing for nine months although some monostearate precipitates from both solvents (143).

REACTIONS. Sucrose stearate does not react with urea to form stearoyl sucrose mono-carbamate (290d).

Sucrose monomyristate

The preparation of the monomyristate has been studied chiefly to obtain data on the reaction mechanism and kinetics of transesterification (100, 103) and to study the composition and structure of the product (16, 97).

As obtained by transesterification in the presence of sodium methoxide with 100% over-all yield of the ester, the monomyristate contains 80% monoester and 20% diester. Catalysis with potassium carbonate is claimed to give similar high yields, as discussed above (143). The two esters can be separated by chromatography on a silicic acid column (97) or by countercurrent distribution (16).

The pure monoester is a white amorphous material that dissolves readily in hot acetone (103). The infrared spectrum is given in Reference 103. Structural studies show that it contains the 6'-ester, 6-ester and unidentified isomers in the proportions 0.62:0.28:0.10 (97).

For analytical studies, a number of derivatives have been prepared from the pure mono-myristate. Among these are:

PENTATOSYL SUCROSE MONOMYRISTATE. Reaction with excess tosyl chloride in pyridine yields a product of 5.18 tosyl groups per molecule of sucrose (97). Treatment of the tosylated product with sodium iodide in acetone replaces two tosyloxy groups, one in primary and the other probably in a secondary position.

HEPTAMETHYL SUCROSE MONOMYRISTATE. The pure monomyristate is reacted with methyl iodide and silver oxide (97). A product is obtained by chromatography identified by its infrared spectrum as the heptaether monoester. Deesterification in boiling methyl alcohol gives heptamethyl sucrose, which is further converted into a monotosyl, monoiodo and monodeoxy derivative of heptamethyl sucrose (see Methyl Ethers, page 19). The composition of the monomyristate was established by the nuclear magnetic resonance spectra of these ether derivatives and by hydrolysis of the methyl ether.

Other monoesters

Various other monoesters have also been prepared by transesterification in good overall yield and quality (143). The composition of these esters was determined indirectly through their fatty acid content. The preparation with an acyl chloride in pyridine is unsuccessful because higher esters are principally formed (143). However, lower esters can be formed when the acylation is carried out in benzene (198).

Monoester (143)	Description
Laurate	Waxy crystalline product. Obtained in 100% purity.
Palmitate	Resembles stearate in most properties. Obtained in 100% purity. Also prepared by transesterification with isopropyl palmitate. Product contains 83% monoester, 15% diester. The preparation of radioactive monopalmitate is given in Reference 16.
Oleate	Semisolid yellow product. Contains 92% monoester, 8% diester. Acylation of three moles of sucrose with one mole of oleyl chloride in pyridine to prepare monooleate is not successful (260c). Product contains 2.3-2.8 oleyl groups per molecule of sucrose.
Behenate	Hard white waxy solid. Obtained in 100% purity.
Ricinoleate	Semisolid, obtained in 100% purity.
Cocoate	Soft, white semitransparent solid, obtained in 100% purity. Gives most stable foam of all esters tried so far.
Linseedate	Orange-colored semisolid, obtained in 100% purity. Acylation with acyl chloride in benzene gives a mixture of mono- and dilinseedate (198).
Linoleate (142)	Brittle, amber-colored, creamy solid.

DIESTERS

Sucrose diesters of fatty acids are made by reacting sucrose with the theoretical amount of the methyl ester of a fatty acid in the presence of 12 grams of potassium carbonate catalyst and 2 liters of dimethyl formamide per mole of sucrose (143). The reaction proceeds at 90°C and 70 mm pressure for about ten hours. This reaction was developed simultaneously with that for the monoesters, discussed above. The diesters are obtained in good yield. The products are mostly semisolid or oily in appearance. Most esters are obtained in high purity, often without any monoester or other contaminants according to their fatty acid content (143). However, only the dimyristate has been purified and analyzed by chromatography (103).

The diesters are more soluble than the monoesters in such nonpolar solvents as aliphatic and aromatic hydrocarbons or oils. Sucrose dipalmitate appears toxic to rats at the level of 5% in the feed ration. However, sucrose cottonseedate, containing approximately 60% monoester and 40% diester, shows no overt toxic symptoms at a level of 25% (143).

The diesters are recommended as emulsifiers for water-in-oil emulsions.

Sucrose distearate

Sucrose distearate is a white crystalline solid obtained in about 80% yield by transesterification (143). It is the most thoroughly studied sucrose diester since it was used as the model in studying the optimal conditions for preparation. The diester (with 10% monoester content) is very soluble in benzene (51 g per 100 ml) as compared with the monoester (1.24 g). This solvent can be used to separate the sucrose stearates by recrystallization. The distearate is also more soluble in hot dimethyl formamide (over 118 g) than the monostearate (20 g). The distearate is sparingly soluble in other organic solvents and in water. For detailed data on solubility, see Reference 143.

Stability tests conducted with 5% solutions in dimethyl formamide (143) show that on standing gels form that are not completely stable.

Other diesters

Other diesters prepared by transesterification are (143):

Diester	Description
Sucrose dimyristate	Solid, pure product obtained by chromatography (103). Presently it is probably the only well characterized diester of high purity (Table 3-1).
Sucrose dioleate	Almost fluid. 100% diester.
Sucrose diricinoleate	Semisolid. Contains monoester.
Sucrose dicocoate	Soft semisolid. Contains 30% monococoate.
Sucrose dicottonseedate	Pure diester. Also prepared in an impure form with low toxicity and good dispersibility.
Sucrose ditallate	Dark brown liquid, pure diester.
Sucrose dilinseedate	Very viscous amber liquid. 100% diester. Also made by acylation of sucrose with linseed oil acid chloride in benzene (198). However, this product may contain mono- and triesters.
Sucrose dilinoleate (142)	Brittle, creamy, solid.

TRIESTERS AND TETRAESTERS

Although more highly substituted esters of sucrose are probably present in standard transesterification reaction mixtures, they have not been obtained in easily isolated amounts from these reactions.

Direct transesterification with a methyl ester and sucrose in the ratio of 3:1 yields sucrose esters with a degree of substitution of 1.25. If the ratio increased to 4:1, the degree of substitution rises to 2 (143).

Transesterification to the triester is achieved by reacting a sucrose diester with one mole of the methyl ester of the fatty acid without solvent in the presence of about 8 grams of potassium carbonate per mole of sucrose diester (143). The reaction is carried out for eight hours at 90 to 120°C and pressures of 2-4 mm.

SUCROSE TRISTEARATE, a white solid of high purity, and *sucrose trioleate* are made by this method. Other triesters can also be prepared similarly. *Sucrose trilinoleate*, an amber-colored semisolid, is reputedly obtained by direct transesterification of sucrose (142), and the oily *trilinseedate* by acylation of sucrose with acyl chloride in benzene (198). The latter contains some diester.

Tetraesters are made similarly to the triesters by transesterification of the sucrose diesters with the theoretical amount of the methyl ester of the fatty acid in the absence of solvent (57, 143). *Sucrose tetralinseedate* and *sucrose tetraoleate*, both oily products, are made by this method. *Sucrose tetralinoleate* is prepared by direct transesterification of sucrose (142). It is a very viscous, transparent oil.

PENTA-, HEXA-, AND HEPTAESTERS
Pentaacetyl sucrose and derivatives

2,3,6,3',4'-PENTAACETYL SUCROSE. This pentaacetate is an intermediate in the preparation of 1',4,6'-trimethyl sucrose (104) and possibly trivinyl sucrose (221b). It is made by the partial hydrolysis of tritrityl (triphenylmethyl) pentaacetyl (see below) in glacial acetic acid. Some hydrolysis of the glycosidic linkage occurs during the detritylation since the reaction mixture shows a reducing action toward Fehling's solution. The trityl group cannot be completely removed by catalytic hydrogenation. Removal of the trityl groups with hydrogen bromide in acetic acid produces strong inversion (splitting of the glycosidic linkage). During detritylation in acetic acid, acyl migration can take place, which may cause the migration of acetyl groups from the original secondary hydroxyls. One such migration probably takes place from the 4 to the 6 position. The suggested structure thus is 2,3,6,3',4'-pentaacetyl sucrose.

The crystalline product is soluble in methyl alcohol, acetone and chloroform, and insoluble in water and petroleum ether.

Tritritylpentaacetyl, trivinyl pentaacetyl, and trimethyl pentaacetyl sucrose

These mixed ether-esters are intermediates in the preparation of trimethyl and vinyl sucrose. They are discussed under Methyl, Vinyl, and Trityl Ethers, pages 19, 34, and 25.

LINOLEATES AND RELATED ESTERS

During the past ten years considerable work has been carried out to develop an economical and standardized process for the preparation of the higher esters of fatty acids. The unsaturated esters have promising coating properties in oleoresinous formulations and possibly in latex paints (see Surface Coatings, page 192). Transesterification is the only economic process since acylation with acid chloride or anhydride is either technically unfeasible or too costly. Also, products made by the acid chloride process in general possess poorer coating qualities than products of transesterification (141).

These esters are mixtures with an average degree of substitution of six to seven. A high degree of substitution is necessary to obtain products with the high content of unsaturates required for good drying properties. Also, the elimination of hydroxyl groups by esterification increases the water resistance of the products. The octaesters would fit these requirements ideally, but they are very difficult to prepare economically by transesterification. Esters with a lower degree of substitution may be useful in compounded products.

The transesterification process has been patented (57). The process has been considerably refined and improved (22, 43, 47, 52, 151). However, further work is needed to standardize production methods.

The reaction is carried out with 100% excess of the methyl ester in dimethyl formamide at reflux temperature at 115 mm pressure. Potassium carbonate is used as the catalyst at 85 grams per mole of sucrose. The amount of solvent is about 8.3 liters per mole of sucrose. The ester is obtained in a yield of over 90%, based on the converted sucrose. The unreacted fatty ester can be recycled.

Potassium carbonate, originally recommended for the production of monoesters and later for higher esters, is the preferred catalyst for this reaction also. A variety of other catalysts, including ion-exchange resins, have been tested. Only barium hydroxide shows good activity. Alcoholysis between sucrose and methyl linseedate with this catalyst gives esters with a degree of substitution of five to six. Similar reactions catalyzed by soda-lime produce lower esters. Most other catalysts are ineffective.

In further studies reproducible process conditions have been established for the laboratory-scale synthesis of sucrose esters with a degree of substitution of about six. Additional modifications have yielded products of better quality and a higher degree of substitution, as described below. The important developments on preparation and properties have recently been summarized in reports available from the Foundation (141, 142).

Preparation of sucrose esters with a degree of substitution of five and six can also be carried out in a manner similar to the preparation of triesters—namely, from the sucrose diester plus the methyl ester without a solvent (143).

Sucrose linoleates

Methyl linoleate was chosen for the pilot plant experiments on unsaturated esters because, unlike methyl linseedate, its color remains stable when it is heated or aged in a paint film. The reaction is carried out in a nitrogen atmosphere to prevent the formation of undesirable products. Process modifications such as more vigorous stirring for rapid removal of the methyl alcohol produced gives a product with a degree of substitution of 6.4-7.0 and improved color and viscosity in a shorter reaction time than in previous work (141).

One of the important accomplishments of the pilot plant program has been the development of a method for separating the unreacted excess of methyl ester from the sucrose ester. Recovery is important both for economic reasons and because retention of as little as 0.1% of methyl ester significantly inhibits the drying rate of the films (21).

The improved transesterification process on the laboratory scale is described in Reference 141. Engineering and pilot-plant data are briefly summarized in Reference 23 and described in detail in References 142 and 206. Further improvements are given in Reference 286.

ANALYSIS. Methods suggested to determine the extent of esterification include saponification and hydroxyl numbers, measurement of the recovered methyl alcohol and methyl linoleate, and possibly molecular weight (23, 141, 142, 206). More recently infrared spectroscopy has been recommended as the most convenient method of analysis (286). The infrared spectrum of the heptaester is given in Reference 141.

ECONOMICS. Preliminary calculations indicate a total cost of production of sucrose hexalinoleate of 13-19 ¢ a pound and a selling price of 25-30 ¢ (at 1963 prices) (142).

Sucrose linseedates

Sucrose linseedates have recently been prepared by the improved direct transesterification method (141) and also by acylation with linseed oil chloride in pyridine (198). With both methods an equally high degree of substitution (six to seven) can be achieved. However, the product made by acylation has poorer film-forming properties (52, 141). The linseedate is reportedly obtained in yields up to 90% by the pyridine-acid chloride process (230). The penta- and hexalinseedates can also be prepared from sucrose dilinseedates by transesterification in the presence of potassium sulfite as catalyst (143). The presence of sulfur is claimed to prevent color formation.

Esters of other unsaturated fatty acids

Polyesters of other unsaturated fatty acids or mixtures can be made by a transesterification process similar to that used for sucrose linoleates (141). These products also have a fairly high degree of substitution, as shown in Table 3-2.

Preparation of *sucrose tallates* has been attempted by acylating sucrose in pyridine with the mixed anhydride of tall oil fatty acid and acetic acid (245j, k) and with tall oil anhydride (245k), and by transesterifying sucrose or sucrose octaacetate (245k). Little or no conversion occurred.

Properties

SOLUBILITY. Sucrose oils with an ester content of six or higher are soluble in hydrocarbons and such solvents as cyclohexane and methylethylketone. Rheological measurements show that the esters form complexes in such solvents (20). Only the mono- and diesters are soluble in methyl alcohol; all other esters are insoluble (142). This difference in solubility can be used for large scale purification.

VISCOSITY. The higher esters have low to medium viscosity, as shown in Table 3-2. The pentalinoleate is very viscous, while the lower esters are solids or semisolids (142). The viscosity of products made by acylation is considerably higher, probably as the result of partial polymerization. The dilute solution viscosity, specific and intrinsic viscosities, and critical concentration of sucrose oils are given in References 20 and 141.

COLOR. In general, the products have medium color according to the Gardner standard (Table 3-2). Products made by the new process are somewhat lighter (142).

COMPATABILITY WITH RESINS. Sucrose esters are very compatible with such resins as acrylics, alkyds, some epoxies, phenolics, vinyls and ureas. They are less miscible with some epoxy polyethers and chlorinated rubber (Table 16-2).

EMULSIFICATION. Sucrose esters can be emulsified in water to form stable and homogeneous emulsions (21, 23). The ease of emulsification depends upon the average degree of esterification. Mono- and diesters form microemulsions in water in nearly any concentrations with a clarity resembling the ideal solution. Tri-, tetra-, and pentaesters form stable oil-in-water or water-in-oil emulsions, depending on the conditions of emulsification. Higher esters can be successfully emulsified with the help of electrolytes or surfactants. Products with a high hydroxyl content often do not require any emulsifier. Sucrose mono-linoleate forms stable oil-in-water emulsions of blown and unblown tetra- to heptalinoleates (47).

Among the emulsifiers suggested are the monoesters of sucrose in amounts from 0.01% to 1%, depending on the degree of esterification (21). Blown (oxidized) products need some-what higher concentrations. Stable emulsions, with good shelf life over a two-month period, can also be obtained with the help of a nonionic castor oil surfactant at 2% (141), and soaps and other ionic and nonionic emulsifiers at less than 5% (23).

The self-emulsifying properties of sucrose esters allow the preparation of emulsions with a minimal amount of additive compared to that necessary for natural drying oils. The prep-aration of stable emulsions is a prime requirement in the emulsion copolymerization of sucrose oils with styrene and styrene-butadiene (21).

POLYMERIZATION AND COPOLYMERIZATION. The tetra-, penta-, and hexaesters can be copolymerized with such reactive vinyl monomers as styrene, or with diisocyanates to urethanes to form potentially valuable coatings and plastics (see Surface Coatings, page 192). Limited tests on homopolymerization of emulsions in the presence of potassium persulfate have been unsuccessful (21).

GENERAL. The properties of sucrose esters of unsaturated fatty acids are given on Table 3-2. For application properties, see Surface Coatings, page 192. Details on testing viscosity, oxidation rates, compatibility and film-forming properties are given in Reference 43. Proper-ties of linseed sucrose esters prepared in pyridine are described in Reference 198.

MISCELLANEOUS ESTERS. The pentaacetyl and four other penta-fatty esters of sucrose have been prepared by reacting pentasodium sucrate with the appropriate acid halide or an-hydride, as shown in Table 9-3.

OCTAESTERS

As discussed above, it is very difficult to prepare the octaesters of sucrose. Acylation with an anhydride or acid chloride in pyridine is the most successful but expensive process. Satu-rated fatty esters with a degree of substitution of 7.1 to 8 can be made by this method in yields of 70 to 87% (Table 3-1). Conventional transesterification does not yield the octa-ester. However, a laboratory-scale method for the preparation of the octalinseedate is given in Reference 216.

Attempts to prepare sucrose octalinseedate from the dilinseedate by transesterification (245e, i) or the reaction of sucrose and the acid chloride of linseed oil in pyridine (198, 230) have been unsuccessful. The products were only the penta, hexa-, or heptaesters. However, the octaesters are claimed to be obtained by reacting sucrose with the phenyl ester of the fatty acid at elevated temperatures in the presence of potassium carbonate (British Patent 925, 718).

Sucrose octaacetate

Sucrose octaacetate is used primarily as a denaturant for alcohol, and also as a plasticizer and a component in adhesive formulations.

Sucrose octaacetate is produced by acylation with acetic anhydride in the presence of pyridine or sodium acetate as catalysts. Successful preparation has been demonstrated from beet molasses (297). The process requires the removal of water from the molasses and decolorization of the crude ester obtained. Attempts to acylate in an aqueous alkaline medium similar to that used for the preparation of alkyloxycarbonyl sucrose have had little success (193b).

Acylation in aqueous caustic soda with a 40-mole excess of acetic anhydride, as described recently in the literature [Prey et al., *Monats. Chem.* **91**, 729 (1960); Ball et al., *J. Org. Chem.* **27**, 4120 (1962)] gives a complex mixture of highly substituted acetates including the octaester (194b). Crystalline, pure octaacetate is then separated by chromatography together with three other products that are apparently pure but have not been characterized.

The octaacetate is a white crystalline compound with a melting point of about 90°C. The hydrolysis of the octaester in normal hydrochloric acid in aqueous dioxane is considerably slower than in aqueous alcohol at room temperature (193b). Its hydrolysis is slower than that of sucrose itself in hydrochloric acid, but considerably faster than the alkyloxycarbonyl sucroses (Figure 4-1).

Attempted condensations with benzaldehyde in the presence of zinc chloride, sulfosalicylic acid or hydrogen chloride have not been successful (193b). Inversion occurred in all cases except with zinc chloride.

Attempts to chlorinate the octaacetate with chlorine or phosphorus pentachloride have been unsuccessful (297). A mixture of chlorinated esters and hydrolysis products are obtained. For the reaction with metal oxides and salts, see Metal Derivatives, page 126.

Octaesters of other fatty acids

Octaesters of sucrose have been prepared with nine saturated fatty acids from propionic to stearic (171) (Table 3-1). The octaesters from caprylate to myristate had not been described previously in the literature. The propionic and butyric acid esters are made with the anhydride, and all others with the acyl chloride in pyridine. The preparation of octastearate has also been attempted by transesterification with the methylester (141). However, the products have a lower degree of substitution (between six and seven), lower melting points, and darker colors.

All the esters except the palmitate and stearate are soluble in acetone. The esters up to sucrose caprylate are also soluble in ethyl alcohol, and those up to caproyl sucrose also in methyl alcohol. All esters are readily soluble in nonpolar solvents (171). The octaester of undecylenic acid has also been prepared and its plastic properties tested (Table 4-3).

Mixed esters

SUCROSE ACETATE ISOBUTYRATE, SAIB®, is a commercial product used as an additive in lacquers and hot melt adhesives. Attempts to prepare a polymeric material of possible adhesive properties by reacting it with zinc chloride have been unsuccessful (306).

SUCROSE HEXAACETATE DISTEARATE is prepared by acetylation of sucrose distearate with acetic anhydride (247a). The reaction is carried out either in pyridine or without a solvent in the presence of a catalytic amount of anhydrous sodium acetate. The yield is up to 92%. The ester is a white, crystalline low-melting compound.

SUCROSE HEXAACETATE DIPALMITATE is made by acetylation of sucrose dipalmitate with acetic anhydride (247b). It is a colorless oil.

SUCROSE HEPTAACETATE MONOPALMITATE is made by acetylation of sucrose monopalmitate with acetic anhydride in pyridine (247c). The product is an oil.

MIXED ACETATE SULFONATE ESTERS. Several mixed esters of this type have been prepared, chiefly to obtain crystalline compounds or to block unreacted hydroxyl groups. The reaction is widely used in organic chemistry (see Sulfonic Acid Esters, page 70).

DERIVATIVES OF SUCROSE ESTERS OF HIGHER FATTY ACIDS

Alkylene oxide adducts

Adducts of sucrose esters with ethylene, propylene and butylene oxide have been prepared and their stability compared to that of the unmodified sucrose ester under the conditions used in the manufacture of detergents (see Surfactants, page 173). The adducts are made with up to eight moles of alkylene oxide per mole sucrose. The ethylene oxide adduct consists of two separate layers, but the propyloxy and butyloxy derivatives are homogenous products.

ETHYLENE OXIDE ADDUCT. Ethylene oxide adducts of sucrose tallowate have been prepared with one, four, and eight moles of epoxide per mole of sucrose tallowate (220c). The product consists of two phases. The lighter-colored upper phase is difficult to disperse in water. The darker lower phase is more readily soluble in water and gives more foam but contains some alcohol-insoluble materials, (220c).

PROPYLENE OXIDE ADDUCTS. Sucrose stearate and sucrose tallowate each react with four moles of propylene oxide to give a dark homogeneous product (220a). The stearate adduct is a hard, brittle, dark brown solid, the tallowate derivative a brown viscous solid. These adducts show somewhat higher stability to hydrolysis than the corresponding unmodified esters in bleaching and crutching tests, as discussed under Surfactants, page 173.

BUTYLENE OXIDE ADDUCTS. Sucrose tallowate reacts with four moles of butylene oxide to produce a hard, dark brown, very viscous syrup (220c). The adduct has properties similar to those of the propylene oxide derivative.

Sulfated fatty esters of sucrose

Sulfated sucrose laurate, stearate and myristate are made by reacting the appropriate acid chloride with sucrose and chlorosulfonic acid in pyridine (290h). The reactants are used in equimolar amounts. The products are complex mixtures.

Halogenated derivatives of the octaesters

Several halogenated esters have been made with the purpose of reacting the halogen further to prepare secondary derivatives of sucrose (297). Among the esters prepared were sucrose octa(trichloroacetate), octa(monochloroacetate), and octa(α-bromopropionate), as described below). The halogen atoms present in the ester in the α-position to the ester group are not sufficiently labile to prepare secondary derivatives.

Attempts to chlorinate sucrose octaacetate result in the formation of compounds varying in chlorine content and degree of degradation of the sucrose molecule, caused by the

E

splitting of the glycosidic linkage. Phosphorus pentachloride and chlorine gas have been used as reactants. The halogenated esters prepared are described below.

SUCROSE OCTA(TRICHLOROACETATE) is prepared by the reaction of sucrose and trichloroacetic anhydride. The reaction is very vigorous and does not require a catalyst. The product is a light amorphous solid.

SUCROSE OCTA(MONOCHLOROACETATE) is prepared similarly. After recrystallization of the amorphous solid in ethyl alcohol, a white hygroscopic product is obtained. It has a low melting point and is very hygroscopic. Saponification with dry ammonia yields chloracetamide in 70% yield. Removal of the chlorine by treatment with sodium hydroxide has not been successful.

SUCROSE OCTA(α-BROMOPROPIONATE) is made by reacting sucrose with α-bromo-propionic anhydride in the presence of a catalytic amount of pyridine. The product is a viscous oil. Attempts to prepare the acrylate by treatment with alkalies have been unsuccessful.

MISCELLANEOUS FATTY ESTERS

A number of fatty esters have been prepared with the sole purpose of testing their activity as agricultural chemicals as shown in Table 21-1. None has been isolated in a sufficiently pure state to be characterized by melting point or other physical properties.

Table 3-1
Physical properties of fatty esters of sucrose

The esters listed in this table are often claimed to be, but probably are not always the pure compounds. Except for the mono- and dimyristates, which have been purified by chromatography, none of the other esters has been satisfactorily separated from the contaminants. The 2,3,6,3′,4′-pentaacetate is well characterized because of the route of synthesis. Some of the octaesters, if fully substituted, are probably of good quality.

See Table 3-2 for properties of higher unsaturated esters of sucrose.

MONOESTERS

Sucrose acetate
White crystals. M.p. 80-82.5°C. Very hygroscopic, and may be difficult to crystallize (93). Found to contain only 70% monoacetate and also diacetate and higher esters (179).

Sucrose laurate
White solid. M.p. 90-91°C^{-a}. $[\alpha]_D^{20}$ +42.5° in C_2H_5OH. (124)

Sucrose myristate
White amorphous solid. M.p. 180-186°C. $[\alpha]_D^{20}$ + 36.7°, c. 4.8, $CHCl_3$. Pure compound obtained by chromatography. Infrared spectrum given in reference. (103)

White solid. M.p. 67-69°C^{-a}. $[\alpha]_D^{20}$ +42.2° in C_2H_5OH. (124)

Sucrose palmitate
White solid. M.p. 60-62°C^{-a}. $[\alpha]_D^{20}$ +39.8° in C_2H_5OH. (124)
Sucrose stearate
White solid. M.p. 52-53°C^{-a}. $[\alpha]_D^{20}$ +39.3° in C_2H_5OH. (124)
Sucrose oleate
White solid. M.p. 50-54°C^{-a}. $[\alpha]_D^{20}$ +37.6° in C_2H_5OH. (124)

DIESTERS

Sucrose dimyristate
White amorphous. M.p. 139-145°C. $[\alpha]_D^{20}$ + 29.7°, c. 5.2, $CHCl_3$. Pure compound obtained by chromatography. Contains some higher esters. (103)

PENTAESTERS

Sucrose 2,3,6,3',4'-pentaacetate
Colorless needles. M.p. 156°C. $[\alpha]_D^{22}$ +22.0°, c. 3.1, $CHCl_3$. Structure well established. Intermediate in the preparation of trimethyl sucrose and vinyl sucrose (104, 221b). See Table 9-3 for properties of esters made from pentasodium sucrate.

OCTAESTERS

Sucrose octapropionate
Colorless powder. M.p. 45-46°C. $[\alpha]_D^{25}$ +51.8° in $CHCl_3$. n_D^{25} 1.4588. Degree of substitution 8. (171)
Also prepared in noncrystalline, glassy form (297)
Sucrose octabutyrate
Light yellow oil. $[\alpha]_D^{25}$ +46.0° in $CHCl_3$. n_D^{25} 1.4550. Degree of substitution 8. (171)
Sucrose octacaprolate
Brown oil. $[\alpha]_D^{25}$ +33.4° in $CHCl_3$. n_D^{25} 1.4582. Degree of substitution 7.8. (171)
Sucrose octacaprylate
Brown oil. $[\alpha]_D^{25}$ +26.7° in $CHCl_3$. n_D^{25} 1.4615. Degree of substitution 8. (171)
Sucrose octacaprate
Brown oil. $[\alpha]_D^{25}$ +19.7° in $CHCl_3$. n_D^{25} 1.4677. Degree of substitution 7.8. (171)
Sucrose octalaurate
Colorless semisolid. $[\alpha]_D^{25}$ +20.7° in $CHCl_3$. n_D^{25} 1.4683. Degree of substitution 8. (171)

OCTAESTERS—*continued*

Sucrose octamyristate
Off-white amorphous powder. M.p. 41-42°C. $[\alpha]_D^{25}$ +18.0° in CHCl$_3$. Degree of substitution 7.3. (171)

Sucrose octapalmitate
Off-white amorphous powder. M.p. 52-53°C. $[\alpha]_D^{25}$ +17.4° in CHCl$_3$. Degree of substitution 7.1. (171)

Sucrose octastearate
White amorphous powder. M.p. 60-61°C. (Reference 311a gives m.p. as 57°C.) $[\alpha]_D^{25}$ +16.9° in CHCl$_3$. Degree of substitution 7.5. (171)

Sucrose octamonochloroacetate
White powder. M.p. 35-50°C. Very hygroscopic. (297)

Sucrose hexaacetatedistearate
White crystals. M.p. 35°C. Suppository ingredient. (247a)

a – This compound was claimed to be essentially pure. However, comparison of the melting points of the myristate prepared by the same method (69c) and that obtained by chromatography (186c) indicates that the lower-melting monoesters listed in this table are not pure, but are probably mixtures of mono- and higher esters.

Table 3-2
Physical properties of higher sucrose esters of linoleic and other unsaturated fatty acids (141)

Derivative of sucrose	Composition of mixed ester reagent	Degree of substitution	Total iodine value	Gardner viscosity	Gardner color-a	Intrinsic viscosity-f
Linoleate		5.6	153	Z-Z_1	8	
		5.7	151	V-W	10	
	(b)	6.5	132	R	14	3.7
	(b)	6.4	132, 134	K, L	9, 12	3.6
Linoleate-stearate	85:15-b	6.7	121	I	7	
	50-90:10-50-c	5.7-6.3	83-148	U-V, Y-d	13-14	3.8
Linoleate-eleostearate	80:20	6.3	152	S	14	
		6.6	156	J-K	9	
Linoleate-linseed oil	50:50	6.1	175	X	17	
	90:10-c	7.1	168	M	12	3.6
Linoleate-palmitate + oleate	80:20	6.7	118	H	10	
Linseed oil ester		6.1	191	U	13	3.1
Linseed oil ester-e		6.6	189	Z_3-Z_4	17	
Eleostearate-stearate	50:50	6.6	124	M	8	

NOTE: The compounds are prepared by transesterification of sucrose with the methyl ester of the fatty acid in dimethyl formamide. Those with higher degree of substitution and generally lighter color are made by the new improved method in nitrogen atmosphere and more efficient stirring.

a – As specified in Paint Testing Manual by Gardner and Sward, published by Gardner Laboratory, Bethesda, Md. The darkest solution designated as No. 18 is dark red. Each solution except No. 1 is 50% darker than the preceding solution.

b – Linoleate methyl ester contains some methyl oleate.

c – Linoleate methyl ester contains some methyl linolenate.

d – Esters with high stearoyl content are solid at 25°C.

e – Made with acid chloride in pyridine (230).

f – Calculated from dilute solution in methyl ethyl ketone at 30°C.

4

Other esters

SULFONIC ACID ESTERS

T_{HE} preparation of tosyl (*p*-toluenesulfonyl), mesyl (methanelsulfonyl), and other sulfonic esters of sucrose is of considerable interest because these products are simple to prepare and undergo a large number of important reactions. Preparation of these esters is conventionally carried out by reacting sucrose with the appropriate sulfonyl chloride (RSO_2Cl) in pyridine or less frequently in aqueous alkaline solution.

The latter method, sometimes called the Schotten-Bauman reaction, does not seem to be as dependable as the pyridine process. For example, recent experiments with mesyl chloride failed completely; and with tosyl chloride, complex mixtures with at least 11 components have been reported (194b). Tosylation by the Schotten-Bauman method reportedly gives highly esterified sucrose almost entirely (12).

Sulfonic acid esters have also been prepared by reacting pentasodium sucrate with the acid chloride (see Metal Derivatives, page 126). Depending on the molar ratio of sucrose and the acid chloride, partial or full esterification may occur.

As with other carbohydrates, tosylation and mesylation of sucrose are claimed to proceed chiefly on the primary hydroxyl groups (6,1',6') of the sucrose molecule. However, acylation with three moles of tosyl chloride per mole sucrose in pyridine at 0-18°C gives only 25-30% 6,1',6'-tritosyl sucrose (12, 96). The rest consists chiefly of di- and also tetra- and pentatosyl derivatives, and uncharacterized tritosyl sucrose. Di- and triesters are actually formed in equal amounts, accounting for about 85% of the reaction products.

Complete selectivity is claimed when the esterification temperature is lowered from the conventional 0°C to −40°C (264). The reduced speed of the reaction increases the selective acylation of primary hydroxyls. In other words, selectivity is inversely proportional to the speed of reaction.

It has also been claimed that tosylation to the triester is more selective than mesylation (264). Chromatographic analysis reportedly shows that acylation at −40°C with three moles of tosyl chloride per mole sucrose yields exclusively one product, tritosyl sucrose, while mesylation under the same conditions is incomplete, and gives other derivatives as well (264).

70

However, further experiments have demonstrated that mono- or diesterification cannot be successfully performed with either of these reactants so as to obtain only one product at $-40°C$ (264) or at $0°C$ (96).

Tosylation with two moles of tosyl chloride per mole of sucrose in pyridine gives about 50% ditosylate, 40% tritosylate, and 10% tetratosylate (12, 96). Nearly half the diester is 6,6'-ditosyl sucrose and nearly half the triester is 6,1'6'-tritosylate. The heterogeneity of the reaction mixture from the tosylation or mesylation of sucrose is also reported elsewhere (213a, b).

Also, hydrolysis of the conventional tritosyl sucrose to trianhydrosucrose demonstrates the heterogeneity of the reaction mixture. The trianhydrosucrose corresponding to the 6,1',6'-tritosylate is obtained in the very low yield of 3.5% (95). On the other hand, a tri-anhydrosucrose corresponding to the 4,1',6' isomer is also claimed to be isolated in high yield (255c).

Tosylation with three moles of acid chloride per mole of sucrose according to Schotten-Bauman also gives heterogeneous mixtures of tosyl sucroses (260d). However, acylation with four moles of tosyl chloride is claimed to produce a uniform tetraester (264). Similarly, reaction with one mole of tosyl chloride under modified Schotten-Bauman conditions gives monotosyl sucrose in good yield (260d).

In general, these studies indicate (a) that the 6- and 6'-positions both undergo tosylation somewhat more rapidly than does the 1'-position, and (b) that the hydroxyls in the three primary positions have greater reactivity than those in the secondary positions in sucrose (96).

Little is known of the reactivity of the secondary hydroxyl groups. However, based on the literature and dimesylation of methyl glucopyranoside (108), the glucose moiety is probably acylated preferentially in the 2-position rather than on the 3- or 4-locations. Non-bonded interactions in the transition state are important and probably mainly responsible for the generally greater reactivity of the primary positions in carbohydrates (96). Intra-molecular hydrogen bonding can also influence strongly the rate of reaction (99).

The sulfonyl groups serve as easily removable protective or blocking agents in the synthesis of sucrose derivatives. Secondary tosyl groups are difficult to eliminate by conventional methods of hydrolysis with aqueous alkali or sodium methoxide. However, all acyl groups can be easily eliminated by reductive deacylation with sodium amalgam. A newer method of hydrolysis uses strongly basic exchange resins. Another method of elimination employs lithium aluminum hydride. Primary tosyloxy groups are removed reductively with the formation of deoxy groups and secondary tosylates are cleaved into secondary alcohols and ditolyl disulfide (35, 272a).

Aqueous alkaline hydrolysis of tosylates often leads through a Walden inversion to a change in the configuration of the related carbon atom. Hydrolysis of tosyl esters proceeds through cleavage between the alkyl radical and the oxygen that can lead to inversion. Halogen, amino, nitrate and other sulfate derivatives can similarly undergo the Walden inversion. During the hydrolysis of tosylates, internal ethers can also be formed by intramolecular reaction (see Internal Ethers, page 43). As Figure 2-1 indicates, the formation of ethers also may proceed by the Walden inversion.

The difference in ease of nucleophilic replacement of tosyl groups on the hydroxyls is well known in the literature. For example, upon treatment with sodium iodide in acetone (Finkelstein's reagent), only primary tosyloxy groups can be replaced by iodine:

$$\underset{\underset{H_2-C-O-Tosyl}{\overset{|}{H-C-O-Tosyl}}}{\overset{|}{-C-}} + NaI \longrightarrow \underset{\underset{H_2-C-I}{\overset{|}{H-C-O-Tosyl}}}{\overset{|}{-C-}}$$

Tosylesters of secondary hydroxyls are usually unaffected (95), though their occasional replacement with iodine has been reported (97).

In the sucrose molecule two (6 and 6') of the three primary sulfonyloxy groups are readily replaced by iodine or similar nucleophilic substituents. The tosyloxy group in the 1' position is resistant to replacement when treated with sodium iodide in acetone at 100°C (12). Further studies with octatosylates (16, 35, 96) and octamesylates (194c, h) confirmed the selectivity of reaction on the 6- and 6'-positions. The 1'-carbon is claimed to be relatively unreactive because of electronic interactions of the neighboring carbon-oxygen valencies at the anomeric center (194h).

The ease of replacement of the tosyl and mesyl groups is an important tool in the analysis, and particularly in the preparation, of derivatives of sucrose. Various attempts, often unsuccessful, have been made to prepare fluoride derivatives with hydrogen fluoride (255c) or alkali metal fluorides (182, 213b, 255a); nitrilo, amino, and hydrazino derivatives (264); sulfur compounds with hydrogen sulfide (180a); aldehydes via oxidation (260a); and replacement with sodium thioethoxide (180a).

A number of crystalline derivatives have been recently prepared by reacting the pure 6,6'-ditosyl hexamesylate, hexaacetate or hexabenzoate directly or through the intermediate diiodo compound. Among these were the dithiocyanate, prepared with potassium thiocyanate (194g); dianhydrosucrose (194d, e); mono- and dichloro derivatives with pyridine hydrochloride (194e, f); diaminosucrose through the diazidosucrose (194g, h), all directly from the ditosylate; and the preparation of dideoxy, diene and other derivatives through the iodine intermediate (see Halogen and Sulfur Derivatives, page 120).

A number of promising polymeric materials have also been made from the tosyl esters (see Resins and Polymers, page 147). The properties of some sulfonic esters are listed in Tables 4-1 and 9-3. For a review on the subject, see Sulfonic esters of carbohydrates, by R. S. Tipson, in *Advances in Carbohydrate Chemistry*, **8**, p. 107 (1953).

Tosyl esters and derivatives

MONOTOSYL SUCROSE. Monotosyl sucrose is made by reacting sucrose with equimolar amounts of tosyl chloride under modified Schotten-Bauman conditions (260d). The sucrose and sodium hydroxide are taken up on an absorbent column (Celite 535), which is then reacted for several hours with tosyl chloride dissolved in benzene. The reaction is claimed to produce mainly monotosyl sucrose along with some ditosyl derivative, according to chromatography. The yield is about 40%.

The product resists acid hydrolysis and does not react with sodium iodide. Based on these reactions and theoretical expectations, the tosyl group is most likely at the 2,1′ and 3′ positions.

DITOSYL SUCROSE. When one mole of sucrose is acylated with two moles of tosyl chloride in pyridine at 0°C, the ditosyl ester is obtained in 50% yield (12, 96). Chromatographic analysis indicates that nearly half the ditosylate is the 6,6′ isomer (see below); the rest has not been identified. Further analysis indicates that the combined ditosylate fraction may be entirely composed of not greatly different amounts of the 1′,6-, 1′6′-, and 6,6′-ditosylates. The other half of the reaction product consists chiefly of tritosylate (mainly 6,1′,6′-derivatives) and some tetratosylate. A considerable amount of diester is also obtained in the reaction of one mole of sucrose with three moles of tosyl chloride.

6,6′-DITOSYL SUCROSE. The pure, crystalline 6,6′-ditosylate is obtained in 20% yield by chromatography of the mixture made by the reaction of one mole of sucrose plus two moles of tosyl chloride, or in 10% yield when prepared with three moles of tosyl chloride (12, 96). Additional improvements in production reported later (194d) have led to the successful preparation of the crystalline hexaacetate, hitherto prepared in amorphous form only. Benzoylation with benzoyl chloride in pyridine yielded the ditosylate hexabenzoate (194e). The compound is soluble in pyridine and chloroform (194j).

6,6′-Ditosyl sucrose has been an important starting material in the recent preparation of a number of well-defined crystalline bifunctional derivatives of sucrose (194). These include the 6,6′-chloro and iodo, 6-chloro-6-deoxy, 5-5′-diene, 6,6′-dideoxy, 6,6′-diazido and 6,6′-dithiocyanate derivatives of sucrose. The compounds are discussed in the appropriate chapters elsewhere in this volume.

6,6′-DITOSYL-2,3,4,1′,3′,4′-HEXAACETYL SUCROSE. This compound is prepared by treating 6,6′-ditosyl sucrose with acetic anhydride in pyridine at about 0°C (12, 96). The reaction product is an amorphous solid that resists crystallization and gives a syrupy diiodo derivative (12, 96). However, a crystalline compound has been prepared later from a purer ditosylate starting material (194d). The yield is 90% (194j). The compound is soluble in chloroform and hot methyl and ethyl alcohols (194j). It can be converted into a crystalline 6,6′-diido derivative with sodium iodide (194d). Treatment of the crystalline iodo compound with potassium thiocyanate gives the dithiocyanate ester (194d).

6,6′-DITOSYL-2,3,4,1′,3′,4′-HEXABENZOYL SUCROSE. This compound is made in 73% yield (194j) by benzoylation of the chromatographically pure 6,6′-ditosyl sucrose in pyridine with cooling (194e). When the acylation is carried out at room temperature, three products are obtained that can be separated into crystalline form by chromatography (194e). They are monochloromonotosyl sucrose hexabenzoate, 6,6′-dichloro sucrose hexabenzoate and 6,6′-ditosyl sucrose hexabenzoate. The chloro compounds are formed by nucleophilic substitution of the sulfonyloxy groups by chloride, since treatment of the ditosyl hexabenzoate itself with pyridine hydrochloride at 40°C also gives the chlorinated compounds.

The ditosyl hexabenzoyl sucrose is soluble in chloroform and hot ethyl and methyl alcohols (194j). It is crystalline and well suited for the preparation of a number of equally crystalline derivatives—for example, the diiodo hexabenzoate with sodium iodide in methyl ethyl ketone (194e), and the monochloro (194f) and dichloro (194e) derivatives with pyridine hydrochloride in pyridine.

6,6′-DITOSYL-2,3,4,1′,3′,4′-HEXAMESYL SUCROSE. 6,6′-Ditosyl sucrose is reacted with mesyl chloride to obtain the hexamesylate, which is isolated in chromatographically homogenous form (194c). It is an amorphous powder. Treatment with sodium iodide gives the 6,6′-diiodo hexamesylate (194c, g). Treatment of the iodide compound with silver fluoride gives the corresponding crystalline 5,5′-diene of sucrose hexamesylate (194g).

TRITOSYL SUCROSE AND 6,1′,6′-TRITOSYL SUCROSE. Tritosyl sucrose is made by the conventional method of reacting sucrose with three moles of tosyl chloride in pyridine at 0°C (72). Structural analysis of the methylated derivative is claimed to show that the product contains 84% of the tosyl groups on the primary hydroxyls (6,1′,6′) (35).

Detailed chromatographic analysis of the tritosylate prepared by this method indicates that the product is a mixture and contains penta-, tetra-, tri-, and ditosyl sucroses in the molar ratios of 0.05:0.33:1:1 respectively (12, 96). The composition of the product is substantially the same when the reaction is performed at −18°C (12, 96). Acylation at −40°C is claimed to yield 6,1′,6′-tritosyl sucrose only, reportedly because of the increased selectivity of acylation of the primary hydroxyls at lower temperatures (264). The claim is based only on a chromatographic analysis that is not too detailed. Further exploration of this reaction could lead to the preparation of pure 6,1′,6′ acyl derivatives that have not yet been obtained.

Tritosyl sucrose contains only 25-29% of 6,1′,6′-tritosyl sucrose, as indicated by the yield of the corresponding 1′,2:3,6:3′,6′-trianhydrosucrose (12, 96). The trianhydro derivative is made by alkaline hydrolysis. (See Internal Ethers, page 43.)

Tritosyl sucrose is also obtained in an overall yield of about 40% when one mole of sucrose is reacted with two moles of tosyl chloride (12, 96). Over half of the product is the 6,1′,6′ derivative.

The acylation of sucrose with three moles of tosyl chloride under Schotten-Bauman conditions also yields a heterogenous mixture consisting of mono- to hexatosylates (260d). The modified reaction successfully used for the preparation of monotosylate cannot be applied with three moles of tosyl chloride (260d).

The product obtained in pyridine is a white amorphous foam that cannot be crystallized (35). The tritosylate of sucrose reportedly shows great stability towards acids (180a). Attempts to obtain a crystalline derivative by benzoylation have been unsuccessful (264). Preliminary experiments to replace two tosyl groups with nitrilo, amino or hydrazine functions have also been unsuccessful (264).

Similarly, the replacement of the tosyloxy groups with aqueous ammonia (290k) or with hydrogen sulfide in pyridine (180a) has also been unsuccessful. However, with sodium thioethoxide in dimethyl formamide at 150°C, all three tosyloxy groups are reportedly replaced, but a number of side reactions also occur (180a). However, the tosyl groups can be partially replaced by halogen or hydrolyzed into a trianhydride, as discussed below.

TRITOSYLPENTAACETYL SUCROSE. Tritosylpentaacetyl sucrose is prepared by acetylating tritosyl sucrose in pyridine according to conventional methods (72). On heating the compound with pyridine hydrochloride at 100°C the dichloromonotosylpentaacetate is formed (255c). Treatment with sodium iodide gives monotosyldiiodopentaacetyl sucrose (35, 96, 272a).

TRITOSYLPENTAMETHYL SUCROSE. Tritosylpentamethyl sucrose is made by reacting tritosyl sucrose with excess methyl iodide and silver oxide in dimethylformamide (35). The product is a syrup with a methoxy content that suggests contamination with dimethyl formamide. Detosylation is carried out in aqueous methyl alcohol with 4% sodium amalgam (35).

4,1',6'-TRITOSYL-2,3,6,3',4'-PENTAACETYL SUCROSE. This compound is made by tosylation of the 2,3,6,3',4' pentaacetate of sucrose with excess tosyl chloride in pyridine (95). The pentaacetate is an intermediate in the preparation of 4,1',6'-trimethyl sucrose (see Ethers, page 17). An amorphous product is obtained in 91% yield. Treatment with sodium iodide gives 6'-iodo-4,1'-ditosyl-2,3,6,3',4'-pentaacetyl (95).

TRITOSYLPENTABENZOYL SUCROSE. This compound is prepared by reacting tritosyl sucrose with benzoyl chloride in pyridine (182). Elemental analysis indicates that the material contains some ditosyl derivative. The mixed ester has been reacted with potassium or cesium fluoride in boiling ethylene glycol in an attempt to produce a fluorinated sucrose derivative (182). However, the volatile reaction product does not contain fluorine. Its structure has not been further investigated.

TETRATOSYL SUCROSE. Tetratosyl sucrose is made by acylation with four moles of tosyl chloride in pyridine at −40°C (264). Esterification is equally successful in aqueous alkali or in mixtures of water and dimethoxyethane according to Schotten-Bauman (264). A foamy white product is obtained that can be pulverized into a free-flowing powder. The product is the uniform tetra-derivative, according to chromatography. Methylation gives tetramethyltetratosyl sucrose (264). Reductive detosylation with sodium amalgam yields a colorless oily product (264).

OCTATOSYL SUCROSE. The octatosylate of sucrose is made by reacting sucrose with eight moles of tosyl chloride per mole of sucrose in pyridine at 0°C (72). The product is an amorphous powder.

OTHER TOSYL DERIVATIVES. The following tosyl derivatives are discussed elsewhere:

> *Under Halogen Derivatives*:
> 6-Iodo-4, 1'-ditosyl-2,3,6,3',4'-pentaacetyl sucrose (page 122)
> 6-Chloro-6'-tosyl-2,3,4,1',3',4'-hexabenzoyl sucrose (page 121)
> Diiodo monotosyl pentaacetyl sucrose (page 122)
> Dichloromonotosyl pentaacetyl sucrose (page 122)
> *Under Methyl Ethers*:
> Heptamethylmonotosyl sucrose (page 22)

Mesyl esters

DIMESYL SUCROSE. The reaction of one mole of sucrose with two moles of mesyl chloride in pyridine at 25°C yields a mixture of products, as discussed above (213a). This can be further converted into dimesyl sucrose hexabenzoate.

TETRAMESYL SUCROSE. This compound is reportedly made by reacting one mole of sucrose with four moles of mesyl chloride in pyridine at −40°C (264). The product is an amorphous powder. Tetramesyl sucrose can be acetylated or methylated into fully substituted derivatives.

TETRAMESYLTETRAACETYL SUCROSE. This compound is prepared by acylation of the tetramesyl derivative with acetic anhydride in pyridine (264). The product is also amorphous.

TETRAMESYLTETRAMETHYL SUCROSE. Methylation of the tetramesyl derivative with methyl iodine and silver oxide in dimethyl formamide yields tetramesyltetramethyl sucrose (264). The product is also an amorphous material. Attempted demesylation with aqueous sodium hydroxide or sodium amalgam, according to Freudenberg has been unsuccessful. Zemplen's method of hydrolysis in absolute methyl alcohol with sodium methoxide proceeds with complete hydrolysis of all sulfonyl esters.

DIMESYLHEXABENZOYL SUCROSE. The compound is made by benzoylation of dimesyl sucrose (213a). The product is noncrystalline and nonhygroscopic. According to chromatographic analysis, it probably consists of a mixture of isomers. The attempted replacement of the mesyl groups by fluoride with potassium fluoride has been unsuccessful (213b).

OCTAMESYL SUCROSE. The octamesylate of sucrose is made by reacting sucrose with eight moles of mesyl chloride in pyridine at 0°C (72). The product is an amorphous powder. Treatment with 3.5 moles of sodium iodide per mole of compound in methyl ethyl ketone yielded 6,6'-diiodohexamesylate (194c).

The reaction indicated preferred replacement in the 6- and 6'-positions. Reduction with lithium aluminium hydride to obtain deoxy sucrose gives a complex mixture (194c). Reactions with sodium azide in methyl ethyl ketone yields a crystalline derivative with azide content (194a, b). Reaction with potassium thioacetate gives a crystalline product (194a). None of these derivatives has been further examined.

OCTA(TRICHLOROMESYL) SUCROSE. This octaester has been prepared for the sole purpose of testing it as an agricultural chemical (Table 21-1). The product was not characterized by its melting point or other physical properties.

OTHER MESYL DERIVATIVES. Other products of this type include:

> 6,6'-Ditosyl sucrose hexamesylate (see Tosyl Esters above).
> 6,6'-Diiodosucrose hexamesylate (see Halogen and Sulfur Derivatives, page 120).

Although little work has been done with these mesyl derivatives, they, like the sucrose tosylates, may be of interest as intermediates in the preparation of crystalline derivatives or polymeric materials.

Brosyl esters

Sucrose can be reacted with *p*-bromobenzenesulfonyl chloride (brosyl chloride) to prepare brosyl esters, analogous to the tosyl esters.

TRIBROSYL SUCROSE. Tribrosyl sucrose is made by reacting brosyl chloride with sucrose in pyridine at 37°C (182). The attempted selective replacement of the brosyl groups with fluoride by treatment with cesium fluoride has been unsuccessful (182).

Naphthalene sulfonyl esters

NAPHTHALENE-2-SULFONYL ESTERS. Naphthalene-2-sulfonyl chloride gives esters in good yields when reacted with sucrose in pyridine (255b). With 0.33 mole of sulfonyl chloride per mole of sucrose, the monosulfonate is the major product. Reaction of three moles of the acid chloride with one mole of sucrose gives a mixture consisting of mainly the *disulfonate*. Both products are amorphous, crisp solids with no surface-active properties.

NAPHTHALENE-1,5-DISULFONYL ESTERS. Only a small amount of sucrose ester is formed when naphthalene-1,5-disulfonyl chloride is reacted with sucrose in pyridine because the acid chloride reacts with traces of water in the pyridine solvent (255b).

NAPHTHALENE-1,3,6-TRISULFONYL ESTERS. Only two moles of sucrose appear to react with one mole of acyl chloride (255b). The introduction of the third sucrose may be hindered sterically. The presence of free sulfonic acid groups causes hydrolysis (inversion) of sucrose and thus lowers the yield.

Other sulfonic acid esters

LAURYL (DODECYL) SULFONYL SUCROSE. One mole of dodecyl sulfonyl chloride, reacted with three moles of sucrose in pyridine, gives a sucrose product that consists mainly of the monoester (255b). Half of the reactant does not appear to react with sucrose. The reaction is reportedly also successful with dodecyl sulfonic acid and sucrose in concentrated sulfuric acid (292). The product is gummy and cannot be crystallized. The removal of impurities is carried out by treatment with an anion-exchange resin (292). It is reported to have high surface activity. (See Surfactants, page 173.)

Experiments have been carried out to prepare the sulfonate with a commerical acylating agent, Alkanol TL® of duPont (199). It consists of 50% lauryl sulfonyl chloride, free sulfonic acid, and hydrocarbons. Acylation with about 0.5 mole of acyl chloride per mole of sucrose in pyridine yields some solids and gum. The latter contains a reducing sugar, thus indicating hydrolysis, but it shows good foaming on shaking.

DODECYL BENZENE SULFONYL SUCROSE. Sucrose is reacted with three moles of dodecyl benzene sulfonyl chloride in mixtures of pyridine and carbon tetrachloride or in alkaline water (290h). A solid product is obtained in yields of up to 47%. The degree of substitution is not specified. The product shows good stability in acid and alkaline media and also promising surface activity. Acylation with the benzene sulfonic acid in the presence of sulfuric acid has also been described (290h).

SULFATED DODECYL BENZENE SULFONYL SUCROSE. Sulfation of the above sulfonyl sucrose is carried out with one mole of chlorosulfonic acid at 0°C (290h). A crystalline product is isolated in very poor yield.

MYRISTYL (TETRADECYL) SULFONYL SUCROSE. Attempts to react tetradecyl sulfonyl chloride and sucrose in dimethyl formamide in the presence of pyridine are described in Reference 290m.

CARBONATES
Cyclic carbonates

Carbohydrates are known to form cyclic carbonates when reacted with phosgene or alkyl chloroformate or when transesterified with carbonate esters:

$$
\begin{array}{ccc}
\begin{matrix} | \\ -\text{C--OH} \\ | \\ | \\ -\text{C--OH} \\ | \end{matrix}
&
\begin{matrix} \\ \\ + \end{matrix}
\quad
\begin{matrix} \text{CL} \\ \diagdown \\ \quad \text{C} = \text{O} \\ \diagup \\ \text{Cl} \end{matrix}
\quad\longrightarrow\quad
&
\begin{matrix} | \\ -\text{C--O} \\ | \quad\diagdown \\ \cdot \quad\quad \text{C} = \text{O} \\ | \quad\diagup \\ -\text{C--O} \\ | \end{matrix}
\end{array}
$$

Phosgene

The reaction between sucrose or other carbohydrates and diphenyl carbonate was first described by Hochstetter in 1913. The "sucrose carbonate" made by this method was later found to be a polymeric material.

In the case of sucrose and other polysaccharides, the bridging might occur between the monosaccharide units, such as the glucose and sucrose moieties in sucrose. The bridge could thus link the two monosaccharide units even after hydrolysis of the glycosidic linkage. [The only known such bridged derivative is an internal ether (Figure 2-1, Compound 1).]

Unfortunately, experiments have indicated that sucrose cannot form cyclic derivatives with these reactants. With alkyl chloroformate or phenyl chloroformate open-chain carbonyl derivatives are formed. Phosgene, diphenyl carbonate, or other carbonates yield directly crosslinked polymeric materials, as discussed below. When sucrose is reacted with phosgene according to the method of Haworth and Porter, a "carbonate" is obtained in a very low yield (183k). Transesterification of sucrose with the carbonate of ethylene glycol also fails to give an appreciable yield of product (183k).

However, other carbohydrates could yield cyclic carbonates or derivatives that contain both a cyclic group and an open chain ester. Among these are derivatives of glucose (53) and mannose (75, 76) and methyl or benzyl glycosides of ribose and galactose (77).

The structure of the carbonates of sucrose and of other carbohydrates has been determined with the help of infrared spectra. The absorption band of the carbonyl group in cyclic carbonates differs from that in the open chain, as given in Reference 77.

Sugar alcohols, such as sorbitol, dulcitol, and mannitol, can also form cyclic carbonates (74). Glycerol gives a tricarbonate that contains two molecules of glycerol bridged with a carbonyl group (73).

Mixed carbonates

ALKYL AND ARYL OXYCARBONYL SUCROSES. These straight-chain carbonate esters of sucrose are prepared by reacting sucrose with the appropriate chloroformate in the presence of aqueous alkali (147) or in pyridine (74, 173).

$$
\text{ROH} + \text{ClCOOR}' \longrightarrow \text{ROCOOR}' + \text{HCl}
$$

Several lower alkyl derivatives have been prepared in up to 98% yield (Table 4-2). Except in the case of benzyl chloroformate, complete substitution of sucrose cannot be achieved by this method. The tribenzyloxyester can be prepared by using only four moles of reagent per mole of sucrose. *Octamethoxycarbonyl sucrose* with a degree of substitution of 7.5 is reportedly obtained by reacting a large excess (20 moles) of reagent in aqueous dioxane

(193c). Further acylation of the triester with ethyl chloroformate in pyridine also gives *octa-ethoxycarbonyl sucrose* (147).

Reaction with chloroformate proceeds more slowly than tosylation. For example, when eight moles each of methyl chloroformate and tosyl chloride are reacted simultaneously with one mole of sucrose in pyridine, the product approximates a *monomethoxycarbonyl hepta-tosyl sucrose* in composition (193c).

The reaction with ethylene dichloroformate produces polymers (148). Transesterification with diethyl carbonate gives low-substituted esters in low yield (149). The reaction is carried out in boiling dimethyl sulfoxide in the presence of sodium bicarbonate.

Except for the octaethoxycarbonyl derivative, these esters are oils. Analysis indicates that they are mixtures of isomers. For example, methoxy carbonyl sucrose with a degree of substitution of 6.8 has at least eight components according to chromatography (147). Infrared spectra indicate the absence of cyclic carbonate (147). Structural analysis shows that the substitution in ethyoxycarbonyl sucrose and also in its polymer is partly random, but mainly preferential at positions 3, 6, 1' and 3' (149).

The oils dissolve in the most common organic solvents with the exception of light petroleum fractions. Treatment with aqueous-alcoholic barium hydroxide or other alkaline materials causes rapid hydrolysis with the precipitation of barium carbonate (147). Secondary butyloxycarbonyl sucrose, and to lesser extent the isopropyl derivative, are much more stable to ammonia than any of the primary esters (193j).

Alkyl oxycarbonyl sucroses are quite resistant to acids. In general they are more stable than other esters and acetals (147). The extreme acid sensitivity of the glycoside linkage is also considerably modified. Comparative data on the change in optical rotation (inversion) indicate that ethoxycarbonyl sucroses are more stable to acids than sucrose or sucrose octaacetate (Figure 4-1). The octaethoxy derivative also shows resistance to concentrated sulfuric acid (147).

Triethoxycarbonyl sucrose suffers complete alcoholysis in methyl alcohol, and in normal butyl alcohol in six hours at 100°C (148). The addition of dimethyl sulfoxide prevents decomposition significantly in butyl alcohol, but not in methyl. Tertiary butyl alcohol is inactive (148). Solvents such as acetone, chloroform, dioxane and dimethyl formamide are also largely inert (193e). Penta- and higher carbonates are stable in all alcoholic solvents (193e).

Triethoxycarbonyl sucrose, which is an amorphous solid, flows into a colorless transparent mass after being exposed to the atmosphere for 24 hours (294b). Triesters of this type should be particularly rapidly polymerized into polycarbonate resins at elevated temperatures (see Resins and Polymers, page 147). The preparation of such a triester in high yield is given in Reference 148. Attempts to condense the triester with acetone in the presence of sodium ethoxide have resulted only in deesterification of the sucrose (193i).

The presence of an alkaline impurity can catalyze polymerization of ethoxycarbonyl sucrose (147) or deesterification in lower alcohols (148). Traces of the alkaline catalyst can remain in the substance during preparation. Such traces should be eliminated from the final product by methods given in Reference 148.

The triester is scarcely attacked by aniline at 140°C but condenses with stronger bases such as *n*-hexylamine, to a product that may be of urethane type (193i).

Figure 4-1
Hydrolysis of sucrose and some of its esters (147)

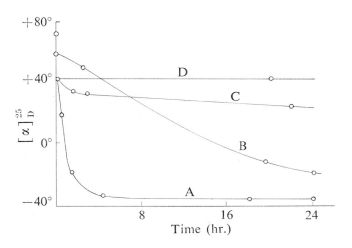

(A) Sucrose. (B) Sucrose octaacetate. (C) Ethoxycarbonyl sucrose (DS 3.1).
(D) Ethoxycarbonyl sucrose (DS 4.9).
Hydrolysis is carried out in 1-N aqueous-alcoholic hydrochloric acid.
Measurement of reducing power during hydrolysis indicates that the minor
change in the rotation of ethoxycarbonyl sucrose is caused by a slight fission
of the glycosidic linkage, rather than inhibited configurational change, such as
that caused by substitution at the 6′ position.

Attempts to polymerize butyloxycarbonyl sucrose and to crosslink octaethoxycarbonyl sucrose have been largely unsuccessful, as described under Resins and Polymers, page 147. Other condensations to polymers are also discussed there.

The properties of selected alkyl oxycarbonyl esters of sucrose are given in Table 4-2.

PHENOXYCARBONYL SUCROSE. Triphenoxycarbonyl sucrose is made from one mole of sucrose and five moles of phenyl chloroformate in pyridine at 0°C (74). The colorless syrup has an average degree of substitution of 3.4. The product can be polymerized in dimethyl sulfoxide at 100°C in the presence of 1% sodium bicarbonate. The polymer is identical to that obtained from diphenyl carbonate in one step (74). (See Resins and Polymers, page 147.)

THIOCARBONATES, XANTHATES, ALKYL, AND ARYL THIOCARBONATES

Thiocarbonates and xanthates are sulfur analogs of open-chain mixed carbonate esters:

ROCOSR′	ROCSSR′
Sucrose thiocarbonate	Sucrose xanthate, dithiocarbonate, or thiolthiocarbonyl sucrose

In the exploratory tests made this far only a few of these products have been obtained in pure form. They have some interest as monomers for polymerization to polythiocarbonate resins, similar to the cellulose xanthates, which are important intermediates in the manufacture of viscose rayon.

Thiocarbonates

Exploratory experiments indicate that the reaction between sucrose and chlorothiolformates yields predominately the symmetrical dithiolcarbonate, RSCOSR, where R is an alkyl or benzyl group (193q). The reaction is carried out in aqueous alkali similarly to that with alkyl chloroformates.

Attempts to prepare *monomethylthiocarbonyl sucrose* through the silver salt show some success (193p).

Xanthates

Sucrose xanthate is prepared by reacting sucrose and carbon disulfide in the presence of aqueous sodium hydroxide (197) or saturated barium hydroxide (193n):

$$ROH + CS_2 + NaOH \longrightarrow ROCSS^-Na^+ + H_2O$$

The degree of substitution depends upon the ratio of sucrose and sodium hydroxide. The dixanthate is made with a ratio of sucrose to base of 1:3.5 (197). The reaction in the presence of barium hydroxide is claimed to yield the monoxanthate (193n).

The solution of sucrose xanthate is unstable. Iodine or other oxidizing agents convert it to the xanthogen (ROCSS)$_2$. Reaction with a methyl halide gives the S-methyl ester. Both products are obtained in an impure state (197).

An attempt to react sucrose xanthate with cellulose xanthate by oxidative coupling has been unsuccessful. The reaction to produce the mixed xanthogen:

Cellulose—OCS—S—S—CSO—Sucrose

F

yields an insoluble product which contains the cellulose derivative only (197).

The barium salt reacts with copper acetate or silver salts to produce the copper or silver xanthate (193n). None of these salts has been prepared in pure form (193o). The copper salt contains *sucrose dixanthogen,* and the silver salt contains silver sulfide. The silver salt reacts with methyl iodide (193n), but analysis indicates that the monomethylolthiocarbonyl sucrose formed is not pure (193o). Methylation of the barium salt of sucrose xanthate with dimethyl sulfate gives an even less pure derivative (193n).

Alkyl and aryl thiocarbonates

Esterification with an alkyl or aryl thiocarbonyl group is often used in organic synthesis for temporary protection of hydroxyls. This protective group is very stable in acid, but can be removed either by alkaline treatment or by oxidation with organic peracids or lead tetra-acetate. The reaction is carried out by acylating with the alkyl or aryl thiochloroformate in pyridine, or under Schotten-Bauman conditions in aqueous alkali:

$$ROH + R'SCOCl \longrightarrow ROCOSR'$$

Sucrose   Thiochloroformate   Thiocarbonate

Sucrose has been successfully acylated to the octaester with methyl, ethyl, phenyl, and benzyl thiochloroformates, but attempts to prepare the trityl sucrose pentabenzylthio-carbonate have failed (see Trityl Ethers, page 25).

Except for the *phenylthiocarbonyl sucrose,* all other esters are oils and cannot be crystallized. The compounds listed on Table 4-2 are made by reacting sucrose with excess reagent in pyridine at 0°C (194a, c).

CARBAMATES

Sucrose carbamates can be used in the production of resins. They have also been tried in exploratory experiments as modifiers for sucrose esters of fatty acids to obtain a more water-soluble and possibly more stable product of good surfactant qualities. They are made by reacting sucrose and urea (228a, 290d, e):

$$ROH + NH_2CONH_2 \longrightarrow ROCONH_2 + NH_3$$

The reaction is carried out by condensing one to eight moles of urea with one mole of sucrose in a melt at 140-160°C. However, as discussed under Resins and Polymers, the reaction does not produce pure sucrose carbamate, as was formerly believed. Thus the products may be of poor quality.

The properties of sucrose carbamates are discussed briefly under Sucrose Carbamate-Formaldehyde Resins, page 151.

Stearate and other fatty acid sucrose carbamates

Sucrose monocarbamate has been reacted with C_{12}-C_{18} fatty acid chlorides (290d) and their methyl esters (290d, e). The stearate derivative is obtained in purer form than other members of this series (290d). Preliminary evaluation indicates that the carbamates are more soluble in water than the corresponding fatty esters of sucrose, and that they have similarly good surface activity (see Surfactants, page 173).

Attempts to condense sucrose octacarbamate with stearic acid, its amide, and its methyl ester have failed (290d). The di- and other polycarbamates have also been reacted with fatty acid chlorides (290d, e) or their methyl esters (290e). The reactions between sucrose mono-carbamate and a fatty acid, fatty nitrile, nonyl phenol, and myristyl bromide have all failed to yield any products (290k).

N-Stearate and N-laurate sucrose monocarbamates have been prepared in small yields by condensing the appropriate acyl urea with sucrose (290e).

SULFATE AND SULFITE ESTERS

Sulfate esters are obtained by the action of sulfur trioxide, chlorosulfonic acid (HSO_3Cl) or sulfuryl chloride (SO_2Cl_2) on sucrose. Esterification with sulfur trioxide produces a mixture of sucrose sulfates with various degrees of substitution. The reaction with sulfuryl chloride or thionyl chloride yields sucrose derivatives that contain chlorine as well as sulfate, sulfite, or sulfonyl chloride groups. Chlorination can be somewhat restricted in the presence of pyridine. Structural studies show that the Walden inversion occurs during chlorination of the hydroxyl position 4 on the glucose portion (36, 272d). (See Figure 4-2.)

The sucrose sulfates do not seem to undergo reactions analogous to those of tosyl or mesyl compounds. For example, the sulfate group in the disulfate cannot be replaced with iodide by treatment with sodium iodide (272a). Sulfuric acid is readily lost and causes widespread degradation of the rest of the acid-sensitive molecule. Similarly, alkaline hydrolysis does not lead to anhydrosugars. For instance, when the barium salt of sucrose disulfate is treated with ammonium hydroxide, extensive desulfation occurs with the liberation of sucrose (272a).

The chlorosulfonyl group cannot be removed by alkaline hydrolysis (272d). Hydrogenation in the presence of Raney nickel and calcium carbonate successfully eliminates these groups without splitting the glycosidic linkage (272e).

Sulfate esters of sucrose have been little explored in the past. Further experiments to obtain derivatives by selective replacement of the chlorosulfonyl groups could lead to interesting new reactions.

The properties of sulfate and related esters of sucrose are given in Table 4-2.

Reaction with sulfur trioxide

Sucrose sulfates are prepared by the action of sulfur trioxide on sucrose in mixtures of dimethyl formamide and pyridine (215, 272a). Stabilized liquid sulfur trioxide or its solution in 1,2-dichloroethane can be used. The reaction is carried out in the presence of barium carbonate, which neutralizes the excess sulfur trioxide and converts the sucrose sulfate into the barium salt.

The degree of sulfation of products prepared by this method ranges from 1.5 to 6.8 (283a). Increasing the ratio of sulfur trioxide to sucrose increases the degree of sulfation. However, attempts to prepare the octasulfate of sucrose have been unsuccessful (283a).

The reaction product is an oily syrup, which can be solidified by treatment with methyl alcohol (215). The pure sulfates can be separated from the mixture by ionophoresis of the barium salts (272a).

Figure 4-2
The structure of reaction products of sulfuryl chloride and sucrose

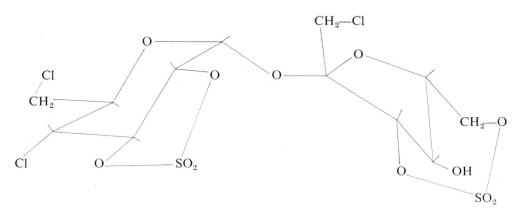

(I) 4, 6, 1′ -Trichloro-2(3),3′(6′)-disulfonyl sucrose (36)-a

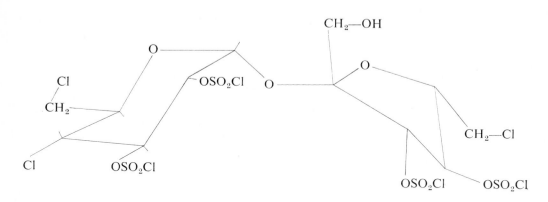

(II) 4,6,6′-Trichloro-2,(3),3′,(4′)-dichlorosulfonyl sucrose (272d)
Chlorination on carbon *4* in the glucose moiety proceeds with Walden inversion into galactose structure.

a – The sulfate group in the fructose portion may form a bridge between 1′ and 4′ and the chlorine on 6′.

STABILITY. In general, sulfates are easily degradable compounds because sulfuric acid is readily lost, and the acidic medium causes heavy deterioration in the acid-sensitive sucrose molecule. The glycosidic bond in these products appears to become more resistant to acid hydrolysis as the degree of sulfation increases (283a).

Treatment of the barium salt of sucrose disulfate with ammonia produces extensive de-sulfation with liberation of sucrose (272a). The pentasulfate is more stable under these condi-tions. Other tests indicate that the less highly sulfated product is slightly more stable than the more highly sulfated product in an atmosphere of ammonia, but that they both are sensitive to the moist ammonia atmosphere (283b).

Quantitative and rapid liberation of barium sulfate occurs when an aqueous solution of the barium salt of *sucrose pentasulfate* is heated at 100°C (272a). Similarly, hydrolysis of su-crose sulfate proceeds readily at 100°C but only very slowly at room temperature (283a). Desulfation is inhibited in the presence of hexamethylene tetramine (272a).

REACTIONS. The barium salt of sucrose pentasulfate yields 5-hydroxymethyl furfural and related polymeric materials in boiling dimethyl formamide. The sulfate groups in su-crose disulfate are not replaced with iodine by heating it with sodium iodide in acetone. Pro-longed treatment of sucrose pentasulfate with ethylene diamine causes no replacement, but only partial degradation of the sucrose sulfate (272a).

Reaction with sulfuryl chloride

In the reaction of sulfuryl chloride with sucrose, replacement of some hydroxyl groups with chlorine takes place in addition to esterification. This halogenation reportedly occurs with the Walden inversion on the 4-position, so that the glucose portion of sucrose is transformed into a galactose. The structure of some of the derivatives is given in Figure 4-2.

DI- AND TRICHLORODISULFONYL SUCROSE. When sucrose is reacted with sulfuryl chloride in a mixture of pyridine and chloroform at about 5°C, a product is obtained that is claimed to be a mixture of di- and trichlorosucrose disulfates (36). The sulfate groups are in a cyclic form that span two carbon atoms within both the glucose (inverted to galactose) and the fructose moieties (Figure 4-2, Formula I). Degradation studies indicate that two of the three chlorine groups are in the 4- and 6-positions. The structure of the fructose portion can-not be determined but has been deduced by comparison.

The product is an oil that can be precipitated into a pale yellow solid in chloroform with ether.

TRICHLORODICHLOROSULFONYL SUCROSE. When sucrose is treated with sulfuryl chloride at −40°C and insufficient pyridine to remove the acids produced, an oily product is obtained (272b). The product crystallizes on treatment with alcohol. Infrared examination and analytical data indicate that it contains four-OSO_2Cl groups in the molecule and three, or possibly four, chlorine atoms (272e). One of the two suggested structures is given in Figure 4-2, Formula II. The fourth chlorine, probably labile, is on the 1'-position. Some re-actions suggest that the compound may contain a cyclic sulfonyl group in the former glucose moiety (now galactose) similar to the disulfonyl derivative shown in Figure 4-2, Formula I (272d). Treatment in cold pyridine could convert the chlorosulfate into a similar, partially cyclic sulfate (272e).

The crystalline compound can be recrystallized from ethyl or n-propyl alcohol. In pure form it is stable for months when kept in a dry atmosphere. It is quite stable in acids and dissolves in cold cencentrated sulfuric acid without charring (272e). It withstands concentrated sulfuric acid at 100°C for 10 minutes and is unaffected by boiling for 24 hours in 2-N sulfuric acid (272b). However, it is rapidly decomposed in alkaline solution, and it reacts vigorously with nonaqueous solutions of sodium iodide to yield sulfur dioxide and iodine (272e).

Aqueous sodium iodide does not satisfactorily remove the sulfochloride groups, but hydrogenation in the presence of Raney nickel and calcium carbonate gives an oil that analyzes as a *trichloro sucrose* (272e). Attempts to condense the chlorosulfonyl compound with amines such as aniline or hydrazine result in decomposition (272e). The reaction with potassium cyanide is also unsuccessful (203d).

Reaction with thionyl chloride

Unlike other alcohols, sucrose does not give halogenated derivatives when reacted with thionyl chloride. Instead it gives halogen-free sulfite esters at lower temperature and halogenated sucrose sulfites at higher temperature. No pure chlorosucrose can be obtained by this method.

The reaction with excess thionyl chloride in pyridine carried out at 5-10°C for 15 minutes and followed by moderate heating at 60°C for 30 minutes gives an almost quantitative yield of a low-melting (185-190°C) product (298c). The elemental analysis indicates that the material is *dichlorosucrose disulfite*. It is a white solid, which is soluble in methyl alcohol and acetone (298d).

Reaction at 15°C for a period of 3.5 hours similarly gives a product melting at 245-250°C (298c). It is a *polymeric sucrose sulfite*. This product is also obtained when the reaction is carried out in dimethyl formamide and in the presence of 2-methyl-5-ethyl pyridine (298d). The product is a white material, insoluble in acetone (298d). The polymer can be acetylated into a number of sucrose products containing sulfite and acetyl groups (298d, e). The sulfite groups in the polymer are quite resistant to displacement reactions with iodide or thiocyanate (298e).

The reaction of sucrose with thionyl chloride in an acetic acid-acetic anhydride medium produces partially acetylated chlorosucroses, including some *monochlorosucrose heptaacetate* (298b). Additional exploratory experiments are given in Reference 298a.

Other reactions

REACTIONS WITH SULFAMIC ACID. Mixture of sulfate esters are formed when sucrose is reacted with sulfamic acid in dimethyl formamide (272c). Similar reactions in pyridine cause extensive decomposition of sucrose (272c). The reaction is very slow at room temperature, and decomposition takes place above 60°C (255e).

REACTION WITH POTASSIUM PYROSULFATE. Attempts have been made to sulfate sucrose with potassium pyrosulfate in aqueous alkali (290k). The product with no isolation has been reacted with ammonia in an effort to obtain sucrose amine. No reaction occurred.

REACTIONS WITH CHLOROSULFONIC ACID. Sulfation of dodecylbenzyl sulfonyl sucrose is carried out with chlorosulfonic acid as discussed under Sulfonic Acid Esters, page 70. *Sulfated fatty acid esters of sucrose* are reportedly made with sucrose, the appropriate fatty acid chloride, and chlorosulfonic acid in pyridine (290h). *Sucrose sulfate* is prepared by reacting sucrose mole for mole with chlorosulfonic acid in a mixture of pyridine and chloroform (290k). The unidentified crude product does not react further with aqueous ammonia to give sucrose amine.

REACTIONS WITH SULFURIC ACID. The reactions of sulfuric acid with sucrose alone or with such other reactants as fatty alcohols, benzaldehyde, and acetone in dimethyl formamide have been briefly studied (290e).

THIOCYANATES

The thiocyanate esters of sucrose are prepared by reacting tosyl sucrose with potassium thiocyanate in dimethyl formamide:

$$RO{-}Tosyl \xrightarrow{KSCN} ROSCN$$

Preliminary experiments indicate that the thiocyanates could possibly be used for the preparation of such other derivatives as the isothiocyanates by rearrangement and thiosucrose by reaction with sodium sulfide.

The physical properties of the crystalline compounds are given in Table 4-2.

6,6'-Dithiocyanate-2,3,4,1',3,'4'-hexabenzoyl sucrose

This compound is prepared from the corresponding 6,6'-ditosyl hexabenzoate by replacement with potassium thiocyanate (194g). The reaction is carried out at 140°C in dimethyl formamide. It includes a rebenzoylation step because of deesterification during the replacement. The yield is 73% (194j). The product is a white crystalline powder, soluble in chloroform (194j). Rearrangement to the isothiocyanate (RSOCN) is under investigation (194h).

6,6'-Dithiocyanate-2,3,4,1',3',4'-hexaacetyl sucrose

This compound is made from the 6,6'-ditosyl hexaacetate with sodium thiocyanate in dry dimethyl formamide at 120-130°C (194d). A white crystalline powder is obtained after chromatography. Its deacetylation by treatment with sodium methoxide has been studied (194e).

NITRATE ESTERS

Sucrose nitrates have been prepared and tested in many exchange reactions in an effort to produce derivatives useful in polymers or other products. However, the nitrates in general do not readily undergo such reactions.

Several methods have been investigated for the nitration. Of these, nitration with 100% nitric acid in a mixture of acetic acid and acetic anhydride (Brissaud method) yields the octanitrate as a clear syrup (197). Its infrared spectrum shows that it is a fully nitrated product. Since catalytic hydrogenation yields pure sucrose, no acid hydrolysis occurs in the nitrating medium. *Sucrose octanitrate* had formerly been described in the literature as a solid product melting at 85.5°C with rotation $[\alpha]_D = 55.9°$ by Hoffman and Hawse, [*J. Am. Chem. Soc.* **41**, 235 (1919)].

Partial denitration of the octanitrate can be effected by boiling it in a solution of sodium nitrite in aqueous ethyl alcohol (197). The product, with a degree of substitution of 3.5-4.5, presumably has the nitrate group mainly on the primary positions. The hydroxyl group of partially nitrated sucrose can be acetylated to a glassy sucrose nitrate acetate that may have useful plasticizing properties. A better yield of such ester mixtures is obtained by first acetylating sucrose and subsequently nitrating. A good chromatographic method has been developed for the separation and detection of nitrates (197).

When sucrose nitrate (degree of substitution 3.75) is heated with sodium iodide in dimethyl formamide at 100°C, approximately one iodine atom per molecule of sucrose is introduced slowly by replacement of the nitrate group. Many other reagents have also been examined for similar nucleophilic exchange reactions. The replacement by fluorine is unsuccessful under a wide variety of conditions. Other unsuccessful reactions include those with potassium cyanide and thiocyanate; sodium benzoate, formate, methoxide, phenate, thiosulfate, metabisulfite, and *p*-aminobenzoate; thiourea, hydrogen sulfide, and sulfur dioxide. Many of these reagents cause some degradation. The extent depends on the temperature, pH, and time of reaction (197).

Ethylamine and diethylamine react vigorously with sucrose nitrates, giving complex tarry products (197).

ACRYLATES AND OTHER UNSATURATED ESTERS

Sucrose acrylates and other unsaturated esters have potential interest as monomers. The physical properties of five unsaturated octaesters of sucrose are given in Table 4-3. They are prepared with sucrose and the appropriate acyl chloride or anhydride in pyridine. Of the several highly substituted esters tested, the methacrylate shows a promising gelation time. The esters of methacrylic, crotonic, and cinnamic acid give hard glassy copolymers with styrene or methyl methacrylate.

Attempts to prepare *sucrose acrylate* from sucrose and acrylic anhydride have been unsuccessful. The preparation of the anhydride itself, presented great problems because of its great ease of polymerization. Indirect preparation of sucrose acrylate by the dehydrohalogenation of the α-bromopropionyl ester of sucrose with alkalies has not been successful (297).

Sucrose methacrylate is reportedly obtained when sucrose octaacetate is transesterified with methyl methacrylate in the presence of sodium as catalyst and hydroquinone as inhibitor to prevent the polymerization (183k).

DICARBOXYLIC ACID ESTERS

Attempts to prepare sucrose esters of dicarboxylic acids have had little success. The reactions have mostly been attempted by transesterification in dimethyl formamide, similar to the method successfully used for the preparation of sucrose esters of fatty acids. Under similar conditions, polyesters can also be formed, as discussed under Resins and Polymers, page 147. Experiments have been conducted with the following esters:

SUCROSE ADIPATE (245b, c, d). Some reaction occurs on transesterification. Reaction between pentasodium sucrate and adipic acid chloride gives a polymer (17).

SUCROSE SEBACATE (245c, d). Transesterification is unsuccessful.

SUCROSE ABIETATE (245d, e, f, g, h). Conversion is reportedly up to 90% in transesterification. This compound is also prepared by the reaction of sucrose with the acid chloride.

SUCROSE OXALATE (245d, e).

SUCROSE MALONATE (272c). Some transesterification is reported.

SUCROSE FUMARATE, TEREPHTHALATE AND PHTHALATE. Reactions between pentasodium sucrate and fumaric and terephthalic acid chloride or phthalic anhydride gives polymeric materials insoluble in chloroform (17). Attempts to prepare sucrose phthalate by transesterification have been unsuccessful (229).

SUCROSE MALEATE (290n). The reaction has been attempted without success with maleic anhydrides and sucrose in dimethyl formamide in the presence of pyridine.

HALF ESTERS. Half esters of sucrose have been reported with succinic, maleic, phthalic, pyromellitic, and itaconic acids (306). The esters have been reacted with metal salts and oxides in an attempt to produce useful metal derivatives (see Metal Derivatives, page 126).

MISCELLANEOUS ESTERS
Sucrose alginate

Attempts to prepare sucrose alginate by transesterification of sucrose with ethyl alginate have been unsuccessful. However, some reaction reportedly occurs with ethylene glycol alginate (306).

Sucrose benzoates

Benzoylation of sucrose derivatives has been carried out frequently to prepare crystalline, well-defined derivatives of sucrose. Among these are mixed sulfonic acid esters and halogen, deoxy, and unsaturated derivatives. These compounds have been discussed above under the sections on the appropriate functional groups.

The benzoyl derivatives reportedly form better crystals than similar acetates (194e).

Miscellaneous esters poorly characterized

Several esters have been prepared for the sole purpose of testing their activity as agricultural chemicals. They are listed in Table 21-1. They include phosphates and other phosphorus esters, benzoates, xanthates, and carbamates. None of these products has been characterized by its melting point or other physical data. All have been screened in more or less crude form.

ESTERS OF OTHER CARBOHYDRATES AND RELATED COMPOUNDS
Borates of aliphatic alcohols

Eighteen aliphatic borates have been prepared (127) by the method described in the literature (Organic Syntheses, Collective Vol. II, p. 106, J. Wiley & Sons, N.Y., 1943). The method uses boiling boric acid with excess alcohol. Water is removed as an azeotropic distillate with the respective alcohol. The process has been successfully applied to all primary and secondary alcohols studied, but has not been successful in the case of the three tertiary alcohols tried.

Sulfonic acid esters of glucose

Several sulfonic acid esters of 1,2;5,6-diisopropylidene glucose have been prepared and studied (107). The original aim to produce allose from the esters by treatment with sodium methoxide through a Walden inversion has not been achieved. Other displacements and hydrolysis have also been studied.

Glycol trichloroacetates

Trichloroacetate esters have been prepared from ethylene glycol and 1,2-cyclohexanediol (129). They serve as model substances for carbohydrate trichloroacetates. The esters are prepared either directly from the glycol and trichloroacetic acid or with trichloroacetyl chloride in pyridine.

1,3,4,6-Tetrabenzoyl fructose

An improved preparation of this compound has been developed (87). Attempts to alkylate or acylate the tetrabenzoate, and also to prepare the 1,6-dibenzoate by direct acylation of fructose have proved unsuccessful.

Fructose acetates

Attempts to prepare new acetates of fructose have been unsuccessful (87).

Table 4-1
Properties of sulfonic acid esters of sucrose

NOTE: This table lists only products with well-defined melting point or good elemental analysis if not crystalline. For tosylates made from pentasodium sucrate see Table 9-3.

Mesyl = methanelsulfonyl   Tosyl = *p*-toluenesulfonyl

Brosyl = *p*-bromobenzenesulfonyl

Tetramesyl sucrose
White amorphous powder. Probable structure: 2,6,1′,6′-mesylate. (264)
Tetramesyltetraacetyl sucrose
Amorphous powder. Derivative of tetramesylate. (264)
Tetramesyltetramethyl sucrose
Off white, amorphous powder. $[\alpha]_D$ +49.38° (23°C), c. 2.44, CHCl$_3$. Derivative of tetramesylate. (264)
Tritosyl sucrose
White amorphous powder. M.p. 66-69°C. $[\alpha]_D$ +42.35° (27.6°C), c. 2.42, CHCl$_3$ (72). Contains 45% tritosyl, 40% ditosyl, and 15% other derivatives (96), see text. $[\alpha]_D^{15}$ + 41.3°, c. 2.06, CHCl$_3$ (35); m.p. 65-85°C, $[\alpha]_D$ +43.0°, c. 2.88, CHCl$_3$ (96).
Tetratosyl sucrose
White powder, M.p. 80-90°C. $[\alpha]_D$ +27.05° (25°C), c. 1.992, CHCl$_3$. Probable structure: 2,6,1′,6′-tosylate. (264)

Table 4-1—*continued*

Tritosylpentaacetyl sucrose
White amorphous powder. M.p. 58-61°C. $[\alpha]_D$ +53.3° (24.9°C), c. 3.94, $CHCl_3$.
Compound is made from the heterogeneous tritosyl sucrose described above.
(72)

Octamesyl sucrose
White amorphous powder. M.p. 86-94°C. $[\alpha]_D$ +43.7° (30°C), c. 2.29,
$(CH_3)_2CO$. (72)

Octatosyl sucrose
White amorphous powder. M.p. 82-86°C. $[\alpha]_D$ +41.78° (25.9°C), c. 7.623,
$CHCl_3$. (72)

Tritosylpentamethyl sucrose
Oil. $[\alpha]_D$ +49.5° (24°C), c. 4.05, $CHCl_3$. Contains some dimethyl formamide.
Compound is made from the heterogeneous tritosyl sucrose described above.
(35)

6,6'-Ditosyl sucrose
Crystalline. M.p. 108-110°C. $[\alpha]_D$ 54.0° in C_2H_5OH. (96)
M.p. 113-114 (194j).

6,6'-Ditosyl-2,3,4,1',3',4'-hexabenzoyl sucrose
White crystals. M.p. 86-89°C. $[\alpha]_D$ +31.8° (24.5°C), c. 1, $CHCl_3$. (194j)

6,6'-Ditosyl-2,3,4,1',3',4'-hexaacetyl sucrose
Amorphous solid. (96)
White crystals. M.p. 64-67°C. $[\alpha]_D$ +51.8° (22°C), c. 1, $CHCl_3$. (194j)

4,1',6'-Tritosyl-2,3,6,3',4'-Pentaacetyl sucrose
Amorphous solid. M.p. 85-91°C. (95)

Tritosylpentabenzoyl sucrose
M.p. 80°C. $[\alpha]_D$ +21° in $CHCl_3$. Softens at 65°C. Elemental analysis indicates
that it contains ditosylhexabenzoyl derivative. (182)

Tribrosyl sucrose
Yellow amorphous solid. M.p. 90°C. Softens at 60°C; chars at 150°C. (182)

Table 4-2
Physical properties of some esters of sucrose

ALKYL (OR ARYL) OXYCARBONYL SUCROSE ESTERS (ROCOOR')

Methyl ester
Degree of substitution 4.9. Oil. $[\alpha]_D^{25}$ +50.6°, c. 4.34, ethanol. Yield 76%. (147)

Ethyl ester
Degree of substitution 4.9. Oil. $[\alpha]_D^{25}$ +43.6°, c. 5.55, ethanol. Yield 86%. (147)
Degree of substitution 7.9. M.p. 79-80°C. $[\alpha]_D^{25}$ +43.8°, c. 0.913, ethanol.
Yield 97%. (147)

Table 4-2—*continued*

Propyl ester
Degree of substitution 5.0. Oil. $[\alpha]_D^{25}$ +37.3°, c. 3.84, ethanol. Yield 87%. (147)
Isopropyl ester
Degree of substitution 6.0. Oil. $[\alpha]_D^{25}$ +37.5°, c. 1.68, ethanol. Yield 90%. (147)
Butyl ester
Degree of substitution 5.0. Oil. $[\alpha]_D^{25}$ +33.3°, c. 6.04, ethanol. Yield 92%. (147)
Isobutyl ester
Degree of substitution 5.5. Oil. $[\alpha]_D^{25}$ +29.5°, c. 5.51, ethanol. Yield 89%. (147)
Sec-butyl ester
Degree of substitution 6.0. Oil. $[\alpha]_D^{25}$ +31.5°, c. 4.52, ethanol. Yield 70%. (147)
Benzyl ester
Degree of substitution 8.0. Oil. $[\alpha]_D^{25}$ +21.2°, c. 2.04, chloroform. Yield 79%.
(147)
Allyl ester
Degree of substitution 7.8. Oil. $[\alpha]_D^{25}$ +39.6° in chloroform. n_D^{25} 1.4778. Yield
34%. Shows poor reactivity in polymerization and copolymerization. (173)

ALKYL (OR ARYL) THIOCARBONYL SUCROSE ESTERS (ROCOSR')

Methyl ester
Degree of substitution 8. Oil. $[\alpha]_D^{25}$ +46° in chloroform. (194a)
Ethyl ester
Degree of substitution 8. Oil. $[\alpha]_D^{25}$ +47° in chloroform. (194a)
Phenyl ester
Degree of substitution 8. M.p. 75-77°C. $[\alpha]_D^{25}$ +71° in chloroform. Gives
crystalline compound with sodium azide, m.p. 63-64°C, $[\alpha]$ +20°. (194a)
Benzyl ester
Degree of substitution 8. Oil. Chromatographically homogeneous. (194c.)

SULFATES AND RELATED ESTERS

Trichlorodisulfonyl sucrose
Pale yellow solid. M.p. 94-99°C. Contains some dichloro derivatives. See
structure in Figure 4-2. (36)
Dichlorosucrose disulfite
White solid. M.p. 185-190°C. Made with thionyl chloride in shorter reaction
time. (298d)
Sucrose sulfite (polymeric)
White solid. M.p. 245-250°C. Made with thionyl chloride in longer reaction
time. (298d)

Table 4-2—*continued*

THIOCYANATES

6,6′-Dithiocyanate-2,3,4,1′,3′,4′-hexaacetyl sucrose
White crystalline powder. M.p. 169-171°C. $[\alpha]_D^{23}$ +71°, c. 2.0, chloroform. (194k)
6,6′-Dithiocyanate-2,3,4,1′,3′,4′-hexabenzoyl sucrose
M.p. 93-95°C. $[\alpha]_D^{22}$ +32.9°, c. 1.0, chloroform. (194j)

Table 4-3
Physical properties of unsaturated sucrose esters (173)

Derivatives of sucrose	Methacrylate	Crotonate	Cinnamate	Furoate	Undecylenate
Degree of substitution	7.7	7.8	8	7.8	8
Melting point, °C	—	—	84-86	90-99	—
Yield, %	54	95	75	69	81
$[\alpha]_D^{25}$, CHCl$_3$	+30.8°	+39.3°	+11.6°	+48.2°	+21.0°
n^{25}	1.4847	1.4980	—	—	1.4720
Physical appearance	Colorless oil	Brown oil	Yellow powder	Powder	Yellow oil
Gelation time, min 1% benzoyl peroxide, 100°C	3	270	(a)	(a)	(b)
Blowing with O$_2$, 100°C	30-c	327	(a)	(a)	(d)
Copolymer with: Styrene-e	Clear hard glass	Clear hard glass	Clear hard glass	Heterogeneous gel	Heterogeneous viscous liq. + colorless solid
Methyl methacrylate-e	Clear hard glass	Clear hard glass	Opaque solid	Heterogeneous gel	Heterogeneous gel

a – No change in 48 hours.
b – Slight increase in viscosity in 36 hours.
c – Heating alone.
d – Viscosity increases from 14.3 centistokes to 40.5 in 349 minutes.
e – Equal weights, 1% benzoyl peroxide, at 100°C.
NOTE: For unsaturated esters made from pentasodium sucrate, see Table 9-3. Allyloxycarbonyl sucrose (degree of substitution 7.8) similarly tested had a gelation time of 1080 minutes (with benzoyl peroxide).

5

Acetals, thioacetals, and ketals

Lɪᴋᴇ other aliphatic alcohols carbohydrates react with aldehydes to form cyclic acetals and with ketones to form cyclic ketals:

$$RCHO + \begin{array}{c} OH-C- \\ | \\ OH-C- \\ | \end{array} \longrightarrow RCH \begin{array}{c} O-C- \\ | \\ O-C- \\ | \end{array}$$

and

$$\begin{array}{c} R \\ \diagdown \\ C=O + \\ \diagup \\ R \end{array} \begin{array}{c} OH-C- \\ | \\ OH-C- \\ | \end{array} \longrightarrow \begin{array}{c} R \\ \diagdown \\ C \\ \diagup \\ R \end{array} \begin{array}{c} O-C- \\ | \\ O-C- \\ | \end{array}$$

The reaction is catalyzed by such reagents as mineral acids, zinc chloride, and copper sulfate.

The preparation of cyclic acetals or ketals of sucrose has had only modest success. The drastic acidic conditions normally required for the preparation invariably cause rupture of the glycosidic linkage, often with concomitant degradation of the monosaccharides into 5-hydroxymethyl furfural and other derivatives. Attempts to prepare acetals of sucrose give chiefly the acetals of glucose (44, 71). A short review of the literature on this topic is given in Reference 280.

The reaction of sucrose with paraldehyde in the presence of freshly fused zinc chloride as catalyst reportedly yields crystalline products, which are claimed to be sucrose derivatives of cyclic acetal structure (Figure 5-1). The reaction is sensitive to temperature, humidity, and

Figure 5-1
Possible structures of the ethylidene sucroses (280)

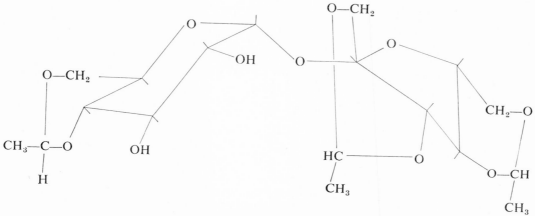

4:6,1′:3′,4′:6′-Triethylidene sucrose

"Penta"-ethylidene sucrose (2:3-Oxidodiethylidene,
4:6,1′:3′,4′:6′-triethylidene sucrose)

other conditions, and isolation of the product is also rather difficult. However, it is the only known crystalline acetal at the present time. Similar reactions with benzaldehyde and propionaldehyde result in partial hydrolysis of sucrose, polymerization, or mixtures of products that cannot be separated (280).

Several noncyclic acetals of sucrose have been prepared with greater ease and in good yield. These derivatives are mixed acetals of sucrose and simpler alcohols with formaldehyde or other aldehydes. They are made by reacting sucrose at low temperatures with the enol ether or the halogen derivatives of the aldehyde or ketone. For example, a mixed methyl alcohol-sucrose acetal of formaldehyde is obtained by treating sucrose or its sodium derivative with chloromethyl methyl ether. Also, mixed acetals of sucrose and lower alcohols with acetaldehyde are made by the reaction of sucrose and vinyl ethers, which can be regarded as the enol ethers of acetaldehyde:

$$ROH + R'OCH_2Cl \longrightarrow R'OCH_2OR + HCl$$

$$ROH + R'OCH = CH_2 \longrightarrow R'OCHCH_3$$
$$\underset{OR}{\overset{|}{}}$$

The reaction with halides is carried out in the presence of an alkaline buffer. The similar reaction with enol ethers is catalyzed with a minute amount of mineral acid, which reportedly does not cause hydrolysis of the glycosidic linkage. Some success has been reported with sodium hydride as condensing agent (208). (See 1-Chloroethoxyethyl Sucrose, page 99.)

A series of new acetals have been prepared by reacting sucrose with a variety of vinyl ethers in dimethyl formamide in the presence of traces of hydrochloric acid. These include the products of reaction with ethyl vinyl ether, 2-chloroethylvinyl ether, isobutyl vinyl ether, 1,10-divinyloxydecane, and the cyclic pyran derivatives described below. The preparation of these derivatives is economically attractive because of the availability of vinyl ethers from alcohols and acetylene and of some pyran derivatives by dimerization of acrolein. However, when sucrose is reacted with similar vinyl ethers at higher temperatures (over 50°C) in the presence of mercuric acetate, vinyl sucrose is obtained. (See Ethers, page 17.)

The products are generally oils or solids with no definite melting point. The degree of substitution can approach eight. The yield ranges from a few percent up to 70-80%. In particular, reaction with vinyl ethers gives highly substituted sucrose acetals in good yield.

A number of other aldehydes and ketones have also been reacted with sucrose under conditions similar to those used for the preparation of acetals or ketals of other carbohydrates. None gives the desired compound.

The properties of condensation products of sucrose with aldehydes and ketones are summarized in Table 5-1.

CYCLIC ACETALS
Ethylidene sucrose

When a mixture of sucrose and excess paraldehyde (polymerized acetaldehyde) is treated with freshly fused zinc chloride initially at 70°C and then for 16 hours at room temperature, ethylidene sucrose is obtained with quantitative conversion of the sucrose (280). The product contains 29% by weight triethylidene sucrose and 71% "penta" ethylidene sucrose. The two acetals can be separated by fractional precipitation in benzene and petroleum ether, and further purified by chromatography. The reaction mixture contains 1 part sucrose by weight, ten parts paraldehyde, and two to three parts zinc chloride. The reaction can also be carried out in dimethyl formamide. However, the use of this solvent is said to inhibit the preparation.

The temperature of 70-80°C is chosen because it is optimal for the depolymerization of paraldehyde. Also, at lower temperature a large portion of the sucrose remains unreacted, and at higher temperatures decomposition occurs. It is also essential to operate under water-free conditions and to use freshly fused zinc chloride.

The structures of the two acetals have been inferred by hydrolysis, molecular weight, elemental analysis, and thorough infrared analysis. Molecular models indicate that strain-less triethylidene sucrose can be formed when the ring formation occurs at the 4:6, 1':3', and 4':6' positions. Introduction of the fourth ethylidene group across the 2:3 positions causes some strain, which is relieved if a seven-membered ring is introduced in these positions with two acetaldehyde molecules reacted to obtain the "penta" acetal. The suggested structures are shown in Figure 5-1.

Further evidence that the product is ethylidene sucrose is given by (a) the exchange reaction with phenyl hydrazine to produce the phenyl hydrazone of acetaldehyde and sucrose, and (b) by the fact that no reaction occurs with Taka-Diastase® and invertase enzymes.

Triethylidene sucrose is a white, powdery solid, soluble in chloroform, benzene, and ethyl acetate and insoluble in petroleum ether and water. Methylation and subsequent hydrolysis yield 2,3-dimethyl glucose.

"Penta"-ethylidene sucrose is an oil of similar solubility. However, it is more soluble in petroleum ether than the triacetal. Methylation followed by hydrolysis causes degradation, but no 2,3-dimethyl glucose can be isolated.

Acetals are also reportedly obtained by transacetalation of sucrose with 1,1-diethoxy-ethane (acetaldehyde diethylacetal) in dimethyl formamide in the presence of zinc chloride (193m). The formation of ethylidene sucrose, among other products, has been reported by the reaction of sucrose with divinyl ether, as discussed below.

Attempts to prepare ethylidene sucrose with paraldehyde or acetaldehyde in the presence of sodium sulfate as a catalyst and barium carbonate as a buffer, either with no solvent or in pyridine, have been unsuccessful (262).

Benzylidene sucrose

Numerous experiments have been carried out to prepare benzylidene sucrose, all without success. These include the treatment of sucrose with benzaldehyde at 150°C under reduced pressure (191) in the presence of zinc chloride catalyst (191, 193m, 280), the anionic resin Amberlite IR-120® (191, 193a), calcium chloride (191), and iodine (191), either with no solvent or in dimethyl formamide. The reaction conditions are those described in the literature for the successful preparation of benzylidene derivatives of other carbohydrates. Either (a) no reaction occurs, (b) the sucrose partially hydrolyzes to fructose and glucose, which

G

then react with the aldehyde, or (c) the formation of polymers is reported (280). Similarly, the reaction between sucrose and benzylidene chloride in the presence of silver oxide in demthyl formamide is also unsuccessful (280).

NONCYCLIC ACETALS

Methoxymethyl sucrose

Methoxymethyl sucrose is a mixed acetal of formaldehyde with methyl alcohol and sucrose. The product is obtained by reacting sucrose with chloromethyl methyl ether (197):

$$CH_3OCH_2Cl + HOR \longrightarrow CH_3OCH_2OR$$

The reaction is carried out in dimethyl formamide with excess reagent in the presence of lead carbonate. The product is a clear syrup with a degree of substitution of 4.2. It is soluble in water and chloroform. Attempts to raise the degree of substitution have been unsuccessful. The reaction with less reagent produces a mixture of lower acetals, according to chromatographic analysis (197).

Methoxymethyl sucrose is also made by reacting pentasodium sucrate with the reagent (17). As the reaction is very violent, it is conducted first at $-70°C$, and the temperature is then gradually raised to room temperature. An oily product is obtained in about 50% yield. Chromatographic analysis indicates that it is a uniform and highly substituted derivative. It is reported as soluble not only in water and chloroform but also in acetone and ethyl acetate. It is slightly soluble in ethyl alcohol and benzene and insoluble in carbon tetrachloride, ether, and light petroleum fractions (17).

Reaction with chloromethyl tridecyl ether

Attempts to prepare *tridecyloxymethyl sucrose* by reacting sucrose with chloromethyl-tridecyl ether have been unsuccessful (199). The reaction is carried out with equimolar proportions of the reactants in pyridine at temperatures up to 90°C. Gummy materials are obtained that cannot be purified.

Acetals with vinyl ethers

1-ETHOXYETHYL, 2-CHLOROETHOXYETHYL-1, AND 1-ISOBUTOXYETHYL SUCROSE. Sucrose reacts with the following vinyl ethers to give the corresponding sucrose acetals (10):

	Ether		
	Ethyl vinyl	2-Chloroethyl vinyl	Isobutyl vinyl
Product	1-Ethoxyethyl sucrose	2-Chloroethoxy-ethyl-1 sucrose	1-Isobutyoxyethyl sucrose
Formula of product	$C_2H_5OCHCH_3$ $\mid$ OR	$CH_2ClCH_2OCHCH_3$ $\mid$ OR	$C_4H_9OCHCH_3$ $\mid$ OR
Degree of substitution of sucrose	7.2	7.6	About 6
Yield	71%	33%	55%

The reaction is carried out with excess reactant in dimethyl formamide at 0°C in the presence of traces of hydrochloric acid. The products are all oils insoluble in water. None distills below 160°C at 0.5 mm. Alkaline hydrolysis of the acetals gives sucrose. Acetaldehyde can be detected among the acid hydrolysis products.

Addition of 2-chloroethyl vinyl ether to sucrose in the presence of sodium hydride in equimolar amount as a condensing agent results in a sluggish reaction and a completely water-soluble product, which has not been further characterized (208). Sodium hydride is a good condensing agent with 1-chloroethyl vinyl ether as described below.

1-CHLOROETHOXYETHYL-1 SUCROSE. This compound is prepared by reacting sucrose with excess 1-chloroethyl vinyl ether in dimethyl formamide in the presence of sodium hydride in equimolar amount as condensing agent (208). The reaction is very vigorous:

$$ROH + CH_3CHClOCH = CH_2 \longrightarrow CH_3CHClOCHCH_3$$
$$\underset{OR}{|}$$

The chloroform-soluble reaction product is an orange, oily syrup of low rotation. Chromatography indicates that it is one compound with slight contamination by another product not characterized.

1-CETYLOXYETHYL SUCROSE. Cetyloxyethyl sucrose is made by reacting excess cetyl vinyl ether with sucrose, as described above for the lower alkyl vinyl ethers (55):

$$C_{16}H_{33}OCH = CH_2 + ROH \longrightarrow C_{16}H_{33}OCHCH_3$$
$$\underset{OR}{|}$$

A white solid product is obtained in low yield. It is soluble in ether, chloroform, and ethyl alcohol and sparingly soluble in methyl alcohol. The average degree of substitution is 3.25. The product is insoluble in water and has no surface-active properties. Acidic hydrolysis yields cetyl alcohol, sucrose, and acetaldehyde.

When the reaction is carried out with one mole of vinyl ether per mole of sucrose, no appreciable quantity of sucrose acetal is formed, but considerable hydrolysis of sucrose occurs (54, 55). The preparation of the monoacetal is of interest because it should be a water-soluble compound, possibly with good surfactant properties.

Condensation with other vinyl ethers

The *vinyl ether of 2-hydroxymethyl tetrahydropyran* has also been reacted with sucrose (217a). The product, a high-boiling viscous liquid, is a mixture of three sucrose derivatives, probably the mono-, di-, and tri-substituted acetal.

Phenyl vinyl ether does not react with sucrose under the mild conditions used for the other ethers. Sucrose is recovered unchanged (82).

The *vinyl ether of tetrahydro-2-hydroxymethylpyran* reacts with sucrose to give a brown oil, containing three compounds with acetal structures (55).

Reaction with divinyl ethers

Divinyl ethers would be expected to react with sucrose (a) intramolecularly, to produce cyclic oxidodiethylidene acetals:

$$
\begin{array}{c}
CH_3 \\
| \\
CH \!-\!-\! O \\
\diagup \qquad\qquad \diagdown \\
O \qquad\qquad\qquad R \\
\diagdown \qquad\qquad \diagup \\
CH \!-\!-\! O \\
| \\
CH_3
\end{array}
$$

or (b) intermolecularly by bridging two sucrose molecules.

An acetal with the cyclic structure has been obtained with divinyl ether. Divinyl ethers of ethylene glycol and of higher glycols give noncyclic acetals similar to those obtained with monovinyl ethers. All reactions are carried out with excess vinyl ether in dimethyl formamide in the presence of traces of acid catalyst.

DIVINYL ETHER TO CYCLIC ACETAL. The reaction of sucrose with the symmetrical ether of vinyl alcohol gives a mixture of acetals and related compounds and unreacted sucrose (10). Chromatographic separation reveals the presence of a sucrose acetal containing three oxiododiethylidene groups for every two sucrose molecules. Such compounds are very unstable and decompose on storage to yield sucrose.

1,10-DIVINYLOXYDECANE TO 10-VINYLOXYDECYLOXYETHYL-1 SUCROSE. Use of a divinyl ether with a long aliphatic chain might overcome the tendency to intramolecular reaction and gives bridged derivatives. However, the reaction of one mole of sucrose with nine moles of 1,10-divinyloxydecane in dimethyl formamide with an acid catalyst gives a noncyclic acetal, 10-vinyloxydecyloxyethyl-1 sucrose (11):

$$
\begin{array}{c}
ROCHCH_3 \\
| \\
OC_{10}H_{20}OCH = CH_2
\end{array}
$$

No bridging occurs. The divinyl compound with a long aliphatic chain thus reacts similarly to the monovinyl ethers with short aliphatic chains discussed above. A white, rubber-like product, analyzed for the hepta-derivative, is obtained in about 70% yield. It is insoluble in organic solvents except chloromethyl cyanide (82). It is completely hydrolyzed by normal hydrochloric acid at 70°C in one hour. The hydrolyzate contains glucose, fructose, and acetaldehyde (11).

ETHANE-1,2-DIVINYL ETHER TO 2-VINYLOXYETHOXYETHYL-1 SUCROSE. Sucrose has been reacted with ethane-1,2-divinyl ether (the vinyl ether of glycol) to prepare a vinyl alkyl acetal of sucrose with a shorter alkyl chain, which should be more soluble in organic solvents than the acetal just described. The 2-vinyloxyethoxyethyl-1 sucrose formed is a hexaacetal with a degree of substitution of 5.6 (82). It is a heavy, white liquid. The acetal is unstable and readily decomposes to sucrose, similarly to the acetal formed from sucrose and divinyl ether. The product does not distill up to 100°C at 0.05 mm pressure.

ADDITIONAL DATA. For more details on the preparation, properties, chromatography, and analysis of the vinyl addition compounds, see References 55, 82, and 83.

2-Tetrahydropyranyl sucrose

Sucrose reacts with 2,3-dihydropyran to form the acetal 2-tetrahydropyranyl sucrose (10):

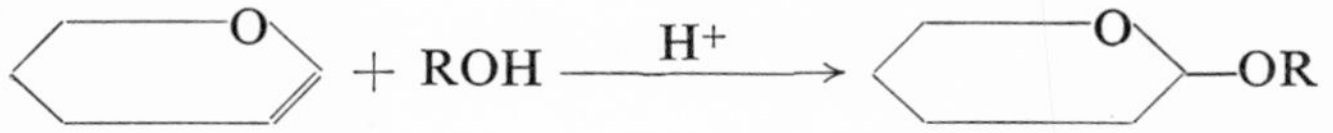

Similar additions are used in organic synthesis to protect hydroxy groups during reactions in basic media. The pyranyl residue is stable to alkalies, but can be readily hydrolyzed by dilute aqueous acids.

The addition of sucrose is carried out with excess reagent in dimethyl formamide in the presence of a trace of hydrochloric acid at 0°C. A white powder is obtained in 64% yield. The compound is a sucrose heptaacetal with a degree of substitution of 6.5. It is readily soluble in ether, lower aliphatic alcohols, pyridine, benzene, and toluene. No sugar can be detected chromatographically in the reaction mixture. This finding indicates that the acid catalyst does not cause hydrolysis and that the conversion of sucrose must be complete.

However, when sucrose is reacted with only 2.5 moles of 2,3-dihydropyran, some unchanged sucrose can be recovered, and glucose and fructose are detected in the reaction mixture. At least three acetals are produced in this reaction. The heptaacetal has been tested as an adhesive and in fiber forming, but without success (294a). For more details on the reaction, see References 82 and 83.

6-Formyl-2-tetrahydropyranyl sucrose

This compound is obtained by reacting sucrose with excess 2-formyl-3,4-dihydro-2H-pyran (acrolein dimer) in dimethyl formamide in the presence of traces of hydrochloric acid (10):

An amorphous solid is obtained in 12% yield. The compound is a heptaacetal with a degree of substitution of 7.4. Analysis indicates that the product contains water of crystallization, probably seven moles.

Similar reaction of sucrose with 3,4-dihydro-2-hydroxymethyl-2H-pyran (obtained by reduction from the above formylpyran) yields a copolymer (see Resins and Polymers, page 147).

More details on this compound are found in References 82 and 83.

ISOPROPYLIDENE DERIVATIVES

Except for esters, acetone is the most widely used blocking agent for hydroxyl groups in carbohydrate chemistry. In most instances condensation takes place between acetone and *cis*-hydroxyl groups on contiguous carbon atoms. The ketals formed are crystalline compounds. The isopropylidene group can be removed easily with dilute acids.

All experiments previously described in the literature for the preparation of isopropylidene sucrose has been unsuccessful because the acidic medium required for the reaction caused hydrolysis of the glycosidic linkage. The Foundation has therefore explored the reaction of sucrose with acetone in the presence of copper sulfate (262). Barium carbonate was added to the mixture to remove any trace of acidity, but the reaction failed.

Catalysis has also been attempted with an acidic ion-exchange resin (Amberlite IR-120®). It gave a mixture of reaction products including glucose, fructose, and their isopropylidene derivatives (191). With mixtures of copper sulfate and calcium sulfate as catalyst no reaction occurred (191). Even such mildly acidic catalysts as ethyl metaphosphate yield a mixture of ketals of glucose and fructose (Pacak et al., *Collection Czech. Chem. Commun.* **24**, 3804 (1959)].

UNSUCCESSFUL METHODS OF PREPARATION

Condensation of sucrose has been attempted unsuccessfully with choral (193m) and propionaldehyde (280) with zinc chloride as catalyst with no solvent. Use of dimethyl formamide as solvent gives mixtures of unidentified sugar-containing compounds. Attempts to condense sucrose with formaldehyde in the presence of an anionic resin or by dehydration with benzene have also been unsuccessful (193a).

The reaction between sucrose and acrolein yields a resinous material. (See Resins and Polymers, page 147.) Polymerization occurs only in solvent-free media. No reaction takes place when sucrose and acrolein are reacted in dimethyl formamide, pyridine, or other basic solvents in the presence of copper, peroxide, and other catalysts (191). The polymerization indicates that the preferred reaction of sucrose with unsaturated aldehydes is addition across the double bond rather than condensation to a cyclic acetal.

However, under solvent-free conditions sorbitol can form cyclic acetals with crotonaldehyde (24). Condensation of sucrose with crotonaldehyde in the presence of zinc chloride yields a mixture of products which can be only partially purified (278a). Analysis indicates that sucrose hydrolyzes during the reaction. Attempts to polymerize some of the reaction products (278a) or to prepare directly a polymer similar to that with acrolein (191) have been unsuccessful.

Other unsuccessful attempts to prepare acetals or ketals have been made: The reaction of sucrose with benzylidene, methylene or ethylidene chloride, iodide, or bromide in the presence of silver oxide results in hydrolysis (191, 280). Disodium sucrate plus benzylidene chloride gives no reaction (280). Disodium sucrate plus chloroacetone give ketose and aldose products not further characterized (280). With dimethyldichlorosilane or diphenyldichlorosilane in pyridine or dimethyl formamide sucrose gives no reaction at room temperature and hydrolyzes at higher temperatures. Treatment with benzylidene chloride in pyridine and sodium carbonate at 100°C gives unreacted sucrose and unidentified materials (191). Sucrose plus 3,4-dihydro-2-hydroxymethyl-2H-pyran yields a copolymer (10). Dibromomethane or dichloromethane and sodium sucrate prepared *in situ* with sodium hydride gives a brown syrup containing a number of water-soluble compounds and polymeric materials (256b).

ACETALS AND KETALS OF OTHER CARBOHYDRATES AND RELATED POLYOLS

Acetals of sorbitol and mannitol

The condensation of sorbitol (glucitol) with crotonaldehyde (24) and n-butyraldehyde (25) has been studied. Cyclic mono-, di-, and triacetals are obtained whose structure has been discussed. Comprehensive investigations have been carried out on the cyclic triacetals of mannitol (8). Their preparation has been simplified and their structures investigated. The cleavage of trimethylene mannitol to polymers of the polyester type has also been studied (281).

Acetals of tris-hydroxymethyl-nitromethane

Tris-hydroxymethyl-nitromethane reacts with several aldehydes to produce cyclic acetals (128):

$$R-CH \overset{O-CH_2}{\underset{O-CH_2}{\Big\backslash \Big/}} C \overset{NO_2}{\underset{CH_2OH}{\Big\backslash \Big/}}$$

The unreacted hydroxyl group can be acylated with benzoyl chloride or tosyl chloride.

4,6-Ethylidene glucose

Crystalline 4,6-ethylidene glucose is prepared from sucrose and paraldehyde in the presence of a catalytic amount of sulfuric acid (44, 71). This product results from hydrolysis of the glycosidic linkage of sucrose, and is identical to that obtained directly from glucose. Hydrogenation of the acetal gives 4,6-ethylidene sorbitol. Other acetals of glucose are similarly obtained from sucrose. (See Davila, O. S., "Preparation and derivatives of the reaction products of sucrose and n-butyraldehyde," and Munck, A. U., "Aldehydolysis of sucrose," Theses, M.Sc., Mass. Inst. Technol., Cambridge, Mass., 1948.)

2,4;3,5-Dimethylene gluconic acid

2,4:3,5-Dimethylene-D-gluconic acid is prepared by reacting trioxane with glucono-δ-lactone in concentrated hydrochloric acid (172). The compound can be oxidized with potassium permanganate to the corresponding saccharic acid.

Dicyclohexylidene glucose and fructose

When cyclohexanone is reacted with glucose or fructose in the presence of sulfuric acid as catalyst, 1,2;5,6-dicyclohexylidene glucose (70) and 1,2;4,5-dicyclohexylidene fructose are obtained (87). Several derivatives have been made from both compounds, and their structure proved.

ACETALS OF SUCROSE WITH UNCHARACTERIZED STRUCTURE

Two acetals of sucrose have been prepared and tested as agricultural chemicals as shown in Table 21-1. Neither has been characterized by melting point or other properties.

DITHIOACETALS OF GLUCOSE FROM SUCROSE AND MOLASSES

Sucrose and molasses have been investigated as a raw material for the dithioacetals of glucose (144, 145). Dithioacetals or mercaptals are obtained by the reaction of the aldehyde function of the glucose moiety of sucrose with a mercaptan. They can also be prepared directly from glucose, a process well known in the literature:

$$\text{R-CHO} + 2C_2H_5SH \xrightarrow[\text{HCl}]{} \text{R-CH}(SC_2H_5)_2 + H_2O$$

Since the reaction proceeds in acidic medium, the sucrose first hydrolyzes into glucose and fructose. Fructose is too acid-sensitive for direct mercaptalation.

The filtrate containing fructose can be treated with hydrochloric acid at elevated temperature to produce levulinic acid.

The reaction is carried out by reacting sucrose with the alkyl mercaptan in 8- to 11-molar hydrochloric acid at about 5°C. Dimethyl, diethyl, di-*n*-propyl, and di-*n*-butyl dithioacetals can be prepared in yields up to 74%. Diethyl and dibutyl dithioacetals of glucose can also be made from raw sugar and molasses in good yields. Mercaptalation is not successful with higher normal alkyl mercaptans or with secondary and tertiary alkyl mercaptans.

Several alkyl dithioacetals have also been made directly from glucose with improved yields (107). Hydrochloric acid alone or in combination with zinc chloride is the condensing agent. Secondary mercaptans, tertiary mercaptans, thiourea, 2-mercaptoethanol, and other reagents do not react with glucose under the conditions tested (145). The higher alkyl mercaptans, such as lauryl mercaptan, react with glucose only under special conditions (145).

In general, the preparation of the dithioacetals from sucrose is more sensitive towards changes in conditions than from glucose (145).

The thioacetals are crystalline, well-characterized compounds. They could serve as useful intermediates for the preparation of other acylic derivatives. They have also been tested as pesticides. Among the derivatives that have been prepared are the benzoates, acetates, methyl ethers (145), and the cyanoethyl and β-carboxyethyl ethers, of glucose diethyl dithioacetal (86). The attempted preparation of the amide of the carboxyethyl ether has shown some success. Attempts to oxidize the dithioacetals or their esters or ethers to a sulfoxide or sulfone have been unsuccessful (145), as have attempts to reduce the cyanoethyl mercaptal to the amine.

Table 5-1
Physical properties of sucrose acetals and ketals

CYCLIC COMPOUNDS

4:6,1′:3′,4′:6′-Triethylidene sucrose
White powder. $[\alpha]_D$ +29.9° in benzene. R_f 0.82 (BuOH:EtOH:H$_2$O). M_G O
(borate, pH 10). (280)
Pentaethylidene sucrose
Oil. $[\alpha]_D$ +29.2° in benzene. R_f 0.86 (BuOH:EtOH:H$_2$O). M_G O (borate,
pH 10). (280)

NONCYCLIC COMPOUNDS

Methoxymethyl sucrose
Yellow syrup. $[\alpha]_D$ +42.0°, c. 1.0, CHCl$_3$. Made from pentasodium sucrate.
Claimed to be highly substituted and uniform. Two other batches similarly
made had lower rotation (20° and 37°). (17)
Clear syrup. $[\alpha]_D$ +35° in CHCl$_2$. Degree of substitution 4.2. Made from
sucrose with excess chloromethyl methyl ether. (197)
2-Tetrahydropyranyl sucrose
White powder. $[\alpha]_D$ +34° (21.5°C), c. 1.6, CHCl$_3$. Degree of substitution 6.5.
(10)
6-Formyl-2-tetrahydropyranyl sucrose
Solid. Degree of substitution 7.4. Product is heptahydrate, according to infrared and elemental analysis. (10)
1-Ethoxyethyl sucrose
Oil. $[\alpha]_D$ +37° (20°C), c. 1.5, CH$_3$OH. Degree of substitution 7.25. (10)
1-Chloroethoxyethyl-1 sucrose
Orange oil. B.p. 100-110°C at 0.1 mm. $[\alpha]_D$ +7.8° (25°C), c. 0.9, CHCl$_3$.
Chromatographically uniform, with slight contamination. (208)
2-Chloroethoxyethyl-1 sucrose
Oil. $[\alpha]_D$ +8.5° (20.5°C), c. 0.8, CH$_3$OH. Degree of substitution 7.65. $n_D^{17.5}$
1.4892. (10)
1-Isobutyoxyethyl sucrose
Oil. $[\alpha]_D$ +30.2° (20.5°C), c. 0.9, CH$_3$OH. Degree of substitution close to six.
$n_D^{17.5}$ 1.4510. (10)
10-Vinyloxydecyloxyethyl-1 sucrose
White, rubbery. $[\alpha]_D$ +14.85° (26°C), c. 0.674, chloromethyl cyanide. Degree of
substitution 6.82. (11)
1-Cetyloxyethyl sucrose
White solid. M.p. 45-50°C. $[\alpha]_D$ +14.2° (16.5°C), c. 2.14, CHCl$_3$. Degree of
substitution 3.25. (55)

6

Oxidation products

THE direct oxidation of sucrose has been studied with a number of oxidizing agents and catalysts. Because of the many oxidizable groups in the molecule, these reactions usually lead to mixtures of products that are either unseparable or can be isolated only with great difficulty. Thus the desired products are generally not easily obtained in good yields.

However, the oxidation of the monosaccharides has greater value. This reaction can produce more uniform products because fewer side reactions are possible. For example, the oxidation of invert sugar by hypobromites gives gluconic acid by oxidation of the glucose plus unreacted fructose. Selective oxidation of the aldehyde group in the glucose can thus be used advantageously for the separation of glucose and fructose. This method may be of interest in the production of fructose.

Arabonic acid has also been prepared by the alkaline oxidation of inverted sucrose or molasses. Arabonic acid is an intermediate in the manufacture of vitamin B_2 (riboflavin).

Further oxidation of gluconic acid, or stronger direct oxidation of glucose, gives saccharic acid. More drastic oxidation with nitric acid splits the molecule to oxalic acid and tartaric acid.

Sucrose and other carbohydrates are also oxidized with lead tetraacetate and periodic acid. Both oxidizing agents are widely used in analytical chemistry and in structural determinations of carbohydrates. These agents split the bonds between adjacent carbon atoms carrying hydroxyl groups to form aldehydes. The formation of *sucrose tetraaldehyde* is reported with lead tetraacetate, but the product has not been sufficiently characterized:

106

CH₂OH ... C
H—C———O———C
H—C—OH   HO—C—H
HO—C—H   O   H—C—OH   O
H—C—OH   H—C
H—C   CH₂OH
CH₂—OH

O′ →

CH₂OH
H—C———O———C
H—C   CHO
CHO   O   CHO   O
CHO   H—C
H—C—OH   CH₂OH
H—C
CH₂OH

Oxidation with periodate reportedly yields a product with no free carbonyl group and the possible structure of a cyclic acetal. Hydrogenation of this oxidation product gives ethylene glycol and glycerol but neither one in the theoretical quantity (three moles of glycerol plus one mole of glycol per mole of sucrose or tetraaldehyde).

Some of the products obtained by the oxidation of sucrose are shown in Figure 6-1.

Figure 6-1
Oxidation of sucrose

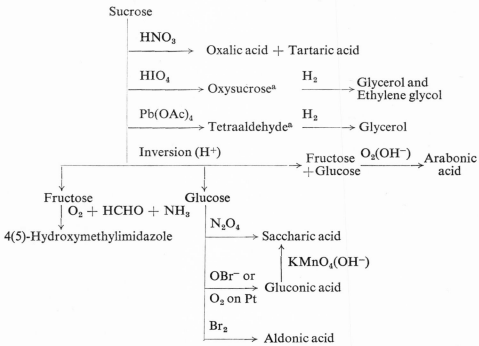

a – Compounds prepared with lead tetraacetate and periodate are probably similar.

OXIDATION WITH PERIODIC ACID TO OXYSUCROSE

Oxidation of sucrose with periodic acid in water gives *oxysucrose*, a white amorphous solid, in 90% yield, (197). Its structure has not been investigated in detail. It reduces Fehling's solution. Infrared absorption shows that it has no free carbonyl groups. Their absence is attributed to the formation of cyclic acetals, probably similar to those obtained from glucose (Guthrie and Honeyman, *Chem. Ind.* **1958**, 388).

The product is very probably identical to that obtained with lead tetraacetate, as shown by the similar properties of its reaction products.

One mole of sucrose is reacted with three moles of periodic acid in water and hydrogenated without the isolation of the supposed tetraaldehyde oxidation product (68). The hydrogenation is carried out at 140°C and 2700 psi. in the presence of Raney nickel. After hydrolysis a viscous liquid product is formed. This product is a mixture of glycerol in 45% yield and ethylene glycol in 66% yield.

OXIDATION WITH LEAD TETRAACETATE TO TETRAALDEHYDE

The oxidation of sucrose in pyridine by lead tetraacetate in a molar ratio of one to three yields a colorless amorphous powder of low rotation ($[\alpha]_D^{26 \cdot 6} + 7.4°$; c. 3.37, H_2O) and no definite melting point (90-115°C) (68). The product reduces Fehling's solution and Schiff's reagent and contains 3.8 aldehyde groups per molecule. It is very soluble in water, slightly soluble in 96% ethyl alcohol, and insoluble in acetone, chloroform and ethylacetate.

The oxidation of sucrose cannot be carried out satisfactorily in aqueous solution since hydrolysis of the lead tetraacetate precedes the oxidation of sucrose.

The tetraaldehyde can be hydrogenated similarly to the product obtained with periodic acid. Glycerol is obtained in a yield of 25%. No ethylene glycol is detected.

Oxidation of the tetraaldehyde to the corresponding acid by strontium hypobromite produces a strontium salt with rotation $[\alpha]_D^{22} + 23°$ (c. 2, H_2O) and other properties identical with those of the product prepared by periodic acid oxidation [Fleury *et al.*, *Compt. Rend.* **214**, 366 (1942); **216**, 65 (1943)].

The rate of oxidation of sucrose with lead tetraacetate has been determined in acetic acid and pyridine. Oxidation is more rapid in pyridine at 0°C than in acetic acid at 25°C but follows a similar course.

CATALYTIC OXIDATION

Oxidation of sucrose has been studied over a platinum catalyst (260b). An aqueous mixture of sodium bicarbonate, sucrose and platinum was shaken in an oxygen atmosphere at an elevated temperature. The reaction was believed to give a *sucronic acid* by oxidation of one or more hydroxyls to carboxyl groups without rupture of the glycosidic linkage. A crystalline, optically active acid obtained in 33% yields was found to be ammonium gluconate. Formation of this product indicates hydrolysis. Several other acidic products were also obtained and analyzed. For more details, see Liston, "The platinum-catalyzed oxidation of sucrose," M. Sc. thesis, University of Ottawa, 1957 (102).

ARABONIC ACID

Arabonic acid is prepared by the alkaline oxidation of inverted sucrose or molasses (116, 268). In alkaline solution oxygen degrades the sugars to acids having one carbon atom less than the starting material. The presence of alkali is necessary for the formation of the en-ediol, which is probably converted into the intermediate peroxide before splitting off formic acid to form the arabonic acid:

$$RCHOHCHO \xrightarrow{\text{OH}^-} RCOH{=}CHOH \xrightarrow{\text{O}_2}$$

Glucose

$$\underset{\overset{|}{O} - \overset{|}{O}}{RCOHCHOH} \xrightarrow{\text{OH}^-} RCOOH + HCOOH$$

Arabonic acid

Fructose similarly yields arabonic acid. The reaction, described previously in the literature, has been further studied to determine the effects of temperature, oxygen pressure, and concentration of sugar and alkali on the reaction rate and yield. Sugar beet molasses can be utilized successfully as a source of invert sugar. Products made from sugar cane molasses have a dark color.

The reaction is carried out in an aqueous alkaline medium. Oxygen is bubbled through the reaction mixture, preferably under pressure. The concentration of dissolved oxygen in the solution is the principal factor determining the yield. At higher temperatures the rate of the reaction greatly increases. Yields up to 60% are reported.

ALDONIC ACID AND ITS AMIDES

Aldonic acid is made by mild oxidation of glucose or other aldose sugars, with silver salts or bromine water. Gluconic acid has also been obtained by catalytic oxidation of sucrose (see above). These acids have the same number of carbons as the sugar starting material.

The acid amides of six aldonic acids have been made by a new method from the corresponding phenyl hydrazides (3). Among these are gluconamide, talonamide, and allonamide. These compounds were prepared in pure form to study the Van't Hoff principle of optical superposition.

SACCHARIC ACID

Glucose can be oxidized directly to saccharic acid by a number of methods. Among these the Foundation has studied the oxidation with nitrogen tetroxide (14, 205):

$$CH_2OH(CHOH)_4CHO \xrightarrow{\text{N}_2\text{O}_4} HOOC(CHOH)_4COOH$$

Glucose   Saccharic acid

The reaction proceeds in nitrogen tetroxide as the solvent at 30°C in the presence of potassium carbonate. Yields are only up to 50% because of the number of side reactions and partial oxidations that accompany the reaction. Numerous unsuccessful attempts have been made to improve the yield by varying the reaction conditions. In addition the by-product glucuronic, guluronic, gluconic, tartaric, and oxalic acids have been isolated to study the reaction mechanism and develop techniques for analyzing the products. However, the yield could not be improved.

ETHERS OF 4(5)-HYDROXYMETHYLIMIDAZOLE

4(5)-Hydroxymethylimidazole is prepared by oxidizing fructose in the presence of formaldehyde and ammonia with cupric carbonate as catalyst. The reaction is carried out at 100°C with air. (See details in Organic Syntheses, **24**, 64, John Wiley & Sons, New York, 1944.) The fructose is cleaved to dihydroxyacetone and glyceric aldehyde, either of which can be oxidized to hydroxymethylglyoxal. The glyoxal then undergoes the conventional condensation with formaldehyde and ammonia to the imidazole. Sucrose may be used as a source for fructose in the reaction:

$$
\begin{array}{c}
CH_2OH \\
|\\
C=O \\
|\\
CHOH \\
|\\
CHOH \\
|\\
CHOH \\
|\\
CH_2OH
\end{array}
\xrightarrow{\;O_2\;}
\begin{array}{c}
CH_2OH \\
|\\
C=O \\
|\\
CH_2OH \\
|\\
CHO \\
|\\
CHOH \\
|\\
CH_2OH
\end{array}
\xrightarrow{\;O_2\;}
\begin{array}{c}
CH_2OH \\
|\\
C=O \\
|\\
CHO
\end{array}
\xrightarrow[NH_3]{CH_2O}
$$

There is a tautomeric equilibrium between the 4- and the 5-isomer, as with all other imidazoles substituted in these positions; hence these compounds are named as 4(5)-imidazoles.

Several ether derivatives of this hydroxymethylimidazole have been prepared including the o-phenylphenoxy and o-benzyl-p-chlorophenoxy ethers (282), similar to those previously prepared [Ruoff and Scott, *J. Am. Chem. Soc.* **72**, 4950 (1950)]. However, attempted N-methylation is reported as unsuccessful (282).

MISCELLANEOUS OXIDATIONS

Oxidation of primary hydroxyls to aldehydes

The oxidation of sucrose via the primary tosyl derivative to aldehyde has met little success (260a). Attempts have included (a) the reaction of the tosylate group with 2-propane nitronate followed by disproportion to the aldehyde and acetoxime and (b) the application of the Hass-Bender reaction using the tosyl ester instead of the halogen derivative.

Oxidation with hexavalent uranium

The original belief that the reaction between photoactivated uranyl (VI) ion and sucrose is a specific photosynthetised hydrolysis of the glycosidic linkage has been disproved. Rather the reaction involves oxidation of the sucrose and reduction of the uranyl ion (61, 112). Similar results are obtained with a wide variety of carbohydrates including glucose, fructose and gluconic acid. The mechanism of the reaction and quantum yields have been thoroughly studied.

OXIDATION OF OTHER CARBOHYDRATES

The oxidation of a number of monosaccharides with lead tetraacetate has been thoroughly studied at Massachusetts Institute of Technology in research partly sponsored by the Foundation (66, 67, 113, 156). This work and other research at the Institute on this subject are summarized in a Foundation report (252).

Among the carbohydrates oxidized are esters, glycosides and other derivatives of mannose, glucose, arabinose, lyxose, galactose and trehalose. Oxidation with lead tetraacetate has also been used for structural studies of glucose, sorbitol, mannitol, and their derivatives.

ERYTHROSE is prepared with good yield by treatment of ethylidene sorbitol with lead tetraacetate (44). Ethylidene sorbitol is made from ethylidene glucose by hydrogenation. Ethylidene glucose itself could not be oxidized into erythrose under similar conditions.

XYLONIC ACID has been made directly by an oxidative process from cottonseed hulls containing xylose (140). Three new compounds of xylonic acid and xylose have been prepared.

Oxidation of 2,4;3,5-dimethylene gluconic acid to 2,4;3,5-dimethylene saccharic acid

2,4;3,5-Dimethylene-D-gluconic acid is prepared by reacting gluconolactone with trioxane in concentrated hydrochloric acid (172). The reaction is a modification of that described previously in the literature. Oxidation of this compound with potassium permanganate in aqueous alkaline medium gives 2,4;3,5-dimethylene-D-saccharic acid, which has been identified as its dimethyl and di-*p*-bromophenacyl esters (172). This reaction has confirmed the finding of other authors that oxidation of the gluconic acid derivative yields the corresponding saccharic acid compound.

7

Reduction products and unsaturated derivatives

CATALYTIC REDUCTION

HYDROGENATION of sucrose has been the subject of much study because several valuable products can be obtained by this process.

Under mild conditions mannitol and sorbitol are formed in the ratio of approximately one to three. Mannitol and sorbitol and their derivatives are used widely in foods and pharmaceuticals. At high temperatures and pressures (230°C, 100 atm) the sucrose chains are severed, and lower alcohols are produced, such as propylene glycol, ethylene glycol, and glycerol. Piperazines and acyclic amino compounds are obtained when hydrogenation is performed in the presence of ammonia or simple organic amines. This reaction has been thoroughly studied by the Foundation.

Nickel is the most widely used catalyst in these hydrogenations.

High temperature cracking of sucrose was probably carried out in Germany during World War II to produce mixed glycols that could be used in place of pure ethylene glycol as an antifreeze. Some glycerol is presently produced by this method.

Production of mannitol

Mannitol is generally produced by the catalytic hydrogenation or electrolytic reduction of invert sugar, but can be made directly from sucrose without inversion (Figure 7-1). Production of one pound of mannitol requires at least four pounds of sucrose. Mannitol is also a by-product of the fermentation of sugar to lactic acid and other products and is produced on a smaller scale from seaweeds.

Sorbitol

Sorbitol can be manufactured from sucrose in high yield, but the commercial production generally is based primarily on corn sugar and starches. The starches are hydrolyzed to glucose first, and then hydrogenated over nickel catalyst.

112

Figure 7-1
Manufacture of mannitol

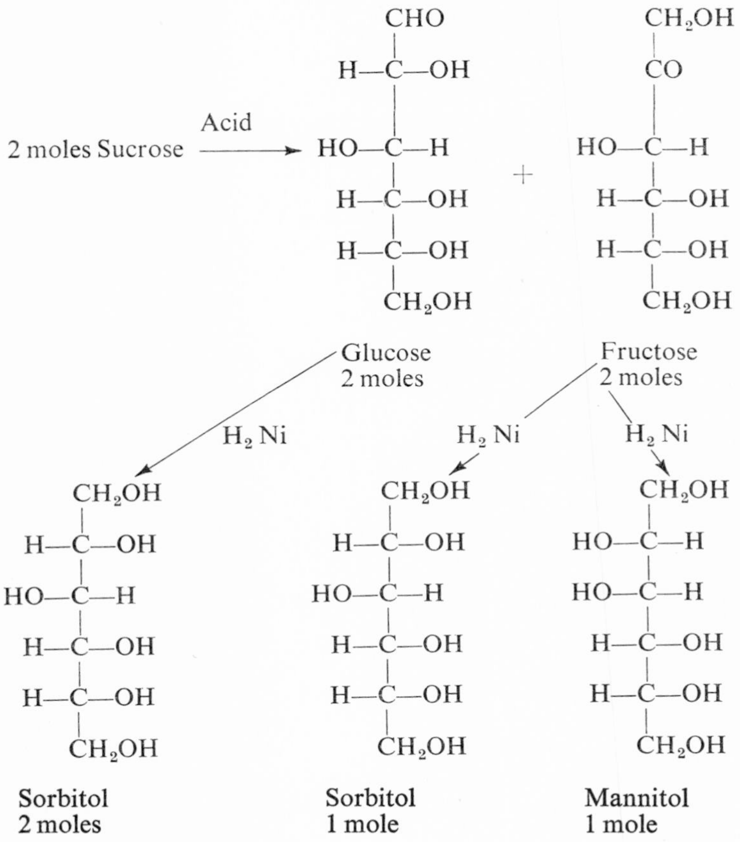

	CHO		CH_2OH
	H—C—OH		CO
2 moles Sucrose $\xrightarrow{\text{Acid}}$	HO—C—H	+	HO—C—H
	H—C—OH		H—C—OH
	H—C—OH		H—C—OH
	CH_2OH		CH_2OH

Glucose 2 moles   Fructose 2 moles

H_2 Ni H_2 Ni H_2 Ni

CH_2OH	CH_2OH	CH_2OH
H—C—OH	H—C—OH	HO—C—H
HO—C—H	HO—C—H	HO—C—H
H—C—OH	H—C—OH	H—C—OH
H—C—OH	H—C—OH	H—C—OH
CH_2OH	CH_2OH	CH_2OH

| Sorbitol 2 moles | Sorbitol 1 mole | Mannitol 1 mole |

REDUCTIVE AMINOLYSIS
Preparation of 2-methyl piperazine

Reductive aminolysis of sucrose was first described by the former I. G. Farbenindustrie [British Patent 449, 474 (1936)]. Sucrose, treated with ammonia and hydrogen in the presence of a nickel catalyst, was claimed to produce a mixture of propylene diamine and polypropylene polyamine.

In similar reactions workers at the Pennsylvania State University have isolated a basic crystalline material which was soon identified as 2-methylpiperazine (289). This process has also been patented (59). Additional work has included the development of an economically feasible process and the study of the chemistry and reaction mechanism (258, 293). By statistical design, the yield of piperazines has been raised to 29% by weight of sucrose (258). This yield corresponds to one mole of 2-methyl piperazine per mole of sucrose.

H

The hydrogenation is carried out in the presence of a large excess of aqueous ammonia at 1150 psi and 215°C. The catalyst is sponge nickel. When the reduction proceeds in the presence of ethylenediamine, propylenediamine, or isopropanolamine, the yield of piperazines is claimed to increase (59, 289).

The piperazine fraction also contains unsubstituted piperazine and 2,5-dimethyl piperazine. Other fractions include aliphatic amines (ethylene and propylene diamine, ethanol amine and 2-aminopropanol) and a series of hydroxyamino compounds.

The primary and secondary amines form weakly basic monomethylol derivatives when reacted with formaldehyde (289).

REACTION MECHANISM. The reaction is believed to start with inversion, and the fructose and glucose condense with ammonia before any cleavage takes place. The mechanism is shown in Figure 7-2.

Figure 7-2
Suggested mechanism of the reductive aminolysis of sucrose (258)

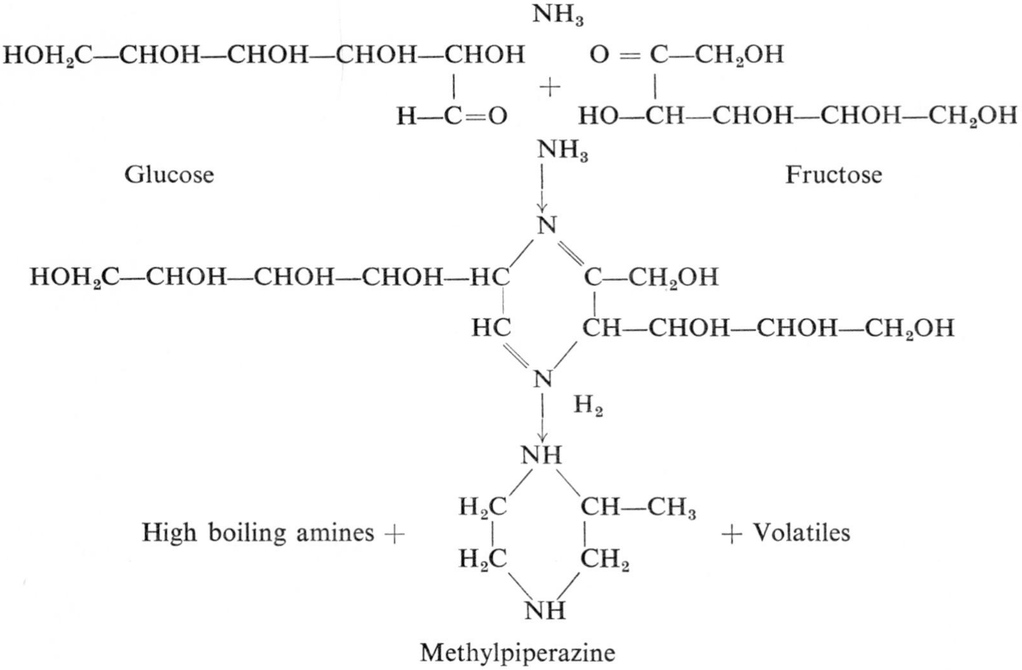

Methylpiperazine

ADDITIONAL DATA. For more details on the reaction conditions, statistical design, analyses of fractions, chemistry, and reaction mechanism, see Reference 258.

SYNTHESIS. Synthetic 2-methyl piperazine is made in good yield by the well known process of cyclizing N-2-hydroxypropyl ethylene diamine (231). The diamine is prepared by the addition of propylene oxide to ethylene diamine. Reductive aminolysis of N-2-hydroxypropyl ethanolamine to 2-methyl piperazine proceeds with a lower yield (265b). The synthetic product was used in this work for identification purposes and also to test the usefulness of the compound in fibers, drugs, and other potential fields.

DERIVATIVES OF PIPERAZINES. Derivatives of piperazines have been made for tests in polymerization reactions. Among these are:

2-METHYL PIPERAZINE-1,4-DICARBOXYLIC ACID CHLORIDE. Attempts have been made to prepare this carbamic acid derivative by reaction with phosgene (241a):

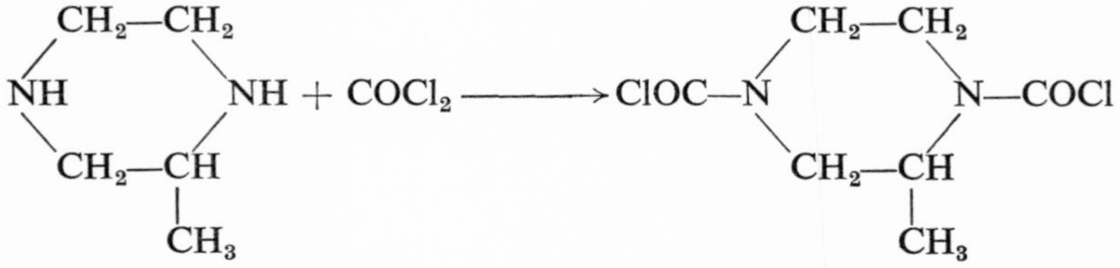

$$
\begin{array}{ccc}
\text{CH}_2\!\!-\!\!\text{CH}_2 & & \text{CH}_2\!\!-\!\!\text{CH}_2 \\
\diagup \qquad \diagdown & & \diagup \qquad \diagdown \\
\text{NH} \qquad \text{NH} + \text{COCl}_2 \longrightarrow \text{ClOC}\!-\!\text{N} & & \text{N}\!-\!\text{COCl} \\
\diagdown \qquad \diagup & & \diagdown \qquad \diagup \\
\text{CH}_2\!\!-\!\!\text{CH} & & \text{CH}_2\!\!-\!\!\text{CH} \\
\qquad | & & \qquad | \\
\qquad \text{CH}_3 & & \qquad \text{CH}_3
\end{array}
$$

No well defined compound can be isolated. The reaction product is either a mixture of white crystals and a cream-colored gum or a white crystalline product with too high a chlorine content.

1,4-DICARBOMETHOXY-2-METHYL PIPERAZINE. The dicarbomethoxy compound is prepared with methyl chloroformate and sucrose as described in the literature. It is used to identify the preceding compound (241a).

1,4-DICARBETHOXY-2-METHYL PIPERAZINE. The dicarbethoxy derivative is made by condensation of sucrose with ethyl chloroformate as described in the literature. Condensation of the carbethoxy derivative with ethylenediamine is unsuccessful (241b).

N-LAURYL-2-METHYL PIPERAZINE. N-Lauryl-2-methyl piperazine is made by reacting 2-methyl piperazine with lauryl bromide (234b).

Reductive aminolysis of sucrose with organic amines

The hydrogenation of sucrose in the presence of a number of organic amines and nickel catalysts has also been studied. N-Substituted 1,2-diaminoethane derivatives were the chief products with both aliphatic and aromatic amines:

Amine	*Major products*	*Reference*
Methyl amine	N,N′-Dimethyl ethylene diamine	59
	N,N′-Dimethyl piperazine	
Diethanol amine	N,N,N′,N′-Tetraethanol ethylene diamine	270
	N,N,N′,N′-Tetraethanol propylene diamine	
Dimethyl amine	N,N,N′,N′-Tetramethyl ethylene diamine	106, 240
	N,N-Dimethyl isopropanol amine	265a, b
	N,N-Dimethyl ethanol amine	
Diethylamine	Not characterized	106
Morpholine or pyrrolidone	1,2-Dimorpholinoethane	106, 270
	1,2-Dimorpholinopropane	
	4-Isopropanol morpholine	
	4-Ethanol morpholine	

For more details of the reaction conditions and study of the products, see Reference 106.

Piperazine and its derivatives are used in the pharmaceutical industry as antihelminthics. Piperazine also shows promising fiber-forming properties in nylon and urethane formulations, as discussed under Fibers, page 210. A survey on additional uses covering the literature through 1959 is given in Reference 293.

Reductive aminolysis of other carbohydrates and related compounds

FRUCTOSE PLUS AMMONIA. Reductive aminolysis of fructose with ammonia gives a poor yield of piperazine, and the product is mostly undistillable (265b).

LEVULINIC ACID PLUS AMMONIA. When levulinic acid is catalytically hydrogenated in the presence of ammonia, 5-methylpyrrolidone is formed (239). The reaction is analogous to the preparation of 1-5-dimethyl-2-pyrrolidone from levulinic acid and methyl amine.

Several attempts have been made to polymerize 5-methylpyrrolidone in the presence of alkaline catalysts (239). No reaction takes place. Copolymerization with 2-pyrrolidone is also unsuccessful. Polymerization of 2-pyrrolidone gives trimers or polymers according to U.S. Patents 2, 638, 463 and 2, 739, 959.

PROPYLENE GLYCOL AND OTHER POLYOLS PLUS AMMONIA. Catalytic reductive amination of propylene glycol yields a mixture consisting mainly of 2,5-dimethyl piperazine and 1,2-propylenediamine. The reaction is described in the literature with a yield of piperazine of 76%. A process has been developed by statistical design to determine the optimum conditions for the reaction (39). The yield is less than 70%, but it can be increased by recycling the unreacted materials.

The work is of interest because it serves as a model for the reduction of sucrose. The reaction gives a high yield of dimethyl piperazine without formation of pyrrol. It is also suspected that propylene glycol may be one of the intermediates in the reduction of sucrose.

Glycerol (289), ethylene glycol (289, 293), sorbitol (289), and deoxyaminosorbitol (293) undergo reductive aminolysis in poor yield.

DEOXYSUCROSES

Deoxysucroses are derivatives of sucrose that contain fewer hydroxyl groups than sucrose itself:

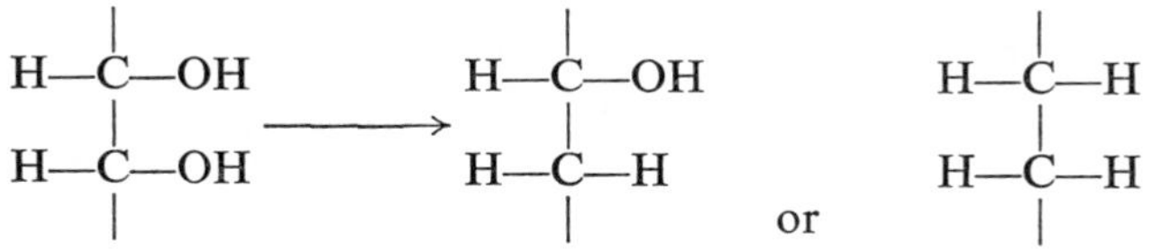

Deoxysucrose cannot be made directly from sucrose. These derivatives are prepared from tosyl, iodo, or other halogen derivatives either by reduction with lithium aluminum hydride or by mild catalytic hydrogenation over palladium on charcoal or Raney nickel.

Lithium aluminum hydride is known to eliminate by reduction primarily tosyloxy groups and halogens and to reduce secondary tosylates to form the secondary alcohol and ditolyl disulfide. Preliminary experiments indicate that the reduction of diiodosucrose mesylate and octamesyl sucrose does not lead to uniform products. This reaction needs further investigation (194c). A mixture of several compounds is also obtained in attempts to treat sucrose pentatosylates with lithium aluminum hydride (16). Hydrogenation at atmospheric pressure at room temperature is reportedly not always successful (194c).

The properties of deoxy sugars are given in Table 7-1.

Heptamethyl monodeoxysucrose

This compound is made by hydrogenation of the corresponding iodo derivative in methyl alcohol solution at atmospheric pressure with palladium on charcoal as the catalyst (103). The hydrogen iodide formed during the reaction is neutralized with diethyl amine.

6,6'-Dideoxysucrose

6,6'- Dideoxysucrose is made by catalytic deesterification of the corresponding hexabenzoate described next (194f, h). The product is a syrup. Dideoxysucrose is also reportedly made by reducing diiodomonotosylpentaacetyl sucrose (272a) or tritosyl sucrose (35) with lithium aluminium hydride. The solid product obtained from tritosyl sucrose is claimed to be 6,6'-dideoxysucrose.

6,6'-Dideoxysucrose is one of the products obtained by the catalytic hydrogenation of sucrose-5,5'-diene (194i). The oily product has been characterized through the hexabenzoate.

6,6'-Dideoxysucrose hexabenzoate

This crystalline compound is obtained by catalytic hydrogenation of 6,6'-diiodosucrose hexabenzoate (194h). The reaction is carried out in the presence of Raney nickel as catalyst. The yield is 63% (194j). The compound is soluble in chloroform and hot methyl and ethyl alcohols (194j). Removal of the benzoyl groups by catalytic deesterification gives the syrupy dideoxysucrose (194f, h).

UNSATURATED DERIVATIVES

The unusual carbohydrates with one or more double bonds in the molecule have not been widely investigated. The only known unsaturated derivative of sucrose has been prepared recently by treating 6,6'-diiodosucrose hexabenzoate with silver fluoride in pyridine:

$$
\begin{array}{ccc}
CH_2I & & CH_2 \\
| & AgF & || \\
HO\!-\!CH & \xrightarrow{} & HO\!-\!C \\
| & Pyridine & |
\end{array}
$$

Other methods of reductive removal include treatment with zinc in acetic acid. As in other unsaturates, several compounds can possibly be added to the double bond, including water, hydrogen halides, and halogenides. However, these reactions have not been investigated. Only saturation of the double bond with lithium hydride has been attempted.

Research on unsaturated derivatives of sucrose has been started only recently and is still in progress. The properties of a few compounds are given in Table 7-1. The structure of the 5-5'-unsaturate is shown in Figure 7-3.

Figure 7-3
The structure of 5,5′-diene-2,3,4,1′,3′,4′-hexabenzoyl sucrose

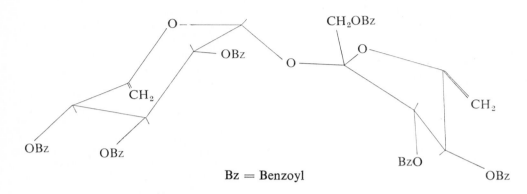

Bz = Benzoyl

5,5′-Sucrosediene

5,5′-Sucrosediene has been prepared by the saponification of 5,5′-sucrosediene-2,3,4,1′,3′,4′-hexabenzoyl sucrose discussed below (194g). The diene does not appear to react with sodium bisulfite to give the 6,6′-disulfo-derivative (194i). Hydrogenation gives a mixture of several products, possibly isomers, including 6,6′-dideoxysucrose (194h, i). Epoxidation and hydroboration are presently being attempted (194h). Results indicate an anti-Markownikow addition during hydroboration, suggesting the possible preparation of 5,5′-dideutero- and 5,5′-ditritiosucrose. [Lehmann, *Carbohydrate Res.* **2**, 1 (1966).]

5,5′-Diene-2,3,4,1′,3′,4′-hexamesyl sucrose

The crystalline compound is prepared from the 6,6′-diiodosucrose hexamesylate with silver fluoride in pyridine (194g). The yield is 20%. The compound is soluble in acetone (194j).

5,5′-Diene-2,3,4,1′,3′,4′-hexaacetyl sucrose

Treatment of the 6,6′-diiodosucrose hexaacetate with silver fluoride yields the corresponding 5,5′-diene (194d).

5,5′-Diene-2,3,4,1′,3′,4′-hexabenzoyl sucrose

The compound is prepared by reacting 6,6′-diiodosucrose hexabenzoate with silver fluoride in dry pyridine (194e). The yield is 63% (194j). The product is a high-melting crystalline material, soluble in chloroform and hot methyl and ethyl alcohols. Hydrogenation of the compound has not been successful (194g). Removal of the benzoyl group is carried out with sodium methoxide in methyl alcohol to produce the 5,5′-diene of sucrose (194g). Reduction with lithium aluminum hydride gives a syrupy product which chromatography indicates is homogenous and has unsaturated character. During reduction one of the double bonds may migrate to the 4,5-position (194i).

Table 7-1

Physical properties of deoxy, unsaturated, and azide derivatives of sucrose

DEOXY COMPOUNDS

Dideoxy sucrose
White solid. $[\alpha]_D$ +49.7°, c. 1.27, water. Structure is claimed to be 6,6′-dideoxy sucrose. Products made by other methods are oily. (35)
6,6′-Dideoxy-2,3,4,1′,3′,4′-hexabenzoyl sucrose
White crystalline powder. M.p. 83-85°C. $[\alpha]_D$ +15.5° (22°C), c. 2, CHCl³.
(194j)

UNSATURATES

5,5′-Diene-2,3,4,1′,3′,4′-hexabenzoyl sucrose
White crystals. M.p. 146-147°C. $[\alpha]_D$ −5.0° (22°C), c. 1, CHCl₃. (194j)
5,5′-Diene-2,3,4,1′,3′,4′-hexaacetyl sucrose
Crystalline. M.p. 113-115°C. (194j)

AZIDES

6,6′-Diazido-2,3,4,1′,3′,4′-hexabenzoyl sucrose
White solid. M.p. 75-77°C. $[\alpha]_D$ +34° (22°C), c. 1, CHCl₃. (194j)

8

Halogen and sulfur derivatives

HALOGEN DERIVATIVES

HALOGEN derivatives of sucrose cannot be prepared by simple treatment with the appropriate hydrogen halogenide. The reaction is preferentially catalyzed by strong acids which would cause hydrolysis of the glycosidic linkage. Experiments have therefore been carried out with thionyl chloride to replace the hydroxyl groups by chlorine atoms. Thionyl chloride is known to react with alcohols to form the halides through the intermediate chlorosulfite, ROSOCl. The reaction with sucrose is claimed to yield either a chlorosucrose sulfite ester or a polymeric sulfite derivative. Similarly, the action of sulfuryl chloride gives sucrose derivatives that contain halogen and cyclic sulfate or chlorosulfonyl groups (see Sulfates and Sulfite Esters, page 83).

One of the most important methods of preparing halogen derivatives utilizes the sulfonic acid esters, chiefly tosyl sucrose. *Iodosucrose* is readily obtained by treating tosyl or mesyl sucrose with sodium iodide (Finkelstein's reagent) in boiling acetone. The reaction is well known and widely used in organic syntheses. As discussed in more detail under Sulfonic Acid Esters (page 70), the esters on the primary hydroxyls of carbohydrates are preferentially exchanged. In the case of sucrose, two of the three primary esters, the 6 and 6', are readily replaceable with iodine.

Similarly, one or two tosyl groups can be replaced with chlorine by treatment with pyridine hydrochloride at elevated temperatures (194e, f; 255c). Some replacement also occurs when sucrose nitrate is treated with sodium iodide (197). However, the preparation of *chlorosucrose* by reacting octa(trimethylsilyl) sucrose with trimethylsilyl chloride has been unsuccessful (217b).

The preparation of *fluorosucrose* has also been investigated. Treatment of tosyl or mesyl derivatives with an alkali metal fluoride, in a method similar to that successfully employed in iodination and chlorination, causes little or no replacement. Other methods also have had little success. Some of the attempted replacement reactions have been carried out at higher temperatures—for example, in boiling ethylene glycol instead of boiling acetone —but the reaction still fails to produce more than a minute amount of fluoridation.

120

Exploratory experiments have been carried out to react tritosyl sucrose and its derivatives with hydrogen fluoride (255c). Treatment at 100°C in pyridine gives a product containing less than one mole of fluorine per mole of sucrose. Other substances are also obtained but have not been sufficiently characterized. Treatment of tritosyl pentaacetyl sucrose (255a), tritosyl pentabenzoyl sucrose (182), or dimesyl hexabenzoyl sucrose (213b) with potassium fluoride in ethylene glycol at elevated (boiling) temperatures or in dimethyl formamide is unsuccessful. Treatment of tritosyl pentabenzoyl sucrose and tribrosyl sucrose with cesium fluoride in boiling ethylene glycol is equally unsuccessful (182).

In all cases only a few per cent (if any) of the required fluoride can be introduced. The fully esterified molecule, in general, is more stable under the conditions of attempted fluoride exchange than the partially substituted sucrose. For example, tritosyl sucrose decomposes extensively under these conditions (213b).

The fluoridation of some monosaccharides and simple alcohols has been thoroughly studied. These experiments serve as models for the potential preparation of fluorosucrose itself (65, 84).

Halogen derivatives are quite stable compounds and often crystalline. Well characterized crystalline derivatives chiefly contain benzoyl groups on the unreacted hydroxyls. These derivatives are prepared from the corresponding mixed esters containing tosyl and benzoyl groups.

The halogen radical can be hydrolyzed in alkaline media. The reaction can proceed with the Walden inversion in the configuration of the related carbon atom. The halogen can be eliminated by catalytic hydrogenation or by reduction with hydrides such as lithium aluminum hydride. The product is deoxysucrose containing less oxygen than sucrose itself. Treatment with silver fluoride gives the unsaturated derivative (see Reduction Products and Unsaturated Derivatives, page 112).

The properties of some halogen derivatives are given in Table 8-1.

Chlorine compounds

The tosyl group is easily replaced by chlorine with pyridine hydrochloride at room or elevated temperatures. The 6,6'-ditosylate yields a mixture of 6-mono- and 6,6'-dichloro-derivatives.

6-CHLORO-6'-TOSYL-2,3,4,1',3',4'-HEXABENZOYL SUCROSE. Reaction of 6,6'-ditosyl sucrose hexabenzoate with pyridine hydrochloride for four hours at 40°C, followed by chromatography, gives a crystalline monochloro-derivative, probably the 6-chloro-6'-tosyl sucrose hexabenzoate (194f). The yield is 9% (194j). The compound is soluble in chloroform and hot ethyl alcohol (194j). Treatment with sodium benzoate in dimethyl formamide gives the crystalline monochloro heptabenzoate, probably the 6-chloro compound (194f, h).

6,6'-DICHLORO-2,3,4,1',3',4'-HEXABENZOYL SUCROSE. This compound is obtained in 67% yield (194j) when the 6,6'-ditosyl hexabenzoate is treated at 40°C with pyridine hydrochloride (194e). It is a white crystalline powder, soluble in chloroform and hot ethyl alcohol (194j).

6-CHLORO-2,3,4,1',3',4',6'-HEPTABENZOYL SUCROSE. The compound is made in 30% yield (194j) by reacting the 6-chloro-6'-tosyl sucrose hexabenzoate with sodium benzoate in dimethyl formamide (194h) or in its 1:1 mixtures with methyl ethyl ketone (194f).

The structure of the product is based on its saponification and hydrolysis to 6-chloroglucose. The full identification is presently under study. The compound is a white crystalline powder, soluble in chloroform and hot ethyl alcohol (194j).

DICHLOROMONOTOSYLPENTAACETYL SUCROSE. Reaction of tritosylpentaacetyl sucrose with pyridine hydrochloride in pyridine at 100°C gives a product that is largely dichloromonotosylpentaacetyl sucrose. Some deacylation can occur during the reaction. Deacylation by passing through a strong anion-exchange resin (Amberlite IRA®) and elution with acetic acid gives inverted anhydrosugars, 3,6-anhydroglucose and anhydroketohexose (255c).

Chlorosucroses that also contain sulfate ester groups are discussed under Sulfates and Sulfite Esters, page 83.

Iodine compounds

6,6'-DIIODO-2,3,4,1',3',4'-HEXAACETYL SUCROSE. The compound is made by treating the corresponding 6,6'-ditosylsucrose hexaacetate with sodium iodide in boiling acetone (12, 96). It is an oily product. Treatment of a purer ditosyl hexaacetate with sodium iodide in methyl ethyl ketone yields a crystalline product (194d). The 5,5'-diene hexaacetate has been made by reacting this product with silver fluoride (194d).

6,6'-DIIODO-2,3,4,1',3',4'-HEXAMESYL SUCROSE. The compound is made in 19% yield (194j) from the 6,6'-ditosyl hexamesylate with sodium iodide in methyl ethyl ketone (194c). It is a crystalline product soluble in acetone. Treatment with silver fluoride in pyridine gives the corresponding crystalline 5,5'-diene of sucrose hexamesylate (194g).

A similar diiodosucrose hexamesylate has been reportedly obtained by treating the octamesylate with excess (3.4 moles) sodium iodide in methyl ethyl ketone. This result indicates the preferred replacement of the mesyl ester moiety in the 6- and 6'-positions (194c).

The reduction to dideoxysucrose by hydrogenation over Raney nickel catalysts at room temperature and atmospheric pressure has been unsuccessful (194c). The reduction product with lithium aluminum hydride has recently been investigated briefly (194c).

6,6'-DIIODO-2,3,4,1',3',4'-HEXABENZOYL SUCROSE. The compound has been prepared by treating the 6,6'-ditosyl sucrose hexabenzoate with sodium iodide in methyl ethyl ketone (194e). The yield is 54% (194j). It is a white crystalline powder soluble in chloroform and hot methyl and ethyl alcohol. It can be converted into the corresponding 6,6'-dideoxy derivative by hydrogenation over Raney nickel (194f, h) and into the corresponding sucrose 5,5'-diene hexabenzoate by treatment with silver fluoride (194e).

6-IODO-4,1'-DITOSYL-2,3,6,3',4'-PENTAACETYL SUCROSE. The compound is made from the corresponding 4,1',6'-tritosyl sucrose pentaacetate with sodium iodide in acetone at 100°C (95). An amorphous product is obtained in 89% yield that analyzes well as the monoiodo derivative.

DIIODOMONOTOSYLPENTAACETYL SUCROSE. When tritosylpentaacetyl sucrose is treated with sodium iodide in boiling acetone, the diiodo derivative is obtained (35, 272a). The product has not been prepared in crystalline form because the tritosyl sucrose starting material was heterogenous. (See Sulfonic Acid Esters, page 70.) Also, acetates are less likely to crystallize than the corresponding benzoylated derivatives.

When chromatographically uniform tritosyl sucroses are acetylated and then treated with sodium iodide, the replacement is only 1.87 and 1.63 tosyloxy groups per molecule (96). Reduction with lithium aluminum hydride gives deoxysucrose (272a). Preliminary experiments show that treatment with 20% sodium thiosulfate in 50% aqueous ethyl alcohol in the presence of magnesium oxide may have resulted in the formation of a disulfide bridge through carbon-6 of the glucose portion (255c). No replacement reaction occurred with sodium nitrite in dimethyl formamide up to 100°C (255a, b). Reaction with tetracyanoethylene was also unsuccessful (255b).

Other products

The following halogenated products are discussed elsewhere:

ESTERS. For 4,6,1'-trichlorodisulfonyl sucrose and 4,6,6'-trichlorodichlorosulfonyl sucrose, see Sulfate and Sulfite Esters, page 83. For miscellaneous halogenated fatty esters of sucrose, see Fatty Esters, page 52.

ETHERS. For heptamethyl monoiodosucrose, see Methyl Ethers.

Halogen derivatives of other carbohydrates

CHLORINATED PRODUCTS OF PENTAACETYL GLUCOSE. The chlorination of pentaacetyl glucose with phosphorus pentachloride according to Brigl has been studied (105). Two crystalline compounds are obtained. Both contain four chlorine atoms per molecule and have a trichloromethyl group. (In 1921 Brigl treated β-D-glucopyranose pentaacetate with phosphorus pentachloride and obtained 2-trichloroacetyl-3,4,6-triacetyl-β-D-glucopyranosyl-1-chloride.) The reaction mechanism assigned by Winslow has also been reconsidered.

THIOSUCROSE AND OTHER SULFUR DERIVATIVES

Reactions with hydrogen sulfide

Thiol derivatives of sugars are usually prepared by reacting halogenated sugar acetates with the sodium or silver salt of hydrogen sulfide:

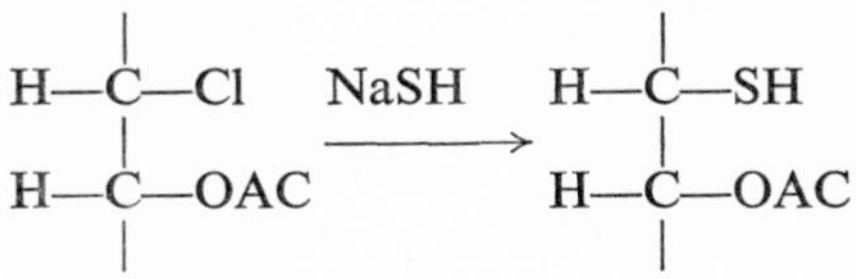

$$
\begin{array}{ccc}
\text{H—C—Cl} & \text{NaSH} & \text{H—C—SH} \\
| & \longrightarrow & | \\
\text{H—C—OAC} & & \text{H—C—OAC} \\
| & & |
\end{array}
$$

The extended direct action of hydrogen sulfide on sugar in pyridine is reported in the literature to also yield thiol sugars. Other methods include the hydrolysis of isomerized sugar xanthate and the hydrogenation of sugar in the presence of hydrogen sulfide. The latter method actually produces a thiosugar alcohol.

The action of low-cost hydrogen sulfide on sucrose is of interest for the preparation of thiosucrose or other sulfur derivatives that might be used as intermediates or for such end uses as pesticides. Some of these reactions have been briefly studied, but with little or no success.

A possible route to thiosucrose is treatment of the thiocyanate ester with sodium sulfide. The thiosucrose could be then converted to a disulfide by oxidation. The reaction with sodium sulfide has been successfully carried out on other carbohydrates, and the possibility of the existence of the disulfide is indicated by studies with molecular models (194c). The thiocyanate of sucrose can be prepared successfully in crystalline form (see Sucrose Thiocyanate, page 87).

Studies have been carried out both with sucrose and with simple sugars, chiefly glucose, and their derivatives to evaluate the reaction on these less complicated models. For example, acetyl derivatives of glucose have been used as a model because sugar acetates have favorable solubility properties and because the acetoxy groups are easier to replace than hydroxyls. Treatment of glucose pentaacetate with hydrogen sulfide in benzene in the presence of an equimolar amount of stannic chloride gives 1-thioglucose-2,3,4,6-tetraacetate (222). However, the product cannot be deacylated to 1-thioglucose. Deacetylation with sodium methylate in methyl alcohol yields a product almost free of the sulfhydryl group. Thio-trehalose is reportedly obtained in large extent. The reaction thus leads to the formation of thioglycosides.

Other model reactions include (a) the reaction of glucose with hydrogen sulfide in concentrated hydrochloric acid, which produces a polymeric sulfur derivative; (b) the explosive reaction of glucose with phosphorus pentasulfide at elevated temperature; and (c) the pyrolysis of glucose in an atmosphere of hydrogen sulfide (222). Pyrolysis of glucose produces sulfur-containing derivatives which have not been further investigated. 1-Thio-glucose and diglucosyl disulfide are reportedly isolated when glucose is treated with liquid hydrogen sulfide in the presence of a catalytic amount of pyridine, or simply with solutions of hydrogen sulfide under pressure (180b).

The preparation of thioglucose with hydrogen sulfide in pyridine, a process reported in the literature to yield thioglucose, has been found to yield a mixture, according to chromato-graphic analysis (180b).

The direct reaction between solutions of sucrose and hydrogen sulfide has also been examined (180a). Under mild conditions at atmospheric pressure and with cooling, no reaction occurs. However, at higher temperatures the sucrose hydrolyzes somewhat, but only a negligible reaction takes place between the monosaccharides and hydrogen sulfide (180a).

Similar experiments under pressure (in sealed tubes) at 80–175°C produce a variety of materials, including dark resinous products, small amounts of glucose and fructose, and thioglucose disulfide compounds (180a). No sucrose can be recovered. The reaction can also be carried out in the presence of catalytic amounts of pyridine hydrochloride, but no pure material can be isolated (180b).

Similarly, no success is reported when sucrose octaacetate or tritosyl sucrose are reacted with hydrogen sulfide (180a). However, replacement reportedly occurs when tritosyl sucrose is treated with sodium thioethoxide in dimethyl formamide at 150°C (180a). *Triethyl thiosucrose* can be isolated from the reaction mixture, which contains at least eight products according to chromatographic analysis.

For a review on thiol sugars, see A. L. Raymond, Thio- and seleno sugars, *Advances in Carbohydrate Chemistry*, **1**, 129–145 (1945).

Reactions with mercaptals

Sucrose and molasses have been successfully reacted with mercaptals to produce the corresponding dithioacetals (mercaptans) of glucose. (See Acetals, page 94.)

Table 8-1
Physical properties of halogen derivatives of sucrose

NOTE: See Table 4-2 for other halogen compounds.

6,6′-Diiodo-2,3,4,1′,3′,4′-hexabenzoyl sucrose
White crystals. M.p. 94-97°C. $[\alpha]_D^{25}$ +2°, c. 2, $CHCl_3$. (194j)

Diiodomonotosylpentaacetyl sucrose
Oil. $[\alpha]_D^{19}$ +40.0°, c. 3.8, $CHCl_3$. Probably structure 6,6′-diiodo-1′-tosyl-2,3,4,4′,4′-pentaacetyl sucrose. Iodine content lower than calculated. (35) Compound was made from tritosyl sucrose, which was found to contain 45% tritosyl, 40% ditosyl, and 15% other esters (96).

6′-Chloro-6′-tosyl-2,3,4,1′,3′,4′-hexabenzoyl sucrose
White crystals. M.p. 83-85°C. $[\alpha]_D^{23}$ +22.2°, c. 2, $CHCl_3$. (194j)

6,6′-Dichloro-2,3,4,1′,3′,4′-hexabenzoyl sucrose
White crystals. M.p. 85-87°C. $[\alpha]_D^{21.5}$ +5.8°, c. 1, $CHCl_3$ (194j)

6-Chloro-2,3,4,1′,3′,4′,6′-heptabenzoyl sucrose
White crystals. M.p. 92-94°C. $[\alpha]_D^{22}$ +13°, c. 1, $CHCl_3$. (194j)
Final identification of a structure under current investigation (194h).

6,6′-Diiodo-2,3,4,1′,3′,4′-hexamesyl sucrose
White crystals. M.p. 210-212°C. $[\alpha]_D^{22}$ +43.5°, c. 1, acetone. (194j)

9

Metal derivatives

METAL SUCRATES

METAL sucrates are sucrose compounds similar to alcoholates where one or all eight hydroxyls are reacted with a metal. Alkali metal sucrates are important intermediates in the preparation of esters, ethers and other derivatives. Metal sucrates also play an important role as catalysts in the preparation of sucrose esters of fatty acids by transesterification (100, 103).

Their application is somewhat limited by their insolubility in inert organic solvents so that all reactions must be carried out in heterogenous phases. Recent research on improved and reproducible methods of preparation and on the reactions of sucrates with organic halogen compounds indicates that this method could become important in the preparation of sucrose derivatives. Further studies will be necessary, particularly to elucidate the structure of the sucrates so as to explore the possibility of preparing selectively substituted derivatives of known structure.

Preparation

WITH METALS. Metallic sodium, lithium, or potassium can be successfully reacted with sucrose to yield the metal sucrate. Sucrose does not dissolve in common inert organic solvents. Of the solvents tested, liquid ammonia is the best medium for the reaction (7). Liquid monomethylamine (19) and N-methyl-2-pyrrolidone (243c) are less suitable since neither the metals nor the sucrates are soluble in these solvents. N-Methyl-2-pyrrolidone and such other solvents for sucrose as dimethyl sulfoxide and dimethyl formamide are decomposed by sodium (7). In morpholine and pyridine the reaction product is similar to the sodium hydroxide addition compound (7).

It is essential to use absolutely dry solvent, or the sodium will be partly consumed and an addition compound will form (7). Laboratory apparatus suitable for the preparation of sodium or other sucrates is described in Reference 7.

WITH METAL ALCOHOLATES. Sodium sucrate is prepared from sucrose with sodium methoxide (285b). The sucrose is dissolved in dimethyl sulfoxide and reacted with the sodium methoxide dissolved in methyl alcohol. The method is described by Gaertner [*J. Am. Oil Chem. Soc.* **38**, 410 (1961)].

WITH METAL AMIDES. Sodium amide prepared *in situ* in liquid ammonia is particularly useful in the preparation of highly substituted metal sucrates that cannot readily be prepared with the metal itself because of the long reaction time. *Sodium hexa-* and *heptasucrates* have been made successfully by this method (7). This method has also been used to prepare lower sodium sucrates (31). *Sodium monosucrate* can be made with sodium amide in dimethyl sulfoxide (285i).

WITH METAL HYDRIDES. A newer method of preparation reacts sucrose with sodium hydride at room temperature in an aprotic solvent, such as dimethyl formamide, dimethyl sulfoxide, or N-methyl pyrrolidone. The sodium sucrate formed is not isolated but reacted *in situ* with an alkyl halide to form sucrose monoethers to octaethers in good yield (90, 196).

WITH METAL HYDROXIDES OR SALTS. Attempts have been made to prepare sodium sucrates by reacting sucrose and sodium hydroxide (243d). The reaction had been described previously using ethanolamine as the solvent and azeotropic distillation with butyl alcohol. However, under such conditions, sodium sucrate is not formed since carbohydrates form addition compounds (the "saccharates") with metallic hydroxides. The addition compound of potassium hydroxide and sucrose is well known and important in structural studies (7).

Copper sucrate has reportedly been made with copper sulfate (299c, d). (See also Reactions with Metal Powder and Metal Derivatives below.)

Properties

Metal sucrates are white or grayish products, often crystalline. Generally they are hygroscopic, but they can be stored in closed containers for several months without undergoing any appreciable decomposition (277). *Sodium octasucrate* and the higher *potassium sucrates* are pyrophoric (7).

Metal sucrates seem to bond one or more moles of the solvent in which they are prepared. Thus monosodium sucrate prepared in ammonia contains one mole of ammonia per mole of sucrate. Higher sucrates have less ammonia (7). The bound ammonia in the trisodium sucrate can be removed almost completely by treatment with dimethoxyethane (19). Extraction with benzene eliminates about half of the bound ammonia (19).

The deammoniation of monosodium sucrate by heat treatment is unsuccessful (285a, b). Desiccation at 100°C *in vacuo* results in decomposition, and 3% ammonia remains in the sample even after prolonged treatment at 50°C. The successful removal of ammonia by this method is described by Prey [*Monatsh. Chem.* **91**, 1185 (1960)]. Similarly, deammoniation of the trisodium sucrate at 100°C *in vacuo* results in a change in composition (285g). (Prey also reported a very efficient method of removing ammonia from monosodium sucrate by extraction with ether and toluene.)

Sucrates are not soluble in common inert organic solvents, but are moderately soluble in dimethyl sulfoxide and dimethyl formamide (277). Urea, which increases the solubility of certain inorganic salts, is said to have no effect on the solubility of sucrates in these solvents (285m).

The sodium sucrates are also slightly soluble in liquid ammonia. Monosodium sucrate reportedly could be kept in solution with the help of excess sucrose (196d). Mono- and disodium sucrate can be redissolved in ammonia with the help of sucrose (196h). Disodium sucrate does not dissolve in dimethyl formamide even when excess sucrose is present (196h).

Some exploratory studies have been carried out to determine the location of the sodium atoms. Methylation of trisodium sucrate indicates that substitution with the methyl group to give the mono-ether occurs chiefly at the 2- and 1'-positions and to a lesser extent at the 6- and 3'-positions (18). Monomethyl sucrose prepared by Prey and co-workers from monosodium sucrate is said to have the methyl groups on the three primary hydroxyls on positions 6,1' and 6' [*Monatsh. Chem.* **92**, 1291 (1961)].

The properties of some metal sucrates are given in Table 9-1. A short review of the literature through 1956 on the preparation and reactions of alkali metal derivatives of sucrose and other carbohydrates is given in References 90 and 207.

Sodium sucrates

Of all true metallic salts those of sodium have been most extensively studied. Sodium is the least expensive alkali metal so that its alcoholates are widely used in sucrose chemistry, as in organic syntheses in general. However, the sucrates are seldom separated but usually reacted *in situ* with another reagent, as described above.

Crystalline sodium sucrates have been made in liquid ammonia with metallic sodium (7, 18, 54, 277). By adding the required amounts of sodium per mole of sucrose, mono- through hexasodium sucrates can be prepared by this method. Since the reaction time of the hexasodium sucrate is over 12 hours, the preparation of higher sucrate is preferably carried out with sodium amide in liquid ammonia (7). Tetra- to octasodium sucrates can be obtained by this procedure in four to nine hours (7).

Sodium sucrates are also prepared with sodium hydride and sodium methoxide, but not isolated in crystalline form. Sodium monosucrate has been made with sodium amide (285c).

Two methods are described for the estimation of sucrose in sodium derivatives (7). Careful analysis of the monosucrate indicates that the reaction yields a mixture (7). Further fractionation is necessary to obtain pure products (277). Attempts to fractionate the di- and tetrasodium derivatives have been unsuccessful (7). Analyses by ignition and infrared spectra are given in Reference 285d.

MONOSODIUM SUCRATE. Monosodium sucrate is a white crystalline material containing one mole of ammonia per mole of sodium sucrate (7). Although the reaction product appears to be homogeneous, it also contains more highly substituted sucrates and unreacted sucrose (7). It is only slightly soluble in ammonia, but can be redissolved slowly in the presence of sucrose (196h). The monosucrate has been used in a number of alkylating studies, particularly in the preparation of methyl sucrose. (See Ethers, page 17.) Removal of the ammonia by desiccation at 100°C although reported in the literature, causes decomposition.

DISODIUM SUCRATE. Preparation of disodium sucrate does not give a pure product by fractionation (7). However, a disodium sucrate has been reacted successfully with alkyl chloride (17). Disodium sucrate is slightly soluble in solvent. It dissolves rapidly in the presence of sucrose in ammonia, but not in dimethyl formamide (196h).

TRISODIUM SUCRATE. Trisodium sucrate contains 2.1-2.6% ammonia (17, 18). All but

0.2% of the bound ammonia can be removed by extraction with dimethoxyethane. Similar treatment with benzene removes only half the ammonia (19). Trisodium sucrate has been reacted to give a polymer with epichlorohydrin (17, 19); a triazine ether (19); or a mixture of methyl ethers (17, 18).

TETRASODIUM SUCRATE. This product is white, hygroscopic, and nonpyrophoric. Purification by fractionation has been unsuccessful (7).

PENTASODIUM SUCRATE. It is a gray hygroscopic powder (7). It has been used extensively in condensation reactions (Tables 9-2 and 9-3) because it is the most highly substituted sucrate that does not contain acidic materials.

HEXASODIUM SUCRATE. This compound is also a gray hygroscopic powder (7).

HEPTASODIUM SUCRATE. This gray hygroscopic powder contains acidic material that may be a product of the degradation of sucrose by sodium amide (7).

OCTASODIUM SUCRATE. Octasodium sucrate is a pyrophoric material that burns shortly after exposure to the atmosphere (7). Makers have suggested that a stable octasucrate might be isolated if a longer reaction time of sucrose with sodium amide were employed (7).

Potassium, lithium, and copper sucrates

A few experiments have been carried out on the preparation and reactions of other sucrates. Sucrates can be prepared similarly to sodium sucrates with sucrose and the metal in liquid ammonia include the *potassium* and *lithium sucrates* (7). Lithium sucrate can also be prepared in monomethylamine because, unlike sodium, the lithium metal is somewhat soluble in the solvent (19). Lithium monosucrate has also been prepared with lithium hydride and sucrose in dimethyl sulfoxide (285i).

MONOPOTASSIUM SUCRATE. This compound is less crystalline than the sodium compound and contains only about 0.6 mole of ammonia per mole of sucrose (7). Its solubility in the liquid ammonia at $-33°C$ is similar to that of the sodium derivative (7).

LITHIUM SUCRATES. Mono- and dilithium sucrates are considerably more soluble in liquid ammonia than the potassium and sodium derivatives (7). *Lithium monosucrate*, prepared in monomethylamine, is a light yellow glassy material (19). The product made with lithium hydride in dimethyl sulfoxide is solid. It is not pure mono-compound (285h). Its metal content is somewhat higher than indicated by its formula.

COPPER SUCRATES. Copper sucrates have been made from sucrose and cupric sulfate, according to U.S. Dept. of Agriculture, U.S. Patent 2, 138, 557 (299c, d). They have been tested as agricultural chemicals with some success. (The products are probably saccharates.)

CONDENSATION OF SODIUM SUCRATES
WITH ORGANIC HALIDES AND ACID CHLORIDES

The two main types of reactions studied with isolated sucrates are condensations (a) with organic halides to ethers and (b) with acyl chlorides to esters. Resins of the epoxy type can be made with epichlorohydrin. An acetal, *methoxymethyl sucrose*, can also be prepared in good yield.

As shown in Tables 9-2 and 9-3, condensations have been carried out with a number of organic halides, acid chlorides, acid anhydrides and other miscellaneous reagents. Since

I

there is no inert solvent that dissolves sodium sucrates, the reactions are unfortunately always heterogeneous. This may be one reason why the reaction often proceeds with little or no success or undesirable side reactions occur (see Ethers, page 17). It has been suggested that cesium or thalium (55) and also lithium derivatives of sucrose could be used more successfully in these condensations because of their greater solubility in organic solvents. Condensation in liquid ammonia (in which sucrates are somewhat soluble) is unsuccessful because of the preferential reaction of the organic halide with ammonia (17).

Because of side reactions, the presence of bound ammonia in the sodium sucrates is a serious disadvantage in carrying out condensations (17). The bound ammonia can be removed successfully by extraction with dimethoxyethane (19). It is said also to be removed by heat treatment [Prey et al., *Monatsh. Chem.* **92**, 1290 (1961)]. However, Prey's method cannot be repeated (285a, b). All attempts to remove ammonia from the sucrates by this method or by modifications of it result in a product that does not analyze to the expected sodium sucrate (285e).

Some reactions have been carried out *in situ* in liquid ammonia. These reactions are either unsuccessful or yield mixtures of compounds. Some success has recently been reported for alkylation in liquid ammonia. The monosodium sucrate is claimed to be kept in a dissolved state in ammonia by the presence of excess sucrose (196e). The sodium sucrate can then be successfully alkylated with methyl iodide *in situ* at $-33°C$ (196d) and to a lesser extent with long-chain alkyl halides (196a).

In general, ethers can be prepared in good yield without isolation of the metal sucrate (see Ethers, page 17). However, the reaction proceeds in specialty solvents such as dimethyl formamide or dimethyl sulfoxide with expensive alkyl bromides or iodides. Often the reaction is complicated.

The preparation of esters is somewhat less complicated. Solid pentasodium sucrate and many acyl chlorides or anhydrides can be successfully reacted in dimethoxyethane.

Reactions with metal sucrates seem to be quite sensitive. Further detailed study on the reaction mechanism and structure of sucrates could lead to a controlled method of preparation of ethers and esters with well-characterized structure. Such a method would be particularly important for the production of sucrose ethers since these derivatives are hard to prepare, particularly unreactive ethers with a long chain.

Condensation with organic halides

Reaction with organic chlorides is generally successful only under drastic conditions, such as high temperatures and pressures. The sodium sucrate is reacted with the chloride either without a solvent or in dimethoxyethane. No reaction occurs with such common methylating agents as methyl iodide or dimethyl sulfate (17), except possibly after the removal of the bound ammonia.

However, as discussed under Ethers, successful alkylation is reported when sucrose is reacted with sodium hydride in an aprotic solvent such as dimethyl sulfoxide or dimethyl formamide and the sodium sucrate is then condensed *in situ*, without isolation, with the appropriate alkyl bromide or iodide (90, 196). *Octamethyl sucrose* and *octaallyl sucrose* are prepared by this method in yields of 69% and 90%, respectively (90). Also, highly substituted octyl sucrose and benzyl sucrose can be made by the same method (90). Solid long-chain monoethers of sucrose have been made with C_8 to C_{18} saturated fatty alcohols in yields up to 50% (196).

The solvent is claimed to react only moderately with sodium hydride, even at elevated temperatures. Other advantages of this method include the absence of bound ammonia and in general greater control and reliability of the reaction. Also sodium hydride, unlike metallic sodium, does not usually react with organic halides at the temperatures employed unless other reactive groups are present.

Sodium sucrates are also used as intermediates for the production of highly substituted sucrose ethers. In such cases the partially etherified sucrose is first reacted with sodium and the resulting sodium sucrates with additional alkyl halide. Octaallyl and octamethallyl sucrose can be prepared by this method (114, 305). A similar two-stage process is described in the literature for the complete methylation of sucrose to octamethyl sucrose, (see Methyl Ethers, page 19).

Table 9-2 lists the organic halides tested in reactions with sodium sucrates.

Condensation with acid chloride or anhydride

Pentasodium sucrate reacts successfully with acid chlorides or anhydrides to produce fatty esters, benzoyl and other aromatic esters, and sulfonic acid esters (17). Table 9-3 shows the properties of these esters. Similar reactions with acid chlorides of dibasic acids, such as adipoyl fumaroyl and terephthaloyl chloride, or with phthalic anhydride result in polymerization (17).

METAL CHELATES

The chelates of sucrose, mannitol, sorbitol, and other carbohydrates are discussed under Chelating Agents and Analytical Chemistry, page 224 and 229.

REACTIONS WITH METAL POWDER AND METAL DERIVATIVES

Attempts have been made to prepare industrially useful products from the reaction between sucrose or its derivatives and metals or metal compounds (306). The objectives were to produce cements, adhesives, or other useful products with good properties, rather than to study the course of the reaction. The reaction products formed were probably of the saccharate type.

The process is based by analogy on that between glycerol and litharge (lead oxide), which gives a cement widely used for its excellent hardness and strength. Among the reactions were:

SUCROSE was reacted with metal oxides under many conditions. None produced a material of comparable quality to the litharge cement. In addition to lead oxide, eighteen other oxides, mainly of heavy metals, were reacted with sucrose in the molten state, in dimethyl sulfoxide, or water; and with mixtures of sucrose plus glycerol. Also, selected metal powders and metal acetates were reacted with sucrose in water or in the molten state. Several of the metal derivatives were reacted with epichlorohydrin with some success and with ethylene oxide without success.

SUCROSE HALF ESTERS OF DIBASIC ACIDS (itaconic, pyromellitic, succinic, maleic, and phthalic acids) were also reacted with a number of metal salts and oxides. The lead product of the succinate was formed into fibers but they were brittle and could not be plasticized. The pyromellitic ester in pyridine gave a brilliant blue pigment with cupric acetate. It also had ion-exchange properties. Attempts to produce a less brittle product by modification with ethylene oxide or epichlorohydrin were unsuccessful.

SUCROSE OCTAACETATE was reacted with litharge to a syrupy polymer soluble in organic solvents. No polymeric material was produced with metal salts. No useful product was obtained when the octaacetate was reacted with zinc chloride, partially saponified, and then reacted with litharge.

INVERT SUGAR was reacted with phenyl hydrazine and the ndiazotized to the formazan. The product was a deep red powder of possible value as a pigment. Its copper salt was of no use. Invert sugar was also reacted with urea or aniline and then with lead oxide to yield a brittle, water-sensitive product. Similar results were obtained with *p*-phenylene diamine.

SUCROSE BORIC ACID POLYMERS could not be made. No reaction occurred when litharge, boric acid, and sucrose were mixed in the cold and then heated. When litharge was added to a polymer prepared from sucrose and boric acid, the product disintegrated.

SUCROSE ACETATE ISOBUTYRATE did not react with zinc chloride.

SUCROSE ALGINATE could not be prepared reliably. Attempts to prepare a product by reacting it with litharge had little success.

URETHANES FROM SUCROSE AND TOLUENE DIISOCYANATE did not react well with litharge. The oxide reacted more successfully when it was added to the reactants before polymerization in mixtures of dimethyl formamide and pyridine. The products had properties comparable to those of commercial litharge cements, but they had no uniform composition and were hard to prepare.

Table 9-1
Physical properties of metal sucrates

Sucrate	Appearance	Metal atoms per mole sucrose	$[\alpha]_D$(a)	NH_3, %	Remarks	Reference
Sodium						
Mono	White crystals	0.98	+56.6°	4.64	(c)	7
Tri		3.15		2.59		17
		3.00		2.13		18
Tetra	White hygroscopic powder	3.95-3.97	+47.3-48.5°	1.58-2.34		7
Penta	Gray powder	4.85	+43.4°	1.4		7
Hexa	Gray powder	6.30	+39.6°	2.38	(d)	7
Hepta	Gray powder	7.71	+36.7°	2.66	(d)	7
Potassium						
Mono	White slightly crystalline powder	0.95	+55.5°	2.76		7
Lithium						
Mono	Light yellow glass	0.90		3.86 (b)	(e)	19

NOTE: Properties given for tetra sucrates and higher derivatives are for compounds prepared with sodium amide.

a – c. 1, in water. The specific rotation is lower than that of pure sucrose (+66.5°) because of the presence of sodium hydroxide, which may cause change in the conformation of the fructose portion. [*J. Am. Chem. Soc.* **79**, 2261 (1957).]

b – Nitrogen content of methylamine complex.

c – Contains some higher sucrates and unreacted sucrose.

d – Contains acidic material.

e – Made in liquid methylamine with metallic lithium.

Table 9-2
Condensation of sodium sucrates with organic halides to ethers, polymers, or acetals

Methyl iodide – a
Butyl bromide – b
Octyl bromide – a, b
Decyl bromide – b
Lauryl bromide – b
Palmityl bromide – b
Stearyl bromide – b
Benzyl bromide – a
Dodecylbenzyl chloride
Perchloromethyl mercaptan – d

Table 9-2 *continued*

Ethylene dichloride – d
Allyl chloride – c
Allyl bromide – a
Crotyl chloride
2-Chloro-4,6-bis(2'-chloro-4'-nitrophenoxy)-5-triazine – d
Methylchloroacetate – e
Polymers – f
Epichlorohydrin
Adipoyl chloride
Acetals
Chloromethyl methyl ether
Little or no reaction (17) – g
o-Chloronitrobenzene
β-Methallyl chloride
Trimethylchlorosilane – h
Triphenyl methyl chloride – i
tert-Butyl chloride
Vinyl bromide – j
Benzyl chloride
Cinnamyl chloride
Picryl chloride – h
Chlorocyclohexane
α-Chloroacetophenone – i
Ethyl mercuric chloride
Dichloroethyl ether – k

NOTE: Details of the successful reactions are found under the reaction products in the appropriate chapters. Some additional derivatives are listed in Table 21-1.

a – Highly or fully substituted derivative prepared in good yield in dimethyl formamide through sodium sucrate made with sodium hydride.

b – Crystalline monoether obtained by reacting monosodium sucrate (prepared from sucrose with sodium hydride in dimethyl sulfoxide) *in situ* with the alkyl bromide.

c – Requires fairly drastic conditions.

d – See, Other Ethers, page 70.

e – See, Carboxymethyl Sucrose, page 37.

f – See, Epoxy Polymers and Polyesters, page 157 and 158. See also Table 13-1.

g – Except for o-chloronitrobenzene, or otherwise noted, all other reagents are reacted with theoretical quantity of sodium pentasucrate in dimethoxyethane at 70-75°C. No reaction occurs or products are obtained in very low yield. o-Chloronitrobenzene does not condense with trisodium sucrate in benzene or dimethyl formamide. o-Chloronitrobenzene also does not react with sucrose in concentrated aqueous alkali (186b).

h – Product is not soluble in chloroform.

i – Product is optically inactive.

j – Sodium sucrate prepared with sodium hydride (256a). Vinyl bromide has low reactivity and also decomposes during reaction in dimethyl formamide.

k – Attempts to achieve cross-linking have been unsuccessful (243e). The reaction is carried out with trisodium sucrate made with sodium hydroxide, so the product is not a real sucrate.

Table 9–3
Sucrose esters made from pentasodium sucrate (17)

Ester derivative of sucrose	Yield, %	$[\alpha]_D$(a)	Remarks
Fatty esters			
Acetate – b	54	+59.3°	DS, 4.14
Propionate	55 – b	+38.9°	DS, 5.4
	51	+29.4°	DS, about 5
Butyrate	63 – b	+33.7°	DS, about 5
	48	+24.8°	DS, about 5
Laurate	74	+ 7.6°	Needles
Palmitate	91	+ 7.4°	Waxy solid
Aromatic esters			
Benzoate	88	+26.5°	
	72 – b	+30.1°	
o-Chlorobenzoate	87	+11.3°	
p-Chlorobenzoate	73	+11.9°	
2,4-Dichlorobenzoate	93	+14.9°	White crystals
Anisate	91	+19.9°	Solid
Cinnamate	95	+16.8°	Solid
Other esters			
Crotonate	79	+21.4°	
p-Toluene sulfonate	61	+22.0°	See also Table 4-1
p-Bromobenzene sulfonate	60	+11.1°	See also Table 4-1
2-Furoate	73	+17.5°	

DS = Degree of substitution
a – In chloroform (no concentration given). All data on crude products.
b – Made with anhydride.

NOTE: All reactions are carried out with pentasodium sucrate and the theoretical quantity of acyl chloride in dimethoxy ethane. The pentasodium sucrate is the most highly substituted derivative free from nonsucrose acidic material. All reactions proceed readily, often in high yield. Only a few products have been analyzed for their acyl content or structure. All derivatives are oils, except where otherwise noted. All ester derivatives are soluble in chloroform, acetone, and ethyl acetate and insoluble in water. See Reference 17 for detailed data. Several other esters have been prepared through the sodium sucrates, as given in Table 21-1.

10

Reaction products of sucrose with acids

Mɪʟᴅ treatment of sucrose with acids results in hydrolysis of the glycosidic linkage. Treatment with concentrated acids leads to the formation of anhydro-rings and double bonds of the inverted sucrose. (See Internal Ethers of Other Carbohydrates, page 47.)

Hydrolysis or inversion

Sucrose is easily hydrolyzed by acids to a mixture of D-glucose and D-fructose. The product is commonly called invert sugar because of the inversion in the direction of optical rotation. Different acids show remarkable variations in their ability to cause inversion. Mineral acids, particularly hydrochloric, hydrobromic, and nitric, have very strong inverting power. Organic acids are weak agents.

Production of invert sugar by enzymatic action with invertase is competitive with inversion by acids because there is no side reaction and loss of fructose, and consumers are often prejudiced against chemical alteration of a food product.

Inversion can also be performed with an ion-exchange resin. The mechanism and rate of hydrolysis with 0.0004-N to 1-N hydrochloric acid at 0°C to 95°C has been thoroughly studied (138, 146).

ꜰʀᴜᴄᴛᴏsᴇ. Sucrose is the most common source for the production of fructose. There is no standardized procedure for its manufacture. Probably the most widely used technique consists of (a) the hydrolysis of sucrose; (b) separation of fructose as an insoluble lime-fructose complex; (c) liberation of fructose by acidification with acids that form insoluble calcium salt, preferably carbon dioxide; (d) removal of the cation and anion contaminants by ion exchange; (e) concentration of the solution; and (f) crystallization of the fructose. The large-scale production by this method was investigated in the late 1940's, and resulted in the development of an almost continuous process (126, 275). Fructose of 98.6–100% purity is obtained because of the use of exchange resins not available to earlier investigators. The production cost of fructose from raw beet or cane sugar syrups was estimated at about 60¢ per pound in 1951 (275).

Fructose can also be made by electrolytic oxidation of invert sugar (48, 49). In the presence of a bromide ion catalyst glucose is oxidized to gluconic acid, while fructose is unattacked. The process is based on that formerly described by Isbell.

GLUCOSE. Glucose is made commercially from corn starch or other cheap sources of starch. The hydrolysis of sucrose can be carried out in ethyl alcohol with sulfuric acid to give a mixture of unreacted glucose and the ethyl glycoside of fructose (113). The reaction is not competitive with present commercial processes, but could be of interest for the production of glucose if crystalline fructose could also be obtained by hydrolysis of the ethyl fructoside. Crystalline glucose is obtained by precipitation with isobutyl alcohol. Eighty-eight per cent of the glucose present can be isolated.

Dehydration to levulinic acid and 5-hydroxymethyl furfuraldehyde

Treatment of glucose or fructose with strong acids produces levulinic acid through the intermediate substituted furfural:

$$
\begin{array}{l}
\text{Glucose or} \quad \text{Acid} + \\
\text{fructose} \qquad \text{heat}
\end{array}
\longrightarrow
\begin{array}{c}
HC\text{————}CH \\
\| \qquad\quad \| \\
HOCH_2\text{—}C \qquad C\text{—}CHO \\
\diagdown \quad \diagup \\
O
\end{array}
\longrightarrow
$$

5-Hydroxymethyl furfural

$$\longrightarrow CH_3COCH_2CH_2COOH + HCOOH$$
Levulinic acid

Fructose is said to transform into the furfural more rapidly than glucose. Both sugars can be converted even without acids at 100 to 150°C.

LEVULINIC ACID. The preparation, reaction mechanism, and properties of levulinic acid from sucrose have been reviewed (302), and the engineering, marketing, and economics of the production have also been studied (177, 233). The cost of levulinic acid (exclusive of sugar) was estimated at 3.5¢ per pound in 1950 (223).

5-HYDROXYMETHYL FURFURALDEHYDE. The intermediate aldehyde has been isolated in the production of levulinic acid (223). The compound can also be prepared from sucrose in dry dimethyl formamide at 100°C in the presence of iodine (26).

Reactions with other carbohydrates

GLYCOSIDES. Five simple alkyl glycosides have been prepared and their hydrolysis studied (150). L-Arabinopyranosides were chosen because they are stereochemically identical with the L-fructopyranosides.

11

Reaction products of sucrose and molasses with alkalies, amines, and azides

Unlike acids, alkalies, as a rule, do not attack the glycosidic linkage of sucrose and other oligosaccharides. However, alkalies do cause a number of reactions including isomerization, rearrangement, or even splitting of the sugar molecule. Sucrose and other nonreducing sugars are said to be far more stable in alkaline solutions than monosaccharides and disaccharides of the reducing type. They are subject to severe decomposition only under drastic conditions.

Thus sucrose, unlike glucose, does not react readily with ammonia or organic amines, even at 200°C (289). Brief comparative studies indicate that such reducing sugars as glucose and fructose react readily with ammonia at lower temperatures, but that sucrose does not react below its melting point (225). The ammoniated sucrose products formed above the melting point have a nitrogen content of up to 4.6%. They are heterocyclic derivatives, chiefly pyrazines and imidazoles, formed through the intermediate 2-amino sugars. (See Stanek and Cermy, "The Oligosaccharides," p. 148 in Selected General References on Sucrose.)

On treatment with strong alkalies above 200°C the sucrose molecule cleaves into smaller fragments, chiefly lactic acid with some acetic and formic acids. The reaction has been extensively studied by the Foundation as a possible method for the manufacture of lactic acid, particularly from molasses. Lactic acid is used primarily as an acidulant in foods and beverages. It also finds applications in the production of leather, in the dyeing of wool, and in plastics as a plasticizer.

Ammoniation of molasses under mild conditions has also been studied. Ammoniated molasses could be used as nutrient additives for animals.

Some studies have been carried out on the effects of alkaline media on ionization of the protons of the hydroxyl groups in sucrose (261a) and other carbohydrates (209). The differences in ionization of the carbohydrates can be used in analytical studies by electrophoresis. (See Analytical Chemistry, page 229.) The effect of aqueous sodium hydroxide on the protons in the sucrose molecule has also been studied in methylations. (See Methyl Sucrose, page 20.)

The successful preparation of *sucrose azide* and its reduction to amine have been recently

138

reported. All former attempts to prepare the amine derivative of sucrose had failed.

For a review on the decomposition of sucrose in alkaline solutions see Athenstedt, *Z. Zuckerind*, **11**, 605 (1961); ibid. **13**, 563 (1963).

LACTIC ACID

PREPARATION. It has been known for many years that lactic acid can be obtained from sucrose and other carbohydrates either by the action of alkaline reagents or by fermentation. (See Fermentation of Sucrose and Molasses, page 144.) A third method is synthesis from acetaldehyde and hydrogen cyanide or carbon monoxide.

Production from molasses was studied extensively in the late 1940's by the Foundation because it was believed to be a simpler method than fermentation in regard to space, operational time, and close control of reaction conditions. A literature survey on the preparation and mechanism of lactic acid formation is given in Reference 110. The work of the Foundation is summarized in References 111 and 266. They include detailed studies on the influence of temperature, time, and other parameters on production, on purification procedures, and on the reaction mechanism.

The crude lactic acid made by treatment with alkali, unlike that made by fermentation, contains acidic by-products. A pure product can be made by fractional distillation of the methyl lactate. Studies on the identification of the organic acid by chromatography are given in References 37 and 109.

Lactic acid is prepared by the action of lime on molasses in water at temperatures of 230–250°C. The yield of acids is dependent on temperature, time of reaction, proportion of lime to sugar, and molarity of the sugar. Effects of these variables are interdependent. Yields of 50–80% of theoretical are obtained together with other acids, which usually amount to 25% of the lactic acid. The acids are separated from the nonacidic components as the zinc salts or methyl esters and by extraction with solvents.

MECHANISM OF THE REACTION. The mechanism of lactic acid formation is not well known. The most generally accepted reaction leading to the formation of lactic acid from glucose is through enolization (I), cleavage to triose fragments by a reverse aldol condensation (II), and finally rearrangement of the fragments (III and IV):

Glucose   Glucose-1,2-enediol   Glyceraldehyde
                  I   II

$$
\begin{array}{c}
\text{OH} \\
\text{HC} \diagdown \\
\diagdown \text{OH} \\
\end{array}
$$

```
              OH
             /
         HC
          |  \
          |   OH
          |
——→      C = O      ——→      COOH
          |                    |
          CH₃                  CHOH
                               |
                               CH₃
       Pyruvaldehyde              Lactic acid
       hydrate

           III                      IV
```

BY-PRODUCTS. Depending on the reaction conditions, five to nine different acidic materials can be detected by chromatography. Among these are such autoesterification products as lactyllactic acid, lactyllactyllactic acid, and higher condensation polymers. Other products include carbon dioxide and glyceraldehyde.

OTHER METHODS OF PREPARATION. Brief experiments have been carried out to prepare lactic acid in aqueous alkaline media in the presence of silver powder (205) and by fusion with alkali (271a). A yield of only 25% (based on the theoretical yield of four moles of lactic acid per mole of sucrose) is obtained in the silver-catalyzed reaction. Further work on the alkaline degradation of sucrose is found in References 205 and 271.

APPLICATION. Several efficient plasticizers for vinyl resins can be made from lactic esters. Lactic acid or its derivatives can also be converted to acrylic derivatives by pyrolysis in the vapor phase. The dehydration of lactonitrile and lactic acid esters, amides or salts to the corresponding acrylic derivatives has recently been studied (125, 253). Conversion up to 5% per pass has been achieved in the dehydration of lactonitrile to acrylonitrile over phosphoric acid at 400–750°C. The ester, amide, or ammonium salt also yield acrylics, but only the nitrile appears capable of giving a high total yield through recycling (253).

SUCROSE AMINES, AMIDES, AND AZIDES

The preparation of these derivatives is of interest because of their potential surface-active properties when linked through the nitrogen to a hydrophobic chain. No success has yet been reported in the direct preparation of amines and amides, but azides can be made and reduced to amines. As discussed above, ammonia does not easily attack the sucrose molecule. When it does react at high temperatures, it yields heterocyclic derivatives.

The preparation of sucrose amines has been attempted unsuccessfully by reacting ammonia with sucrose, anhydro sucrose (290k), sulfated sucrose (290k), and tosyl sucrose (290k, n). However, none of the intermediate sucrose products has been purified or identified thoroughly before further reaction with ammonia. Conversion of the tosyl groups to amino or nitrile groups has been attempted unsuccessfully elsewhere (264). Similarly, chloro-sucroses do not react with alkyl amines (194f). The reaction of sucrose with lauronitrile and lactonitrile does not lead to sucrose amide (290m).

However, amino sucrose has recently been prepared by the hydrogenation of azido sucrose. Azido sucrose itself can be prepared simply from the tosylate by replacement with sodium azide:

$$RO-Tosyl \xrightarrow{\text{NaN}_3} R-N_3 \xrightarrow{\text{H}_2} R-NH_2$$

6,6′-Diazidosucrose

6,6′-Diazidosucrose has been made by the deesterification of the corresponding hexabenzoate, described below, with sodium methoxide in methyl alcohol (194g). The product is an oil. It is converted into diaminosucrose by hydrogenation (194g).

6,6′-Diazido-2, 3, 4, 1′,3′,4′-hexabenzoyl sucrose

This compound is made from the corresponding 6,6′-ditosylate by treatment with sodium azide in dimethyl formamide at 140°C (194g). The reaction mixture contains a number of products caused by deesterification during the reaction, but reesterification with benzoyl chloride gives the crystalline 6,6′-diazidosucrose hexabenzoate. The yield is 50% (194j).

All attempts to convert the compound to the corresponding diaminosucrose by hydrogenation failed (194g). However, after removal of the benzoyl groups by alkaline saponification with sodium methoxide in methyl alcohol, the resulting diazidosucrose can be reduced successfully (194g).

The properties of the compound are given in Table 7-1.

Azidosucrose mesylate

Sucrose octamesylate has been reacted with sodium azide in dimethyl formamide (194b). The product contains an azido group, but has not been further investigated.

6,6′-Diamino sucrose

6,6′-Diaminosucrose is made by catalytic reduction of 6,6′-diazidosucrose (194g). A pure product is isolated by chromatography, but it does not crystallize (194h). The preparation of crystalline derivatives is presently under study (194h).

AMMONIATION OF MOLASSES

The ammoniation of molasses and such other carbohydrate materials as beet and citrus pulp has attracted the attention of sugar and citrus producers and manufacturers of cattle feed because the technique can provide a cheap and readily available protein supplement for ruminant animals (see Food and Feed Additives, page 206). Molasses, beet, and citrus pulp are excellent energy foods for cattle, but they suffer, particularly molasses, from the absence of nitrogen.

The ammoniation of molasses is described in the literature and has been further investigated by the Foundation. A few exploratory experiments have been performed with Hawaiian molasses and invert molasses (225). The best result is obtained by reaction with aqueous ammonia at 87°C for 18 hours in a closed container. The products contain 3.9–11.4% organic nitrogen. Treatment at 37°C requires a reaction time of two weeks. The products are brown or black solids, often soft and hygroscopic, particularly those made from inverted molasses. All soften more or less with increasing humidity and absorb enough water at 80% relative humidity to become completely liquid. The composition of these products has not been determined.

More detailed experiments have been carried out particularly to obtain on a large scale a product with high nitrogen content without side effects on the animals. As some toxic symptoms are reported in feeding studies, the composition of the ammoniated product has been carefully studied.

Small-scale studies indicate that it is essential to hydrolyze all the sucrose in the molasses to obtain a product high in fixed nitrogen (88). The product from normal molasses has a fixed nitrogen content of only 2.1%, while that from inverted molasses under similar conditions has a nitrogen content of 3.9%, which can be increased to 6% under more drastic conditions.

The pilot-scale ammoniation is carried out by first inverting cane molasses by heating with dilute sulfuric acid at 90–95°C for one hour (153, 154). After neutralization with caustic soda and cooling to 50°C, anhydrous ammonia is admitted to the vapor space in the stainless steel reaction vessel, and the mixture is vigorously stirred. The ammonia is rapidly taken up and the temperature rises to 100–120°C. The reaction is completed by maintaining the temperature at about 120°C for two hours. By the carefully controlled admission of ammonia a product can be obtained containing little excess ammonia and 6% nitrogen, equivalent to 37.5% crude protein. The product is a black liquor that is less viscous than ordinary molasses. It has a burnt and rather bitter taste, but no unpleasant odor.

Details on the effects of temperature, pressure, reaction time, and other parameters on the nitrogen content of the product are found in Reference 88.

COMPOSITION. The chemical composition of the product has been thoroughly studied by chromatography and polarography to determine the constituents, particularly those with toxic effects (153, 154, 155). Among the compounds isolated are the following derivatives of imidazole and pyrazine (153, 155):

> 4(5)-Methylimidazole
> 5-Hydroxymethyl-2-methylpyrazine
> 2-Methyl-5-arabotetrahydroxybutylpyrazine
> 2-Methyl-6-arabotetrahydroxybutylpyrazine
> 2,6-Dimethylpyrazine
> 2-Hydroxymethylpyrazine

Imidazoles are reportedly present at a level of 10%, and pyrazines of 20% by weight of the product. Polarography indicates that the pyrazines are formed at a rapidly increasing rate at temperatures over 50°C and pressures over 20 psi. Analysis also shows that ammoniation at 100–120°C destroys all but traces of reducing sugars so that the product does not have the feeding value of ordinary carbohydrates.

TOXICITY. Although previous reports in the literature report no serious problems in feeding tests, later work has shown that some animals show a marked reaction to the ammoniated molasses. Feeding studies with chicks reveal that the imidazoles or pyrazines of low molecular weight are responsible for the toxicity (78, 155). The toxicity can be eliminated by the removal of these compounds, particularly 4(5)-methylimidazole, or by modifying them by acidifying the ammoniated molasses before feeding, preferably with such food acids as phosphoric, acetic, or lactic. These modified products produce no toxic disorders in feeding studies and are palatable to sheep and cattle (153, 155). For detailed feeding studies see Reference 78.

PRODUCTION COSTS. Preliminary estimates indicate that the cost of the product was about $3.44 per 100 lb in 1954 (88). Its crude protein value is 29.7%. The cost of ammoniated molasses with the same crude protein value as 100 lb of soya meal (protein value 45%) was $5.20. The price of 100 lb of soya meal was $5.40 in the U. S. and $12 in Trinidad at that time.

REACTIONS WITH INVERT SUGAR, OTHER CARBOHYDRATES, AND RELATED COMPOUNDS

Alkalies

The action of alkalies (including strong base resins and lime) on glucose (187), and galactose, lactose, and mannose (139) has been investigated. Glucose isomerizes into sorbose and galactose, lactose and mannose into saccharinic acids through internal oxidation, reduction, and group migration.

Glucose, fructose, and the equimolar mixture of these sugars (invert sugar) are completely degraded into nonreducing substances at 100°C in aqueous solutions buffered with carbonate (60). The reaction was formerly believed to result mainly in an equilibrium mixture of glucose, fructose, and mannose without degradation.

The action of ammonia on nitrile derivatives of sugar acids yields acetamide derivatives of an aldose containing one less carbon atom than the starting nitrile (69).

Phenyl hydrazine, urea, aniline

Invert sugar can be reacted with phenyl hydrazine and diazotized into a bright red diphenyl formazan (306).

Resinous products are obtained by reacting invert sugar with urea or aniline in benzene (306).

12

Fermentation of sucrose and molasses

F ERMENTATION of carbohydrates is an important method of production of a number of chemicals. Substances which can be made by this method are:

Products	Organisms	Yield, %
Ethyl alcohol	*Saccharomyces cerevisiae* (brewer's yeast)	>90
	Schizosaccharomyces pombe	
Acetone } 1-Butanol }	*Clostridium acteobutylicum*	9
Citric acid	*Citromyces* or *Aspergillus niger*	50
Dextran	*Leuconostoc mesenteroides* or *L. dextranicum*	25
Fumaric acid	*A. fumaricus* or *Rhizopus nigricans*	50
D-Gluconic acid	*Penicillium chrysogenum* or *A. niger*	50
Itaconic acid	*A. terreus*	15
Kojic acid	*A. flavus* or *A. oryzae*	60
Lactic acid	*R. oryzae*	95
Glycerol	*S. cerevisiae*	≤28
Fat	*Endomyces vernalis*	≤80
	Fusaria lycoperseci	
	Rhodotorula gracilis	
Amino acids	*Bacillus subtilis*	
	Neurospora crassa, etc.	

Because of its low cost molasses is the common source of sucrose and other sugars in these fermentations.

The production of chemicals by fermentation is dependent on supply and demand and competition from such other processes as chemical synthesis. For example, a great deal of attention was given during the last World War to the microbiological production of fat because of possible shortages in natural sources. However, the process cannot compete with

144

the well-established methods of production by extraction from animals and vegetables. Glycerol was produced by fermentation during World War I, but it is now made only by saponification of fats and by synthesis.

Of these processes, the production of lactic acid, citric acid, glycerol and fats and the amino acids, lysine and tryptophane, have been studied by the Foundation. Work has also been done on the use of sugars and beet molasses for the production of baker's yeast.

Lactic acid

The economics of production of lactic and lactates from molasses acid by fermentation were studied in the late 1940's (267). Potential markets, known industrial processes, and patents were also studied.

Citric acid

The most important commercial source of citric acid is the fermentation of carbohydrates. There are two methods of fermentation. The surface method is favored in many countries in Europe. A new submerged-growth process has been successfully used in the United States since 1952. Beet molasses appears to be the main source of carbohydrate in the fermentation.

Production by the submerged technique from sucrose at a concentration of 260 grams per liter of fermentation liquor gives a yield of 70% in 12 days (133). Detailed studies have been made on the effect of variations in the environmental conditions (133) and the composition of the fermentation medium (134, 135).

Glycerol

The possible production of glycerol by fermentation was studied briefly after World War II (176a). The process includes the alcoholic fermentation of glucose (or possibly sucrose) to the intermediate acetaldehyde and fixation with sodium sulfite. The addition of sulfite is accompanied by a large increase in the amount of glycerol formed in the fermentation medium. The highest yield of 28% glycerol (based on glucose) is obtained by fermentation with fresh yeast for about 20 hours in the presence of oxygen at 35°C.

A market survey in 1948 indicated good prospects for the production of glycerol by fermentation (176). However, synthesis from propylene has proved more economic. Natural glycerol continues to be made by hydrolysis of fats and oils.

Fats

Many yeasts, molds, and bacteria, including certain strains of *Fusaria*, can be used for the biochemical transformation of carbohydrates to fat. The formation of fats from glucose with *Fusaria lycoperseci* has been studied (158). The optimum synthesis of fat is observed at pH 7-8. The fatty acid formed can be determined by a newly developed microtitration.

Related studies have been made on intermediates in the synthesis of fats. They include the metabolism (159), synthesis (160) and determination (157) of triacetic acid (β,δ-diketohexanoic acid) and related diketones, and the properties of liver homogenate enzymes which metabolize these ketones (45, 115).

Lysine and tryptophane

Several microorganisms have been tested for the production of materials rich in lysine and

K

tryptophane from sucrose (175). These amino acids are used as additives to foods and feeds. Lysine is used to enrich wheat-based foods, which are deficient in this amino acid. Tryptophane is effective against pellagra. Of the several organisms tested, *Bacillus subtilis* shows promise for lysine (175a) and *Neurospora crassa* and *N. sitophila* for tryptophane (175b).

Baker's and food yeasts

Research related to food yeasts has studied the aeration (136) and biotin content (42) of yeast; the yield from different kinds of molasses (2) and the utilization of the nonsugar carbon of molasses by food yeasts (1).

13

Resins and polymers

OF the many potential industrial uses of sucrose, plastics are the most important. Because of its phenomenal rate of expansion in the past three decades, the plastic industry requires increasing amounts of raw materials of great variety.

Several attempts to form commercially useful resins from pure sugar are recorded in the literature. These include:

—The preparation of a hard insoluble and infusible product from sugar and ammonium persulfate. German Patent 552,380 (1929);

—Sucrose as a condensing agent in the preparation of plastics from formaldehyde and urea. French Patent 714,388 (1930).

—Condensation of sucrose with cyclic ketones. French Patent 728,846 (1931).

—"Sakaloid" plastics made by Industrial Sugar Products from sucrose and an aldehyde plus urea, phthalic aldehyde or aliphatic acid. U.S. Patents 1,949,831-2 (1930) and 1,974,064 (1934).

—"Sucrolite" plastics, a form of phenolics in which sucrose substituted for formaldehyde. *Brit. Plastics* **6**, 503 (1935).

—Polymerization of sucrose in the presence of an inorganic acid to a resin compatible with cellulose acetate and nitrate. U.S. Patent 2,076,795 (1937).

—Condensation of *m*-phenylene diamine with sucrose and formaldehyde to an insoluble anion-exchange resin suitable for the treatment of water. British Patent 472,404 (1937).

However, despite many optimistic claims, none of the sucrose-based resins has achieved commercial success. In the work sponsored by the Foundation, several new resins and polymers have been prepared with desirable properties, particularly as adhesives and laminating resins, surface coatings, and textile chemicals. Only a few of these polymers have been

147

investigated in detail. Most have been prepared with the primary objective of testing their application properties without elucidation of their structure or physical properties.

POLYCARBONATES

Polycarbonate resins can be prepared either in one step directly from sucrose or in two steps by the polymerization of an intermediate such as alkyloxycarbonyl sucrose:

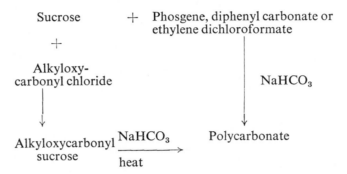

Exploratory tests indicate that molding powders of good quality can be fabricated from the resins made from triethoxycarbonyl sucrose. The resin itself is very brittle and must be compounded with a filler such as asbestos or a cellulosic material. The resin is sensitive to alkalies. Since the condensation itself requires alkaline catalysts, the problem of obtaining a stable final product has not yet been fully solved.

Condensation of alkyloxycarbonyl sucrose with alcohols, amines, or other reagents into a polymer has had little success. Thermosetting and fiber-forming resins can be made from octaethylcarbonyl sucrose with hexamethylenediamine as a cross-linking agent.

Sucrose plus phosgene

A polycarbonate resin is obtained when one mole of sucrose (diluted with toluene) is reacted with five moles of phosgene in pyridine cooled with ice and salt (149). The yield is only 26%. Yields up to 50% are obtained when a large excess of gaseous phosgene is passed through a solution of sucrose in pyridine. Attempts to acylate in aqueous media in the presence of alkali catalysts are less successful (149).

The polymer analyzes well for a polycarbonate type, $(C_{12}H_5O_{11}CO)_n$, both by elemental and infrared analysis. It is rapidly hydrolyzed by excess aqueous ammonia at room temperature (149).

Sucrose plus diphenyl carbonate

Reaction of one mole of sucrose with 1.1 to 4.0 moles of diphenyl carbonate in dimethyl sulfoxide gives a cross-linked polymer (149). The reaction is carried out at 135°C in the presence of 7% powdered soda glass (by weight of sucrose) or preferably with 0.15% sodium bicarbonate. A similar polymer is obtained by the polymerization of triphenoxycarbonyl sucrate in dimethyl sulfoxide at 100°C (74). The polymer is insoluble in water and has phenoxycarbonyl content only up to 0.6% per sucrose. Reaction with about 1.5 moles of diphenyl carbonate gives an almost theoretical yield of cross-linked polymer with a negligible phenoxycarbonyl content.

A similar highly cross-linked polymer is obtained when the reaction is carried out in molten resorcinol. The presence of the catalyst is very important because, contrary to the findings of Hochstetter, with no catalyst hydrolysis occurs in resorcinol rather than polymerization (149).

Polymerization with up to one mole of diphenyl carbonate yields a water-soluble, slightly gelled product (149).

The water-soluble polycarbonate can be hydrolyzed with invertase and mineral acids, but the reaction with acids proceeds more slowly than in the case of sucrose itself (149). This property is analogous to that reported for ethoxycarbonyl sucrose (Figure 4-1).

Analysis indicates the presence of some aromatic residues in the polycarbonate resins, particularly in those made with two and four moles of diphenyl carbonate (149).

Sucrose plus ethylene dichloroformate

A polymer is obtained directly in 31% yield when sucrose is reacted with ethylene dichloroformate in the presence of aqueous sodium hydroxide at 0°C (147). The white polymer is insoluble in all common organic solvents including pyridine, dimethyl formamide, and dimethyl sulfoxide. The material decomposes without melting at 290-300°C. Hydrolysis of its suspension with 0.2-N barium hydroxide yields sucrose as the sole carbohydrate constituent.

Polymerization of ethoxycarbonyl sucroses

Triethoxycarbonyl sucrose and other ethoxycarbonyl sucroses polymerize to form hard, crosslinked resins when heated in the presence of 0.1 to 0.5% sodium bicarbonate at 145–160°C, preferably under reduced pressure (148). Other polymerization catalysts have also been tested because of the sensitivity of the polymer to alkalies (see below) but without success (294d). The process is strongly catalyzed by traces of alkali and inhibited by acids. The rate of polymerization depends on the degree of substitution (DS) of the monomer and the concentration of the catalyst (148). With an increased DS, the setting time increases considerably at the same level of catalyst concentration. Similarly, the higher the DS, the smaller the accelerating effect of increasing catalyst concentration (148):

Degree of substitution	Setting time at 160°C at varying $NaHCO_3$ conc., minutes				Average ethoxy content, %
	0.01%	0.1%	0.25%	0.5%	
3.4	40	4	—	3	14.8
4.7	50	20	6	5	25.0
5.7	90	60	45	25	27.3
7.9	>360	>360	>360	>360	—

The structure of the polymer is not completely known. Structural studies of both the monomer and polymer show that substitution is somewhat random, but preferential at positions 3, 6, 1' and 3' (149). The polymerization process is probably a simple alkali-catalyzed transesterification with the elimination of ethyl alcohol (148):

$$ROCOOC_2H_5 + ROH \rightarrow ROCOOR + C_2H_5OH \quad (I)$$

where R is a substituted sucrose radical.

The presence of large amounts of diethyl carbonate in the reaction mixture indicates that simultaneous alcoholysis also occurs:

$$ROCOOC_2H_5 + C_2H_5OH \text{ ------ } ROH + (C_2H_5)_2CO_3 \quad (II)$$

Elimination of diethyl carbonate from two carbonate esters could yield a carbonate polymer directly. However, such reactions appear to occur only at much higher temperatures (250°C), usually in the presence of a more specific catalyst, such as titanium butoxide (148).

Equation (I) indicates that the presence of free hydroxyl groups is essential in the polymerization. Thus no polymerization can occur with the octaester under normal conditions. Penta- to heptaesters are also unsuitable because their free hydroxyl groups are located in sterically hindered, unreactive positions. The most successful and most rapid polymerizations occur with the tri- and tetraesters (148). The sluggishness of *octaallyloxycarbonyl sucrose* in polymerization may be caused by the absence of such hydroxyl groups (173).

The polymers are sensitive to alkalies, particularly those with a lower DS, which are less hydrophobic (148). The alkali stability of the polymers can be increased by lower levels of catalyst and by polymerization under reduced pressure (294e). The presence of some secondary butoxycarbonyl groups is claimed to enhance the alkali stability of polymerized ethoxycarbonyl sucrose (193o).

The degradation of the resin during storage, particularly in moist air is also caused by the presence of alkaline catalyst (294d). The sodium bicarbonate catalyzes the breakup of crosslinkages and the final decomposition of the polymer into sucrose and ethyl alcohol (294c). Polymers made from monomers with a DS of 4 and over are claimed to resist the ethanolysis better than the lower monomers. For example, 90% or more of the polymer from the penta- and hexaesters is recovered from boiling soap solution. Only 19% of the polymer made from the triester is recovered. For additional studies on polymerization and properties of the polymers, see References 294b, c, d, and e and 193k and l.

Copolymerization and crosslinking

ETHYLENE GLYCOL. Ethylene glycol in low molar ratios (0.5-1.0) reacts with triethoxycarbonyl sucrose to give thermosetting polymers (193i). Their properties are similar to those of resins obtained from the ester alone. Higher molar ratios (1.5-2.0) increasingly inhibit crosslinking, and the products become dispersible in water (193i). Condensation with the octaester (193h) or highly substituted methoxycarbonyl sucroses (193c) is unsuccessful.

MANNITOL. Preliminary experiments show that the condensation of triethoxycarbonyl sucrose with excess mannitol (three moles) gives a new mannitol derivative but causes excessive deesterification (193g). The reaction with higher methoxycarbonyl sucroses is equally unsuccessful (193c).

CELLULOSE. Some condensation occurs when pentaethoxycarbonyl sucrose is reacted with cellulose, although 98% of the unreacted ester is recovered (193f). The reaction was attempted with alkali-treated cellulose, as otherwise the untreated cellulose would have acted as an inhibitor in the polymerization of sucrose carbonates (193e). Condensation with the octaester at 160°C is not successful (193h).

HEXAMETHYLENEDIAMINE. Hexamethoxycarbonyl sucrose reacts mole for mole with this diamine to give a resin that is fiber-forming but water-soluble (193d). Octaethoxy-carbonyl sucrose gives a fiber-forming resin with one mole of diamine and a thermosetting type with two moles (193h). The diamine reacts at elevated temperatures with the poly-carbonate resin to form a semi-fluid mass that sets to a brittle, brownish solid (193d).

HYDRAZINE. One mole of trimethoxycarbonyl sucrose gives a brittle, insoluble mass when reacted at 150°C *in vacuo* with 0.5 moles of hydrazine (193d). Reaction with higher ratios of hydrazine probably forms hydrizides with and without sucrose in the molecule, $ROCONHNH_2$ and $MeOCONHNH_2$ (193d). The reaction is carried out with an alcoholic solution of hydrazine at room temperature. Under similar conditions, *isopropoxycarbonyl sucrose* is attacked by hydrazine much more slowly (193d).

Polymerization of other alkyloxy carbonate esters

Although ethoxycarbonyl sucrose is the best monomer, other less reactive esters have also been tested. In general, esters that are less sensitive to alkalies are also less apt to polymerize.

BENZYLOXYCARBONYL SUCROSE. Tribenzyloxycarbonyl sucrose can also be poly-merized in the presence of 0.5% sodium bicarbonate, similarly to the triethoxycarbonate (148). The process is more sluggish but is accompanied with less simultaneous alcoholysis than for the ethyl derivative. The polymer has solubility characteristics similar to those of the polymerized ethoxy carbonyl sucrose.

BUTYLOXYCARBONYL SUCROSE. Attempts to polymerize secondary butyloxy-carbonyl sucrose in the presence of sodium bicarbonate have failed even under high vacuum (193i).

SUCROSE CARBAMATE-FORMALDEHYDE RESINS

Two-step method

Sucrose is first reacted with urea to form a carbamate, which is then reacted with formalde-hyde to form a resin similar to the urea-formaldehyde resins:

$$ROH + NH_2CONH_2 \longrightarrow ROCONH_2 + NH_3$$
Sucrose   Urea   Carbamate

Mono-, di-, and higher sucrose carbamates can be obtained, depending on the amount of reactants. The preparation of such carbamates has been patented by the Sharples Chemical Division of Pennsalt Manufacturing Co. (U.S. Patent 2,527,839). The preparation of the polymer has been further studied (228a) and later modified into a one-step method.

The sucrose carbamates are made by condensing sucrose and urea in a melt at 140-160°C. The mole ratios of urea to sucrose investigated were 1:1 to 6:1 (228a). A similar process is also used in the preparation of fatty acid esters of sucrose carbamate (290d, e). (See Carba-mate Esters, page 77.) Other methods briefly explored include condensation in such solvents as water, 1% sodium hydroxide, and pyridine (228a). Apparently, none of these reactions produce the desired pure sugar carbamate, as claimed in the patent (228a).

Condensation of equimolecular amounts of sucrose and urea in sulfuric acid, acetic acid or dimethyl formamide probably gives a sucrose-substituted urea or ureide, $RNHCONH_2$. This reaction is analogous to the reaction of alcohols with urea described in Organic Syntheses, Volume 29.

A laboratory and pilot-plant preparation of mono-, di-, and sesquicarbamates is given in Reference 178.

Condensation with formaldehyde gives a yellow viscous solution. The polymerization can be carried out at room temperature, at 80°C (228a), or at the boiling point (249). Alkaline catalysts such as ammonia or sodium bicarbonates are preferred to the acetic or sulfuric acids originally recommended in the patent.

PROPERTIES. Sugar carbamates, contrary to the patent claims, could never be obtained in crystalline white form (228a). They are viscous or glassy products of varying shades of brown and high hygroscopicity. All products are believed to be contaminated with unreacted urea. Often they are mixtures of mono- and polycarbamates. Excess urea may be removed with acetone.

The dry SUCROSE MONOCARBAMATE is a glassy product with a melting point of 70-90°C. It is soluble in water and pyridine, partially soluble in methyl and ethyl alcohol, and insoluble in dioxane and acetone. Fractional precipitation in water and acetone gives products with a high nitrogen content, indicating excess urea or the presence of dicarbamate.

HIGHER CARBAMATES. Carbamates made with mole ratios of urea of sucrose up to 5.7 are oily or amorphous. The resins made with formaldehyde give a viscous yellow solution which contains free formaldehyde. The composition of the sucrose carbamates that have been reacted further to fatty acid derivatives have been less carefully investigated (290d, e).

One-step method

In the one-step method the resins are made by reacting sucrose, urea, and aqueous solutions of formaldehyde (37%) in the presence of 1% zinc oxide (by weight of urea plus sucrose) as catalyst (228b). The reaction is carried out first at room temperature and then at the boiling point. The ratio of reactants is 40-60 g of sucrose to 100 g each of urea and formaldehyde. Since the amount of sucrose is considerably decreased, the resin may be regarded as a sucrose-modified urea-formaldehyde. The reaction mixture is concentrated by removing part of the distillable components. The water-free product can be obtained by further removal of water.

When the resin is modified with melamine, a similar process is used. However, the resin gels when the solution is concentrated by distilling off part of the water. Melamine replaces 25% of the urea. Sodium hydroxide-ammonia is not effective as a polymerization catalyst.

PROPERTIES. The water-free resin is a white amorphous product that is extremely hygroscopic. The resin concentrate is a very viscous oil. Both the unmodified and modified resins are infusible and insoluble in common solvents (228b).

USES. The resin has been tested in surface coatings and textile finishes (see Surface Coatings and Textile Chemicals, page 192 and 216). Other suggested uses include adhesives, laminating syrups, core binders, molding powders, and wet-strength additives for paper. None of these uses has been explored.

SUCROSE MODIFIED PHENOLIC RESINS

Sucrose can be used successfully to modify phenol-formaldehyde resins (40, 91). The optimum formulation contains approximately one-third of sucrose by weight. It replaces an equal weight of phenol—that is, about half the phenol used in conventional formulations. The product is economically attractive because the more expensive phenol can thus be partially replaced with the lower-priced sugar without sacrifice of properties.

The later improved process for these resins condenses phenol, formaldehyde and sucrose in the presence of alkali in water (40, 91). A previous, more complicated preparation (185) gave a resin that contained unreacted sucrose and caused difficulties in processing and inversion of sucrose (259).

Further modification by adding sucrose to the phenol-formaldehyde condensate rather than reacting all three at the same time gives a less stable resin with poorer adhesive properties (204). The preparation of a sucrose-modified resin for casting is given in Reference 284.

The sucrose was originally believed to enter into the matrix of the polymer thus to be chemically bound into the resin molecule. Recent investigations have concluded that about 90% of the sucrose could be extracted by water (204). A casting resin cured at 120°C for several hours has resistance to water at the same level as the unmodified phenolic resin (284, 2851).

The application properties of these resins are given in Tables 18-1 and 18-2. More details on their preparation and properties are found in References 91, 204, 259, 284, 2851. Reference 91 is available from the Foundation on request.

Attempts to extend the phenolic resins with various sugar esters have been unsuccessful (285k). The resin is not compatible with the esters under the conditions normally used for its preparation. Preparation under other conditions including water-free media (285m) have also been tried without success (285k). Among the sucrose esters tested are sucrose monopalmitate (285k, m) and distearate (285m, n, o).

The resin is primarily useful as a plywood adhesive but also shows some promising properties in molding, casting and laminating. (See Plastics and Polymers, page 209.)

Other sugars in phenolic resins

Phenolic resins modified with other sugars, have been prepared in two steps: (a) condensation of sugar with phenols and (b) further reaction of the adduct with phthalic anhydride or formaldehyde (226). All products show poor heat stability.

GLUCOSE-PHENOL condensates are made by reacting phenol and glucose in a solvent, preferably glacial acetic acid, at around room temperature in the presence of hydrogen chloride gas. The mole ratio of phenol to glucose is 1:1 and 2:1. Other solvents, higher temperatures, or other changes in conditions give undesired results. The reaction is based on U.S. Patent 2,252,725. The 1:1-phenol-glucose condensate is a yellow to brown glassy solid with an indistinct melting point of about 80°C. Several fractions are obtained from the 2:1 condensate, including oils and amorphous powders.

Condensation of the condensates with phthalic anhydride in various ratios at 140–200°C gives black, brittle, glassy products with little strength. Condensation of fractionated products gives similar results.

Condensation with formaldehyde in water at up to 102°C in the presence of sulfuric acid gives a glassy solid product. The dried filtrate is hygroscopic, soluble in water, and darkens upon heating. It appears to have some surface activity. Similar condensation with sodium hydroxide gives a brown gum, which darkens when cured at 110°C.

GLUCOSE-CRESOL condensates are made similarly and also in hydrochloric acid. A gummy, yellow, water-soluble product and a brown powdery material insoluble in water are separated. Polymerization with an equal weight of phthalic anhydride gives dark products.

SUCROSE MODIFIED MELAMINE- AND UREA-FORMALDEHYDE RESINS

Melamine resins

Sucrose, invert sugar, glucose, and fructose can be successfully incorporated into melamine-formaldehyde resins on the laboratory scale (274, 307). These sugar-extended resins have been evaluated in textile finishes, molding compounds, laminating resins, and surface coatings. They are equal to or better than the unmodified resins in many applications. Evaluation of overall performance in comparative tests is quite difficult, since these resins may be better in one specific property and poorer in another in the given end use. For example, in textile applications modification with sugar may improve the crease resistance of cotton cloth but lower its shrink resistance. However, on rayon these same resins show the opposite effects.

In any case incorporation of sugar lowers the cost of raw materials. Although many of the modifications have been carried out with invert sugar, sucrose and other sugars are equally useful extenders. For example, sucrose, fructose, glucose, and even corn syrup are equally satisfactory in melamine-based baking primers (307c). Furthermore, sucrose appears to have advantages over invert sugar in molding compositions (307a). The color and water-adsorption properties of the sucrose-extended composition are superior to those of the product extended with invert sugar.

The preparation of the sugar-extended resin is very close to that practiced in the general manufacture of these resins. The addition of sugar has no effect on the reaction rate in poly-condensation. The sugar is probably combined chemically with the melamine-formaldehyde condensate and not present merely as a filler. The sugar may react with the methylol melamine to form ethers. The methylol melamines are precursors of melamine resins and are known to form ethers with alcohols. No free sugar can be detected in resins made for textile applications (274).

Sucrose is added in concentrations of up to 65% by weight of melamine resin. The melamine-formaldehyde resin is prepared according to conventional methods—namely, by condensing melamine and formalin in various ratios in the presence of an acid or alkaline catalyst. Etherified resins, such as trimethylol-melamine, are made by condensing in the presence of methyl alcohol (274). The resin is then processed further as required by the intended end use. Detailed descriptions of the preparation are given for textile finishes (274), molding powders (307b), and surface coatings (307c).

The common trimethylol resins, made with a ratio of formalin to melamine of 3:1, are more or less viscous liquids, depending on the level of condensation and their concentration in the aqueous medium. The hexamethylol and methylated resins are solid products, often crystalline. The presence of sucrose does not seem to alter the physical appearance of the resins appreciably.

The application properties of these sugar-extended resins are discussed under Plastics and Polymers, page 209.

Urea Resins

Sucrose-dimethylolurea resins are made by reacting sucrose and dimethylolurea in aqueous solution (183k). The optimum amounts are 1-1.5 parts sucrose to one part dimethylolurea (183i). The best catalyst is 0.5% *p*-toluene sulfonic acid. Sodium hydroxide is also effective (183i). Attempts to produce the resin as described in U.S. Patent 1,949,831 by reacting sucrose, urea and formaldehyde give a heat-sensitive nonmoldable product.

The resins are clear, colorless, soluble in water, and low in strength. Resins with a high concentration of sucrose have low thermal stability. Experiments to modify the resin to improve its properties have included the incorporation of other resins, acids, anhydrides, diisocyanates, silicone derivatives, plasticizers, and antioxidants (183i). The resins have been tested in coating sheets and as adhesives. (See Plastics and Polymers, page 209.)

SILICONE POLYMERS

The reaction of alkyl or aryl dihalo- and trihalosilanes with sucrose produce polymeric materials (55, 90). These reactions can proceed in a number of ways, including bridging, formation of cyclic acetals, or incomplete substitution of the labile chlorines in the molecule:

$$
\begin{array}{ccc}
\begin{array}{c}
\quad O \\
\diagup\;\diagdown \\
R\quad SiR'_2 \\
\diagdown\;\diagup \\
\quad O
\end{array}
&
\begin{array}{c}
R' \\
| \\
R\text{---}Si\text{---}O\text{---}R \\
|\quad\;|\quad\;| \\
O\quad R'\quad O \\
|\qquad\quad| \\
R'\text{---}Si\text{---}R'\quad R'\text{---}Si\text{---}R' \\
|\qquad\qquad\quad|
\end{array}
&
\begin{array}{c}
R' \\
| \\
RO\text{---}Si\text{---}Cl \\
| \\
R'
\end{array}
\\[2em]
\text{Cyclic acetal} & \text{Bridging} &
\begin{array}{c}\text{Incomplete}\\ \text{substitution}\end{array}
\end{array}
$$

R = Sucrose radical   R' = Alkyl or aryl groups

All three types of linkage may possibly occur simultaneously in varying degrees, which may explain the complex nature of the polymer.

Sucrose reacted with the halosilanes in pyridine gives polymers with molecular weights over 20,000 that are quite insoluble in organic solvents. They have high rotation, which indicates little or no hydrolysis of the sucrose. The polymer made with dichlorodimethylsilane contained chlorine, which can be further reacted with water, methyl alcohol or ammonia. The corresponding diphenyl compound contains only the alkoxide linkage, but it also undergoes modification on treatment with methyl alcohol. The modified products were low polymers of molecular weight below 5,000 therefore soluble in organic solvents. The polymeric materials made with halovinylsilanes are similar in general properties to those obtained with dichlorodimethyl and dichlorodiphenyl silane.

Because of the excellent high-temperature properties of silicone polymers, these materials are of interest for further research.

Dimethylsilyl polymers

One mole of sucrose is reacted with four moles of dichlorodimethylsilane in pyridine at room temperature for 20 hours (55). Addition of water gives a white solid, part of which can be extracted with ether. The infrared spectra of both fractions are identical and consistent with the structure of a sucrose dimethylsilyl ether. The optical rotation of each material was about $+37°$.

Hydrolysis with hydrochloric acid in ethyl alcohol gives glucose, fructose, and a polymeric material containing sucrose and a high portion of siloxane (–Si–O–Si–) linkages. On hydrolysis in neutral aqueous methyl alcohol sucrose is eliminated from both materials.

The ether-soluble material (m.p. 132°C) is very soluble in most common organic solvents. It is either a low polymer or monomer; its molecular weight is 2724. The insoluble portion, which chars at 200–250°C, is soluble in dioxane and chloroform. It is a highly polymeric material of molecular weight over 20,000.

Thorough analysis indicates that the product is a fully substituted sucrose derivative with four $-Si(CH_3)_2-$ groups per sucrose molecule and with some $-Si(CH_3)_2OH$ groups in the polymer, probably formed by hydrolysis.

A chlorine-free polymer is made by a modified process using methyl alcohol to remove pyridine hydrochloride during processing. Its properties are similar to those of the high polymer described above. It can be modified with ammonia to a polymer containing nitrogen with a molecular weight of about 3,900, which is soluble in organic solvents. Modification with methyl alcohol also gives a product with the properties of a low polymer. For more details on the polymers, see Reference 55.

Diphenylsilyl polymers

Sucrose reacts with dichlorodiphenylsilane under the same conditions as those described for the dimethylsilyl compound (55). The properties of the product are similar to those of the dimethylsilyl polymers. Analysis indicates that the polymer contains an average of one $-Si(Ph)_2-$ group per molecule of sucrose and one tetraphenyl disiloxane ($-Si(Ph)_2-O-Si(Ph)_2-$) linkage for every four sucrose molecules. However, it does not have chlorine or hydroxyl groups.

The methyl alcohol-modified product has a low molecular weight (797), indicating that it is almost a monomer. For more details, see Reference 55.

Vinylsilyl polymers

A polymeric material is obtained when sucrose is reacted with dichloromethylvinyl silane in pyridine (90). The polymer is a granular white solid, insoluble in ether, which chars over 200°C. Analysis of the product shows unsaturation, hydroxyl groups, and the absence of chlorine. Neutral hydrolysis of this material gives a hydrolyzate containing sucrose and some glucose and fructose. The positive specific rotation ($[\alpha]_D^{21} = +42.4°$) of the material also proves that hydrolysis is not extensive.

The similar reaction of sucrose with trichlorovinylsilane gives a brown granular solid that is insoluble in organic solvents (90). The product contains unsaturation and free hydroxyl groups, according to infrared analysis. The amount of free hydroxyl is markedly less than for the polymer from dichloromethylvinyl silane, indicating a higher degree of substitution. The reaction can also be carried out in the presence of ammonia (90).

Reaction with dimethyldiethoxysilane

The reaction of sucrose with this silane gives a polymer of low molecular weight (183k).

EPOXY POLYMERS

Epichlorohydrin

Epichlorohydrin reacts with sucrose (17, 183a, k), sodium sucrates (17, 272c), or mixtures of these (17) to a polymer that is probably of the type:

$$- (\text{Sucrose} - \text{OCH}_2\text{CHCH}_2)_{\overline{x}}$$
$$\underset{\displaystyle \text{OH}}{|}$$

The reaction with sucrose occurs only under alkaline conditions, such as the presence of potassium carbonate (17).

Similar polymers are reportedly made from saccharates with potassium and strontium. Barium, lead, and aluminum saccharates give no polymer (306). Attempts to prepare moderately polymerized derivatives in the presence of sulfuric acid, ferric chloride or sodium hydroxide have been unsuccessful (186c).

When sodium sucrate is refluxed with epichlorohydrin, the reaction proceeds slowly. However, heating at 135°C in a sealed tube yields a polymeric material in theoretical yield in a few hours (17). The yield of polymer is calculated by replacing the sodium in the sucrose by glycidyl residues.

Mixtures of sucrose and sodium sucrate can be reacted with epichlorohydrin similarly to sodium sucrate alone. Sucrose does not react completely if used in large excess. For complete reaction, a longer reaction time is necessary even at a mole ratio of 1:1. A syrupy byproduct that is largely nonsucrose in composition is also obtained in these reactions (17).

The products obtained from sucrose are tacky, water-sensitive resins (183a, k), generally inferior to those made from sodium sucrate (17).

The properties of the yellow powder from trisodium sucrate suggest that it is a highly cross-linked polymer of the epoxide type. It is insoluble in water and organic solvents (17, 272c) and quite heat-stable (17). A similar product is obtained from deammoniated trisodium sucrate (19).

The polymers prepared from mono-, tri-, penta- and heptasodium sucrate are all yellow powders that are completely insoluble in water and organic solvents. They are degraded slowly by acid. Treatment with 2-N hydrochloric acid at 100°C for seven hours dissolves the polymer completely. Heating at 210°C produces an odor of burnt sugar, but no visible change (17).

An attempt to induce solubility in organic solvents and limit polymerization by carrying out the condensation with trisodium sucrate in the presence of sodium phenoxide was unsuccessful (17). The sodium phenoxide reacted separately with each reactant. Infrared analysis of the trisodium sucrate showed the presence of free hydroxyl groups. Attempts to acetylate these groups with acetic anhydride or to sulfonate them with chlorosulfonic acid in pyridine have not been successful (17). Irradiation with γ-rays produces a definite degradation to water-soluble products (19).

The properties of polymers made from mixtures of sucrose and sodium sucrate with epichlorohydrin are similar to those of the polymer made from sodium sucrate alone (17). Infrared spectra of the polymer from sucrose, trisodium sucrate, and epichlorohydrin show the presence of free hydroxyl groups that cannot be reacted with acetic anhydride or chlorosulfonic acid (17).

Butylene oxide and propylene oxide

1,2-Butylene oxide does not react with sucrose under normal conditions in aqueous alkaline media. Under pressure in the presence of sodium ethoxide, an oily polymeric material is produced. It is a carbohydrate derivative in which all eight hydroxyls are substituted (272c). The product is a water-insoluble syrup (203c). Similar polymeric materials have also been made from butylene and propylene oxides by other workers (183k). The oily or tacky solids discolor at 130–140°C. For additional details, see Reference 290d.

Styrene oxide

The preparation of a polymeric adduct of sucrose and styrene oxide has also been reported (183k). Like the polymers above, it is unstable to heat.

Other epoxides

The attempted reactions between sucrose and epoxidized divinylbenzene and other epoxy compounds in aqueous alkaline media have been unsuccessful (183h). Allyl glycidyl ether reacts with sucrose to a water-soluble polymer. The product becomes insoluble after treatment with styrene oxide or vinyl acetate (183i). Similar unsuccessful attempts have been reported with glycidaldehyde in an aqueous medium (272c), bisepoxydicyclopentyl ether with potassium carbonate or boron trifluoride (246a) and "Epoxol 7-4®," a commercial product with four epoxide groups (255d).

POLYESTERS

A few experiments have been made to prepare resins of the polyester type by reacting sucrose with dibasic organic acids. A white polymer is obtained in reasonable yield with terephthaloyl chloride by interfacial condensation, and some tacky film-forming solids are made by reaction with dibasic esters.

Condensation with terephthaloyl chloride

Sucrose and some other sugars react with terephthaloyl chloride to produce white, powdery polymers (264; 269a, b). The yield is about 50% when the reaction is carried out in a two-phase system of aqueous alkali and carbon tetrachloride (269b). The reaction is an example of interfacial polycondensation, which—like the Schotten-Baumann reaction—proceeds at the interface between two fluid phases. The polymer consists of two fractions, one soluble in carbon tetrachloride and the other insoluble. Elemental analysis on the polymers made under various conditions has been carried out, but without establishing their structures (269a).

The reaction between pentasodium sucrate and adipoyl chloride also gives a polymeric material (17).

Condensation with dimethyl esters of sebacic, maleic, and other dibasic acids

Dimethyl sebacate, maleate, phthalate, itaconate, epoxy-stearate, and abietate, and diethyl succinate react with sucrose, in most cases, to give tacky solids whose formation indicates some polyester formation (183h, i; 203a; 290a, c). The reaction is carried out in dimethyl formamide with varying ratios of sucrose and diester and with sodium or potassium hydroxide as catalyst. Transesterification in xylene, with or without *p*-toluene sulfonic acid as catalyst, and with tetrabutyl titanate has not proved successful (183k).

Some polymeric material is also obtained by ester interchange between sucrose octaacetate and esters of dibasic acids (183f, k; 290b). The sebacate and succinate polyesters can be modified by further reaction with methyl stearate, linseedate (290a) or oleate (290c). The films prepared from both these modified polymers and the unmodified polymers show good adherence to glass but have poor water resistance. The dry solids are brittle resins (290a). The relative viscosities of some polymer solutions are given in Reference 290c.

Condensation with oxalyl chloride

Attempts to react sucrose with oxalyl chloride result in decomposition of the sucrose even at temperatures as low as −30°C (272c).

Polyesters from mannitol and sorbitol

The preparation of polymeric materials of the polyester type by cleaving the acetal, trimethylene sorbitol, with a mixture of adipic acid and trifluoroacetic anhydride has been described in the literature (Bonner et al., *J. Chem. Soc.* 1960, 2914). Similar polyesters could possibly be formed from the corresponding mannitol acetal. (These acetals are prepared from the sugars with formaldehyde.) Preliminary experiments have been conducted to study the cleavage of the mannitol acetal to produce the polyester (281).

ACRYLIC POLYMERS

Sucrose-acrolein resins

Sucrose reacts with acrolein in the presence of zinc chloride or other catalyst. The reaction does not produce a cyclic acetal, but a resinous material by addition across the double bond of the acrolein molecule. Polymerization occurs in solvent-free media. However, no reaction is observed when sucrose is reacted with an equimolar amount of acrolein in dry dimethyl formamide or in such basic solvents as pyridine and its mixtures, even with copper and calcium salts, organic peroxides, hydroquinone, and basic compounds as catalysts. The reaction in aqueous medium with an equimolar amount of calcium hydroxide as catalyst is equally unsuccessful (191).

Some condensations of sucrose with acrolein have been studied to explore the possibility of preparing pentaerythritol sucrose. Acrolein is an intermediate in the production of pentaerythritol. (See Pentaerythritol Sucrose, page 40.)

The most promising resin is obtained by reacting 5 parts of sucrose with 50 parts of acrolein in the presence of 20 parts of anhydrous zinc chloride (191). Zinc chloride is used in large excess because it not only serves as a catalyst but also functions somewhat as a solvent. For example, no polymer is formed in the presence of only 4 g of zinc chloride. The reaction is exothermic, and cooling is required to keep the mixture at moderate temperatures.

The reaction product is a hard yellow, transparent, slightly hygroscopic resin. It does not contain unreacted sucrose according to chromatographic analysis, but is a true polymer with no acetal content (191). Sucrose cannot be extracted from the polymer with water (294a).

The role of sucrose in the polymerization is indicated by the reaction of acrolein under similar conditions but in the absence of sucrose. The reaction mixture fails to give a clear yellow solution, but remains a milky-white suspension that does not solidify (191).

Pyridine or dimethyl formamide dissolves part of the resin, possibly the zinc chloride not already removed from the reaction product, leaving a yellow or white material insoluble in most common solvents. The extracts do not contain carbohydrates, according to chromatographic and infrared analyses. Water, acetone, and chloroform also attack the crude polymer (191). On prolonged treatment in boiling water, the surface becomes white and opaque (294a).

Some experiments have been made to remove the zinc chloride from the polymer and thus improve its water resistance (294b). Agitation of a partly polymerized syrup with water did not change the properties. Treatment with dry hydrochloric acid decomposed the resin.

Use of other catalysts gives some products with promising properties and others that are brittle or infusible or have other poor qualities. However, none of the reactions has been as fully explored as that with zinc chloride. These reactions are tabulated briefly below. They are generally carried out by simply reacting the components at room temperature:

Reactant with acrolein + catalyst	Products	Reference
Sucrose octaacetate + $POCl_3$	No reaction; only slight increase in viscosity	278c
Sucrose + H_2SO_4	Rubbery orange resin; hardens on standing	278c
Sucrose + methylcellulose + phloroglucinol	Filled product is good molding compound	183f
Sucrose + dimethylol urea + Et_4NOH	Thermally stable resin	183g
Sucrose	Brittle, glossy solid with 3 moles acrolein. Infusible product with 6 moles	183k
Sucrose + $POCl_3$	Rubbery orange resin with little sucrose content	278b
Sorbitol + $POCl_3$	Clear, viscous syrup; hardens to glass-like resin	278b
Mannitol + $POCl_3$	No reaction	278b

Sucrose-crotonaldehyde resin

Experiments to polymerize sucrose and crotonaldehyde under conditions similar to those for acrolein fail to give resinous materials (191). The reaction products have been thoroughly analyzed by chromatography and infrared (191, 278a).

Sucrose acrylate and related unsaturated esters

A number of acrylic and similar unsaturated esters of sucrose have been tested as monomers in polymerization (173, 183k). As Table 4-3 shows, the sucrose octaesters of methacrylic, crotonic, and cinnamic acids can be copolymerized into clear hard glasses with styrene or methyl methacrylate. Octamethacrylyl sucrose has a promising short gelation time. Similar tough, clear films can be made by reacting sucrose octaacetate with methyl methacrylate (183k).

Acrylic and allyl polymers from octamethyl sucrose

Preparation of these monomers from sucrose follows the route below:

Sucrose
│ Methylation
▼
Octamethyl sucrose
│ Hydrolysis

Tetramethyl glucose ◄――――――――――► Tetramethyl fructose

The tetramethyl monosaccharides are separated. Each one can be reacted with acrylic chloride, vinyl isocyanate, allyl chloride or other polymerizable groups on the glycosidic hydroxyl:

$$CH_2OCH_3 \quad \cdots O \cdots \quad CH_3O \quad OCH_3 \quad OH \quad OCH_3 \xrightarrow{\quad RCl \quad} CH_2OCH_3 \quad \cdots O \cdots \quad CH_3O \quad OCH_3 \quad OR \quad OCH_3$$

The monomer is then polymerized to a polymer or copolymer. Of the monomers listed below, tetramethylglucosyl methacrylate and its acrylate can be polymerized. Attempts to polymerize allyl tetramethylfructoside have been unsuccessful (269g).

The polymers are white, water-insoluble solids. They are formed from the α- and β-isomers of the glucosidic derivatives. Isomerization of the product apparently occurs during the preparation of the monomer through the intermediate sodium derivative.

L

The monomer is actually the full acetal of the glucose or fructose when the sugar is reacted with an organic chloride, or the ester derivative of the half acetal when the sugar is reacted with an acyl chloride. The monomers successfully prepared are:

Reactants	Monomer
Tetramethyl glucose + Methacrylic chloride	Tetramethyl glucosyl methacrylate (269f)
Acrylic chloride	Tetramethyl glucosyl acrylate (269g)
Tetramethyl fructose + Allyl bromide	Allyl tetramethylfructoside (269g)

The reaction is preferably carried out by reacting the sodium tetramethyl sugar with a slight excess of the reactant in ether (269f). The oily products are mixtures of anomers (isomers of α- and β-glucosides), which cannot be separated successfully by chromatography (269d). Partial separation can be achieved by simple fractional distillation. The various fractions can be tested in polymerizations.

The reactions of tetramethyl fructose with vinyl isocyanate to tetramethylfructosyl N-vinyl carbamate or with isopropenyl isocyanate to the corresponding carbamate give products that are not crystalline and are not stable to heat (269b, c). Attempts to prepare the vinyl derivative by reaction of the sodium glucoside of either methylated sugar with vinyl bromide or ethylene bromide have been unsuccessful (269f).

Polymers from tetramethyl glucosyl methacrylate
Various fractions of the monomeric mixtures of the α-and β-isomers have been polymerized in boiling acetone for 24 hours. A white, water-insoluble polymer is obtained with over 90% conversion of each fraction (269f). Optical rotation and dispersion properties of the polymers are given in Reference 269e.

Polymers from tetramethylglucosyl acrylate
Fractions of the monomer boiled in acetone for 20 hours produce white polymeric materials with 66-77% conversion (269g).

POLYURETHANES
Some sucrose polymers of the polyurethane type show promising properties as coatings and foams.

Sucrose
When sucrose is reacted with tolylene-2,4-diisocyanate in pyridine (or possibly in dimethyl sulfoxide), a rigid, highly cross-linked polymer is formed (264). The light-colored product is hard and brittle. It stays rigid and does not decompose up to 200°C. Prolonged boiling with water, ethyl acetate, butyl alcohol, ethyl alcohol or 0.2-N aqueous hydrochloric acid does not alter its appearance or consistency. It is also insoluble in boiling phenol and dimethyl formamide. Boiling in concentrated hydrochloric acid blackens the material, and boiling in aqueous sodium hydroxide causes disintegration.

Resins of varying viscosity can be prepared in pyridine at 160°C, depending on the reaction time (306). The product has adhesive properties after curing, but is brittle. Attempts to incorporate metal oxides into the polymer have been unsuccessful. Polymerization in dimethyl formamide gives a solid product (285m). Polymerization in acetic anhydride gives a hard, brittle product (264). A gummy product has also been obtained (183k).

Sucrose linoleate and other unsaturated esters

Urethane polymers useful as surface coatings are made by reacting the higher sucrose esters of unsaturated fatty acids with diisocyanates by several methods, as described under Surface Coatings, page 192. Urethane foams can also be prepared from these esters. They are discussed under Plastic Foams, page 213.

Sucrose tetratosylate

The tetratosylate copolymerizes with tolylene diisocyanate to a hard polymer. (See Miscellaneous Polymers, below).

ALKYD RESINS

Sucrose polyoxyethylene plus phthalic anhydride

Attempts to obtain alkyd resins by condensing the impure sucrose tetra- or octaethers of ethylene oxide with phthalic anhydride in a melt give dark brown, brittle, glassy products (224).

Sucrose polyoxyethylene plus formaldehyde

Condensation of impure sucrose tetra- or octaethers of ethylene oxide with formaldehyde does not produce a resin (224).

Sucrose plus maleic anhydride

When sucrose is reacted with maleic anhydride in pyridine, a solid product is separated from the tarry reaction mixture by trituration with water (184). During the reaction a large volume of carbon dioxide is formed. The hygroscopic product contains nitrogen. Further treatment under vacuum yields a nitrogen-free material that is soluble in water. Exploratory tests indicate that dimers or higher polymers are obtained when the nitrogen-free material is treated with potassium persulfate. However, the hard molding compositions made with wood flour are sensitive to water (184).

The reaction of sucrose and maleic anhydride in the presence of acetic anhydride or acetic acid gives an amber resin (183c). Copolymerization with styrene produces a rigid product and with vinyl acetate a flexible material (183c). Condensation of maleic anhydride with sucrose in the presence of formic acid yields a crystalline product (183c). Its copolymer with vinyl acetate is a semisolid.

MISCELLANEOUS POLYMERS

Sucrose tosylates and their copolymers

Sucrose tetratosylate forms a clear, hard film on evaporation from a suitable solvent (264). Addition of a plasticizer improves film properties.

The bifunctional property of sucrose tri- or tetratosylates has been explored in attempts to prepare resins. When reacted with other bifunctional compounds, they form polymeric compounds, some of which show good water and heat resistance. Among these copolymers are (264):

2,4-DIAMINOTOLUENE. A brown polymeric material is obtained when the tritosylate is first reacted with 2,4-diaminotoluene in dimethyl formamide at 100-130°C and then diluted with ammonia.

BENZENE-1,3-DITHIOL. The reaction of benzene-1,3-dithiol with sucrose tritosylate in a mixture of dimethyl formamide and acetonitrile in the presence of potassium carbonate gives an elastic gum that becomes hard and brittle on trituration with hot water. The product is soluble in hot dimethyl formamide and phenol, and insoluble in chloroform and all hydrocarbon solvents. It gels in dioxane and pyridine. When heated, it becomes temporarily elastic.

TOLYLENE DIISOCYANATE. Reaction in dichloromethane catalyzed by triethylamine gives a hard, colorless substance that does not decompose up to 200°C and is resistant to water and organic solvents.

ETHYLENEDIAMINE. Reaction with ethylene diamine and acetonitrile could produce a polymer with the structure -(NH-Sucrose-(O-Tosyl)$_2$-NH CH$_2$CH)$_x$-.

The reaction is carried out in the presence of potassium carbonate at 110°C. The yellow powder is insoluble in water, benzene and toluene: partly soluble in anisole; and soluble in methyl alcohol, ethyl alcohol, acetone, dioxane and dichloromethane. It fuses to a viscous mass on heating.

Condensation of sucrose with diallylidene pentaerythritol

Condensation of sucrose with diallylidene pentaerythritol gives a dark, brittle resin (235). The reaction is catalyzed with *p*-toluene sulfonic acid or boron trifluoride. Catalysis with choline gives an unhomogeneous product containing a black tar. The attempted reaction is an analog of that described for mannitol, which gives a pale yellow, slightly elastic resin.

Polymers by reaction with metal oxides and salts

Sucrose, its octaacetate, and several half esters with dibasic organic acids have been reacted with a number of metal powders, oxides or salts (306). The objective was to make products useful as cements and adhesives, similar to those made from glycerol and litharge, or to sorel cements. (See Metal Compounds of Sucrose and Its Derivatives, page 210.)

Polymers with boric acid

A polymeric material is reportedly formed when a solution of sucrose is reacted with boric acid at about 115°C (306).

Oxysucrose-urea resins

Oxysucrose has been reacted with urea in acidic solutions to yield a variety of products whose composition depends upon the molar ratio of the reactants and the concentration of catalyst (197). However, later experiments indicate that this reaction does not yield satisfactory material (294c, d).

Heat-curing of the adduct gives polymers that are substantially insoluble in water (197). The product has been tested in textile finishing.

Copolymerization of sucrose and 3,4-dihydro-2-hydroxymethyl-2H-pyran

When sucrose is reacted with an excess of the pyran derivative in dimethyl formamide in the presence of traces of hydrochloric acid, a polymer is obtained in 11% yield (10, 82, 83). Its sucrose content corresponds to the combination of one mole of sucrose with 19.8 moles of the enol ether. The similar reaction with the corresponding 2-formyl derivative of the pyran gives the acetal. (See Acetals and Ketals, page 94.)

The nondialyzable polymer resembles a polysaccharide in having the pyranose ring structure and an interglycosidic linkage, but differs in its hydrophobic character, caused by the methylene groups in the ring.

Polymers from by-products of reductive aminolysis to 2-methyl piperazine

A large number of experiments have been carried out to produce polymers from various distillation fractions of reductive aminolysis. The fractions are mixtures of aliphatic and cyclic amines. The reactants include formaldehyde alone and with melamine, phenol, or urea; epichlorohydrin; maleic or succinic acid plus glycol; diisocyanates; adipic, sebacic and isosebacic acids; and organic dihalides (293). None of the products has properties comparable with those of polymers obtained from purer and more readily accessible materials.

Polymers with phosphorus halides

Polymers are obtained when sucrose or sodium sucrate is reacted with phosphorus chloride or thiophosphoryl chloride. These polymers have been tested as agricultural chemicals, as shown in Table 21-1.

Other polymers

A number of other attempts to prepare polymeric materials are briefly tabulated in Table 13-1.

Table 13-1
Other polymers made from sucrose

Reactant	Product	Reference
Halogen compounds		
Ethylene chlorohydrin		
(+ di- or pentasodium sucrate)	Oil or tacky hygroscopic solid.	183c
Dichloropentane	Low yield of amber brittle resin.	183k
Dichloro-1,3-hexadiene-2,4	Glassy film. Copolymer with styrene gives	
(+ disodium sucrate)	quickly drying film.	183d
Dichlorohexadiene (+ disodium	Tack free film made with cobalt drier and	
sucrate)	peroxide catalyst.	183c

Table 31-1 *continued*

Reactant	Product	Reference
Sulfur compounds		
Propylene sulfide	Water-insoluble polymer formed under pressure in the presence of sodium ethoxide. Similar polymer obtained with trisodium sucrate.	255d, 272c
Thioglycolic acid	Could not be polymerized by oxidation.	183a
Unsaturates		
Polyvinyl alcohol + formaldehyde	Strong flexible but water-sensitive material.	183i
Vinyl acetate	Vinyl acetate reacted with sucrose or sucrose propylene ether. The latter gives an amber hydrophobic resin.	183i
Acetylene	Some reaction occurs in dimethyl formamide.	183i
Furfural	Water resistant, thermoplastic product obtained by curing with 2-5% BF_3.	183g
Phenols, alcohols, and acids		
Resorcinol, chlororophenols, cresols, or catechol	No useful resin obtained.	185
Sorbic acid + acetic anhydride	Has drying oil properties. Too costly raw material.	183b
β-Propiolactone	The reaction product prepared in dimethyl sulfoxide or dimethyl formamide not isolated. In xylol and naphtha a low molecular weight and a hard glossy solid were isolated respectively. Both are water soluble (183k). Reaction generally proceeds with extensive decomposition of sucrose (272c).	183k, 203c
Tetraethyl orthosilicate	Moldable product. Reaction is hard to repeat.	183k
Cellulose	Exploratory attempts to modify cellulose with sucrose.	203a

14

Miscellaneous products and properties

Condensation with nitromethane

ATTEMPTS to prepare a crystalline condensation product from aldehyde derivatives of sucrose by condensation with nitromethane are unsuccessful (272c). These aldehydes are made with the well-known selective oxidizing agents lead tetraacetate and periodic acid. Successful condensation of nitromethane with other carbohydrates is reported by Fischer and Baer in 1960 (255e). The product can be reduced to aminoderivatives of sucrose.

Eutectic mixtures of sucrose

Experiments have been conducted to prepare eutectic mixtures of sucrose with several nonreactive organic or inorganic chemicals (210). These mixtures could serve as media for the reaction of sucrose with other compounds. Among the results were:

—Dimethyl sulfoxide, and camphor, give syrupy liquids with sucrose that do not solidify.

—Sucrose decomposes when reacted with a number of organic chemicals in the dry state above 100°C. Milling sucrose with other chemicals is also unsuccessful. The reaction of sucrose with diphenyl sulfones and other organic chemicals in aqueous methyl and ethyl alcohol gives viscous or pasty products.

—Promising mixtures with sharp meeting points are obtained with bis (4-aminophenyl)sulfone digalactoside, cyclohexyl-*p*-toluene sulfonamide, and 4,4-sulfonyldiphenol. Ten grams of each chemical are added to 90 grams of sucrose in 1:1 mixture of water and ethyl alcohol. Of some 40 compounds tested under similar conditions in aqueous methyl alcohol, only furan derivatives give stable eutectic mixtures with low and sharp meeting points between 50 to 70°C.

167

The possibility of eutectic mixtures of sucrose with pyridine, dimethyl formamide and other solvents has also been suggested.

Solubility of sucrose in organic solvents

Sucrose is highly soluble in water. It is also soluble in alcohols, glycols and many other protic organic solvents. A summary review of its solubility in non-aqueous solvents is given in Reference 92.

The solubility of sucrose in some unconventional aprotic solvents at various temperatures is given in Table 14-1. Among these morpholine, dimethyl sulfoxide, dimethyl formamide, and N-methyl-2-pyrrolidone are the best solvents. The sulfolanes are good solvents at temperatures of 150°C and over. Additional data may be found in References 92 and 285f.

Solubility of sucrose in urethanes

An exploratory test shows that sucrose is slightly soluble in a mixture of methyl and ethyl urethanes (245e).

Optical rotation of mannitol and sorbitol

The optical rotation of mannitol and sorbitol in tungstate and molybdate solutions and the effect of pH and the relative concentrations of polyols and tungstate are given in Reference 6 and 27. (For additional data, see internal reports of Foundation, project 160.)

Table 14-1
Solubility of sucrose in organic solvents (92)

Solvent	Grams sucrose per 100 grams solution					
	120°C	110°C	100°C	85°C	60°C	30°C
Pyrazine	3.95	3.04-a	2.23-b	1.95	—	—
Methyl pyrazine	2.34	1.84	1.25	0.87	—	—
Mixed pyrazines	—	2.73	2.46	2.02	—	—
Morpholine	50.8	—	45.1	39.8	34.7	30.7
N-Methyl morpholine	0.72	0.56	0.38	0.37	—	—
*Dimethyl sulfoxide	—	61.6	58.7	51.1	49.1	41.6
N-Methyl-2-pyrrolidone	40.4	—	33.5	28.0	22.6	17.3
Dimethyl formamide	42.8	—	29.6	23.6	16.9	14.1
Pyridine	—	7.46	5.99	5.00	3.75	3.12
Dioxane	—	—	0.11	0.11	0.07	—
2-Methyl piperazine	30.1-c	29.6-c	29.5-c	26.1	—	—
Trimethyl cyanurate	0.32-d	—	—	—	—	—
Tetrahydrofuran	—	—	—	—	0.01	—
Dimethyl sulfolane	0.52-c	0.50-c	0.37	0.30	—	—
Sulfolane-e, f	0.20	—	0.17	0.05-i	—	—
3-Methyl sulfolane-e, g	2.9	—	0.07	0.02-i	—	—
Di-n-propyl sulfoxide-h	—	—	42.0-c	38.0-c, i	22.6	—

a – At 107°C.
b – At 97°C.
c – Solution discolored.
d – At 140°C.
e – Reference 285f. Grams sucrose per grams of solvent.
f – 16 g at 150°C; 85 g at 180°C.
g – 7 g at 150°C; 63 g at 180°C.
h – Reference 285j.
i – At 80°C.

Part II

Applications

15

Surfactants

SUCROSE ESTER DETERGENTS, EMULSIFIERS, AND WETTING AGENTS

Sucrose esters have recently been introduced as nonionic surfactants based on sucrose and fatty acid esters as raw materials. They are manufactured on a limited scale. (See the summary report on production available from the Foundation (143) and chapter on Fatty Esters, page 52.)

The sucrose ester surfactants can be used in a variety of products, as shown in Table 15-1. They compare well in overall performance to other surfactants in detergency, emulsification, and related properties. However, because of their composition they differ in many respects from most other surfactants. Among their outstanding properties are:

—Neutrality (pH of solution 7.0–7.5)
—Freedom from taste and odor
—Freedom from skin irritation
—Freedom from toxicity (except possibly for the dipalmitate)
—High biodegradability
—Physiological compatibility and ease of digestibility by the body
—Soft and velvety feel and freedom from tackiness
—Compatibility with other materials

Few, if any, of the common commercial surfactants can claim such a wide combination of qualities necessary in many uses. For example, none of the presently used surfactants is composed of chemicals similar to those found in food. Sucrose esters contain only sucrose and fatty acids, both of which are widely consumed in many foods and are even nutritionally important to the human body.

Conventional anionic surfactants have excellent detergency, but display slow degradability in sewage treatment. Nonionic surfactants are used in specialty detergents for dishwashing and fine fabrics, and also as emulsifiers, dispersants, and stabilizers in cosmetics,

173

food, and other fields. The properties of sucrose esters make them highly competitive with such common nonionics as the polyoxyethylene alkylated phenols (Tritons®) and polyoxyethylene fatty acid-sorbitol adducts (Tweens®).

Among the disadvantages of sucrose esters are their poor stability in acidic media, their relatively high price, and their novelty.

Commercial development studies

The status of the detergent industry, legislation on pollution, and the possible entry of sucrose ester detergents into the market as of 1964 have been reviewed (202). The review concludes that "there is a strong opportunity for sucrose ester surfactants to become a major product entity" provided that their performance and economics are competitive.

The detergent industry is highly price-conscious. Large investments in new equipment and machinery are required when new types of products are introduced. In the past six years, the new and more highly biodegradable linear alkyl sufonates (LAS) have gradually replaced the branched-chained alkyl benzene sulfonates (ABS) of poorer biodegradability. The new surfactants required some changes in the manufacture of complete detergents. However, introduction of the new detergents was required by legislation to control pollution.

Although there are already some indications that LAS is not completely biodegradable, the industry probably will not replace it with higher-priced sucrose esters or other surfactants unless new legislation compels such a change. However, in cosmetics, food additives, and other uses where such qualities as performance, physiological acceptance, and freedom from toxicity and irritation are of major importance, sucrose esters can already compete successfully with the older, established surfactants.

Formulations

The application of sucrose esters in suggested formulations is outlined below. Esters made from tallow or other cheap sources of fatty acids can be used in most formulations. Additional information is available from the manufacturers.

Heavy duty detergents

Sucrose ester detergents are formulated similarly to detergents based on typical other commercial surfactants. A suggested formulation for a heavy-duty laundry detergent powder includes the following (56):

Sucrose monotallowate, cocoate, or oleate	10.0-25.0 parts
Sodium tripolyphosphate	38.0-50.0
Sodium silicate	4.0-6.0
Carboxymethyl cellulose	0.5-1.0
Optical brightener	0.1
Sucrose, moisture, etc.	Up to 10.0
Sodium sulfate (filler), to make	100.0

Sucrose esters can also be used in combination with other nonionic or anionic surfactants. Several compositions are suggested in Reference 56.

A suggested formulation for a light-duty liquid detergent for dishwashing and fine fabrics is:

Sucrose tallowate	5-10 parts
Sodium tripolyphosphate ⎤	
Sodium silicate ⎦	≤ 30
Foam booster	4-5
Isopropyl alcohol	3-5
Water, to make	100 parts

Cosmetics

Sucrose monoester is employed in cosmetic products as emulsifiers in concentrations of 1 to 2.5%. Since they are rather hydrophilic, the monoesters should be used with agents of more lipophilic character, such as sucrose diesters or Spans®. All the compositions suggested below are stable for a minimum of six months (117):

Cleansing cream

Beeswax	10 parts
Mineral oil	35
Paraffins and petrolatum	15
Lanolin	2.5
Arlacel C®	4.0
Propylparaben (preservative)	0.2
Sucrose monostearate	1.0
Water, to make	100.0

Cleansing lotion

Mineral oil	10.0 parts
Span 60®	2.0
Sucrose monostearate	2.5
Methylparaben	0.2
Water, to make	100.0

Dry skin cream

Absorption base	20.0 parts
Mineral oil	35.0
Paraffin wax	10.0
Sucrose monostearate	1.0
Propylene glycol	5.0
Propylparaben	0.2
Water, to make	100.0

Men's hair lotion

Mineral oil	30.0 parts
G1441®	2.0
Beeswax	2.0
Span 60®	2.0
Arlacel C®	2.0
Propylparaben	0.2
Sucrose monpalmitate	2.0
Water, to make	100.0

Sunscreen lotion

Butyl stearate	10.0 parts
Span 60®	2.0
Screening agent	1.5
Silicone oil	2.0
Sucrose monopalmitate	2.5
Methylparaben	0.2
Water, to make	100.0

Other formulations are suggested for toothpaste, waterless hand cleaner, and washable ointment (117).

Latex paints

Sucrose monoesters of the necessary surface activity stabilize emulsion paints prepared from the more highly substituted sucrose esters. For example, sucrose monolinoleate is a good emulsifier for blown or unblown sucrose tetra- to heptalinoleates. Stable oil-in-water emulsions are formed in concentrations of 10 parts sucrose ester in 100 parts water (47). The amount of the monoester required for stabilization is below 1%. The emulsion is then used to prepare styrene copolymers of better quality and higher conversion than those obtained with conventional potassium laurate emulsifiers.

Composition

Sucrose esters are made from fatty esters derived from a variety of such sources as the tallow, which is most commonly used, tall oil, and coconut oil. The sucrose esters can also be made with pure acids, such as lauric and stearic. The composition of five representative sucrose esters as produced by commercial manufacturers is given in Table 15-2. They have been used in recent comparative detergency and related tests. The stearate and laurate esters are mixtures of roughly equal parts of monoester and diester. The others are essentially monoesters. The first four materials were solids.

Commercial products often contain tri- or higher esters. For example, the products made by one U. S. supplier have the following specifications:

Sucrose monoester

Monoester	72-80%
Diester	13-15%
Higher and methyl esters	1- 8%
Dimethyl formamide	0.01-0.5%
Color (Gardner Varnish)	
50% isopropyl alcohol	6-12

Sucrose diester

Monoester	25%
Diester	35%
Higher esters and methyl esters	35%
Dimethyl formamide	0.01%
Color	9

The method of analysis recommended by the Foundation is given in Reference 143.

Stability

Sucrose esters undergo some hydrolysis to sucrose and acid under the alkaline working conditions of common detergents, but the extent is not high enough to influence their detergency and other surface active properties. However, they show poor resistance to hydrolysis during prolonged crutching in the manufacture of formulated detergents.

Hydrolysis has been studied with detergent formulations containing sucrose tallowate, sodium silicate, and sodium tripolyphosphate. Hydrolysis of the ester to the extent of 12–15% is observed when the formulation is heated at 60–80°C for three to six hours. The solution has a pH of 9.3 and contains 0.04% sucrose tallowate, 0.16% sodium phosphate, and 0.024% sodium silicate (220c).

Crutching tests have been carried out with similar formulations containing sucrose tallowate and other esters at 160 to 175°F (220c, d, e). All the sucrose esters tested are saponified to 30% or more by crutching. Resistance to hydrolysis during crutching is somewhat improved when the ester molecule is modified by reaction with alkylene oxide. (See Alkyleneoxy Adducts of Sucrose Esters, page 183.)

All the esters in uncompounded form are hygroscopic. However, they do not seem to pick up excessive amounts of moisture, and appear to reach a saturation point rather early in the exposure period (220c). For earlier stability tests, see Reference 124.

Spray drying tests have been carried out for a number of sucrose esters. The resulting powders were then formulated into heavy-duty detergents (220a). The purpose of the work was (a) to determine whether the sucrose esters were sufficiently stable to hydrolysis in crutching and spraying, and (b) to examine the performance and appearance of the spray-dried products. Because of the shorter times, less saponification was observed than in the prolonged crutching tests (220d).

The bead size and bulk density of the final product looked promising for full-scale or pilot-plant operation. The detergency values (soil removal, lime soap dispersion) of the dried materials were equal to those of the uncrutched and undried controls. However, the foaming power of the spray-dried product was very poor, and had to be improved by foam boosters.

Physiological and biological properties

Sucrose esters are essentially wholesome foods. When sucrose esters enter the digestive system, they are hydrolyzed into glucose, fructose, and fatty acids, all of which are components of common foods.

Detailed studies with enzymes indicate that those found in the liver hydrolyze the esters with the greatest activity (15). The enzymes studied include wheat germ, pancreatic lipase and juice, pancreatin, α-amylase, invertase, and liver homogenates. None of these enzymes cleaves the glycosidic linkage. Unlike normal fats, sucrose esters thus enter the process of metabolism directly in the liver, without circulating in the blood. Therefore, as pointed out by Nobile [*Ann. Chim.* (*Rome*) **53**, 1299 (1963)], the accumulation of cholesterol in the blood vessels is less likely to occur.

Toxicity

All sucrose esters tested except the dipalmitates show good tolerance by animals.

M

SUCROSE MONOSTEARATE. Brief toxicity tests on rats have been carried out with sucrose monostearate (291). The rats accept a diet of Sherman ration containing sucrose monostearate at concentrations of 5% and 10%, unless it is unpurified and of bitter taste (291a), but refuse it at the level of 15% and 25% (291b). However, rats fed on a ration containing 5% sucrose stearate do not gain weight as well as control animals fed on an unsupplemented ration (291b). The poor acceptance by rats may be attributed to the residual odiferous solvents such as dimethyl formamide, an explanation accepted by the Food and Drug Administration (251). Nausea, diarrhea, and other problems caused by the solvent are reported elsewhere (301).

Preliminary toxicity studies indicate that single dosages of five grams of the sucrose ester per kilogram of body weight cause no deleterious symptoms in rats (124).

SUCROSE PALMITATES. Commercial raw and purified samples of sucrose dipalmitate (Sucrodet B-600®) have been fed to rats at a level of 25% of the basal ration (303b). The animals died after 12 days when fed with the raw sample and after seven days when fed with the purified ester. The purified sample contained only 6 ppm of dimethyl formamide. Similar toxicity has been reported previously (303a). The dipalmitate fed at level as low as 5% of the ration appears toxic (143).

SUCROSE COTTONSEEDATE. Cottonseedate, containing 60% monoester and 40% diester, produces no overt toxic symptoms in rats at a level as high as 25% of the ration (303a). The ester was the commercial product Sequol-260® marketed by Pfizer. Its fatty acid contains about 50% linoleic acid, 22% palmitic acid, 22% oleic acid, and some stearic acid.

For detailed data on the ration and the histopathological observations, see Reference 303a. Similar freedom from toxicity has been observed in nutritional studies in humans and rats (301).

Skin irritation

The sugar esters appear to have an extremely low order of irritation to the skin (123). A 10% solution of sucrose stearate applied to the eyes does not sting or smart. Intravenous injection of aqueous solutions of the sugar esters does not produce irritation or redness. Similar lack of reaction on the skin is reported by Nobile [*Ann. Chim. (Rome)* **53**, 1299 (1963)].

Biodegradability

Biodegradability is one of the most important requirements of surfactants. Since surfactants and detergents are used in extremely large quantities, their elimination in waste treatment is of considerable importance.

The surfactants most widely used in detergents until the last few years, the branched chain alkyl benzene sulfonates (ABS) and the nonionic alkylphenoxy polyoxyethylenes are very resistant to biological oxidation. Often as much as 50% of these products passes unchanged through the biological sewage treatment processes. The presence of surfactants in sewage causes foaming and reduces its capacity to take up oxygen from air bubbles, so that the efficiency of the activated sludge processes is reduced. Perhaps the most serious result of the poor biodegradability of these surfactants is the effect of quite small concentrations on rivers and other receiving waters.

The detergent industry has replaced the ABS surfactants with linear alkyl sulfonates, LAS, which are more degradable in the activated sludge and trickling filter processes, but are not easily eliminated in primary treatment and in cesspools (*Proc. of the 20th Industrial Waste Conference*, Purdue Univ., Lafayette, Ind., May 4–6, 1965, Eng. Ext. Ser. No. 118, p. 724).

Like other fat-based surfactants, sucrose esters of fatty acids have the advantage of good degradability during biological treatment. The effect of sucrose esters on the uptake of dissolved oxygen by sewage microorganisms has been studied under the conditions of standard tests on biological oxygen demand (BOD) (79, 81, 85). The sucrose esters tested include sucrose monostearate, sucrose tallowate, sucrose dipalmitate, and sucrose ester of cottonseed oil. The products were not pure; for example, the monostearate contained up to 20% distearate. These preliminary experiments indicated that the biological lability of sugar-based surfactants is far greater than that of the anionic ABS. For additional information see also References 80 and 254.

Sucrose esters are also degradable under anaerobic conditions, such as occur in cesspools and septic tanks (see Wayman and Robertson, "Biodegradation of Anionic and Non-ionic Surfactants under Aerobic and Anaerobic Conditions," U. S. Geological Survey, Denver, Colo.).

Some preliminary comparative studies have been carried out on the pollution of drinking water by formulated detergents based on sucrose esters, LAS, ABS, other anionic surfactants, and soap (295). Studies on the effect of surfactants from a cesspool on Long Island on the ground waters indicate that soap and sucrose esters have the lowest polluting effect. The concentration of phosphate in the disposal system was highest with the sucrose esters and lowest with soap. The study concludes that "it would appear from the data that soap and sucrose ester compounds would result in a more acceptable washing compound than is presently being used on Long Island." Much of Long Island, like many rural and suburban areas, does not have a sewage system. In addition, the soil is sandy. Accordingly the overflow from cesspools and septic tanks sometimes seeps into nearby wells for potable water.

The detergent based on the sucrose ester contained 10% sucrose tallowate, as did the detergents based on sulfated fatty alcohol (273). The detergent formulations based on anionics contained 19% linear alkyl sulfonate (Committee LAS) and 19% ABS (130). All contained inorganic builders (chiefly sodium tripolyphosphate and sodium silicate), carboxymethyl cellulose, and sodium sulfate.

Evaluation in household detergents

Standard heavy-duty household detergent formulations, prepared from a series of well characterized sucrose ester surfactants, have been compared in performance to standard detergents (130). On the whole the sucrose esters performed at least as well in detergency as the standard anionics ABS, sulfated fatty alcohols and α-sulfo-fatty acids. In addition, they retained their effectiveness at lower concentrations. They showed about the same tendency as the anionics, or slightly less, to build up organic residues on the fabric. Both series were much superior to soap in this respect. In redeposition performance and lime soap dispersion the sucrose esters were outstandingly better than any of the standard anionics.

The stearic acid (C_{18}) esters of sucrose gave generally better performance than such lower homologs as the laurate (C_{12}). The saturated esters tended to be better than the unsaturated tall oil and coco esters.

HLB values

The main index used for the choice of a surface active agent in many applications is the hydrophile-lipophile balance or HLB. The HLB index of sucrose esters ranges from four to twelve. The value can be varied either by changing the number of acidic radicals or the chain length of the fatty acids.

For example, the short-chain monolauric or myristic acid esters have high HLB values. They are better foamers and somewhat better detergents than the longer-chain esters. The longer-chain stearates and palmitates have lower HLB values. They give better emulsification and other properties on the interface of two liquids than the C_8–C_{12} homologs. Sucrose di- and triesters have HLB values as low as four.

Detergency

TEXTILES. Detergency tests have been carried out by the carbon soil method (130) and by the more realistic soil accumulation method (Table 15-3). The data indicate that the sucrose esters in conventionally formulated form provide outstanding antiredeposition performance and soil removal at least equal to that of the favored conventional anionic surfactants. The long-chain (C_{18}) esters give better detergent performance than the shorter-chain ones. They are remarkable for their effectiveness at low concentrations. For more data see Reference 219.

Additional detergency tests are given for formulations used in pollution studies (273) and also for the types of sucrose esters prepared formerly (124, 211).

DISHWASHING. Comparative hand dishwashing tests have been carried out with formulations based on sucrose tallowate, and other surfactants used in pollution studies. As Table 15-4 shows, the sucrose ester displays the best cleaning power, but gives the least suds. Sudsy formulations for hand dishwashing have higher acceptance among housewives. (Such products contain a few per cent of a foam stabilizer, commonly lauroyl diethanolamide.) The sucrose tallowate is more effective at a level only 50% of that of the common anionic synthetics.

For additional tests, see Reference 211.

Foam performance

Results of the foam performance tests are shown in Table 15-5. The laurate ester resists the foam-depressing effects of soil somewhat better than the tallow ester, although there is only a little difference after close to full loading. Neither material is as persistent as the commercial anionic surfactant of the high-suds type. The sucrose ester formulations contained no foam booster, but nevertheless performed much more like a high-foaming detergent than a controlled-foamer (130).

Of all sucrose esters tested so far, sucrose monococoate gives the most stable aqueous foam (143). The foaming property of the ester decreases with increase in size of the fatty acid group (124). Sucrose monolaurate and myristate were found better foamers than the palmitate or the stearate. The effect of other surfactants on foaming is discussed below.

A decrease in the foaming of diluted aqueous solutions of sugar esters on standing has been observed (214b). For additional studies on foaming, see References 211 and 214a.

Lime soap dispersion

Lime soap dispersion studies show that sucrose tallowate is similar to other nonionic surfactants and much superior to anionics (Table 15-6). Since sucrose esters can be formulated into solid detergent bars more easily than the conventional polyethylene oxide nonionics, they can be used advantageously in toilet soaps. They can also be used in shampoos, detergents, pesticide emulsions and latices.

Residue in laundered fabrics

Alcohol extraction tests indicate that formulated sugar ester detergents leave less residue in fabrics than soaps. They are as good as commercial anionic detergents in this regard (130).

Surface and interfacial tension

Tests on a number of sucrose monoesters indicate that their surface tension is somewhat lower than that of the common anionic alkyl benzene sulfonates but higher than that of all other nonionic surfactants tested. However, they do not have as high interfacial activity as the anionics (Table 15-7).

The surface activity of sugar esters does not vary with concentration between 1% and 0.05% (124), but rapidly deteriorates at lower concentrations at different critical micelle concentration (CMC) levels (118). The CMC is the lowest concentration at which surface activity starts to fall off. The CMC value for sucrose monolaurate is about 0.02% and for sucrose monostearate less than 0.0005%.

Emulsification properties

Sugar esters are excellent emulsifying agents. A substantial number of lotions, creams, and ointments prepared with the sucrose esters have remained stable after many months of aging (124). In general, the sucrose esters must be employed in combination with more lipophilic emulsifiers (such as the Spans® or glycerol monostearate) to obtain stable emulsions. This behavior is characteristic of synthetic surfactants that are good detergents in aqueous systems.

The comparative data on stability of oil-in-water emulsions in Table 15-8 indicate that sucrose monopalmitate alone is an emulsifying agent of high quality. The tests also show that mixtures of the sucrose palmitate and glyceryl monostearate produce more stable emulsions with both silicone and mineral oils than either emulsifier alone.

Further studies demonstrate that the presence of either sucrose distearate or glyceryl monostearate decreases the stability of preformed mineral oil-in-water emulsions containing sucrose monostearate (121). With adequate concentrations of emulsifier, the stability of milled emulsions passes through a maximum as the ratio of glyceryl monostearate to sucrose monostearate is increased. The experiments suggest that this increased stability results from a decrease in droplet size rather than from the formation of a more tenuous interfacial film.

Emulsion stability depends in large part on the rigidity or compactness of the interfacial film. Because the sucrose moiety of the surfactant molecule is more rigid than the hydrophilic polyoxyethylene groups in conventional nonionic surfactants, it gives a more stable film on the interface. This may partly explain the high interfacial tension values of sucrose esters, as given in Table 15-7.

Wetting

The wetting properties of several fatty monoesters of sucrose (oleate and laurate to stearate) have been tested and compared to those of conventional anionic and nonionic surfactants (124). The tests, conducted according to Draves, indicate that the sucrose esters are only fair wetting agents according to this method of evaluation. The wetting properties decrease with increase in the length of the hydrocarbon chain. Unfortunately, the sucrose esters used in these early tests probably contained large proportions of diesters.

Effect of other surfactants on sucrose esters

The interaction between different surface-active agents is of considerable importance. One surfactant may enhance or destroy the performance of the other. For example, lauryl alcohol improves the foam stability of sodium lauryl sulfate, while polyoxyethylene-base nonionics inactivate phenolic germicides. Accordingly the effect on surfactant properties of one part of sodium lauryl sulfate, polyethylene glycol monolaurate, and lauroyl diethanolamide on nine parts of sucrose ester was investigated (118).

SURFACE TENSION. The CMC value of sucrose monolaurate is lowered somewhat by sodium lauryl sulfate and polyethylene glycol monolaurate, but increased by lauroyl diethanolamide.

FOAM STABILITY. Foam stability is increased by the addition of each of these three surfactants to 0.3% sucrose monolaurate solutions in water. However, at lower concentrations of sucrose ester the tests reveal little or no effect, or a deleterious effect of the other surfactants. For viscosity values and other details, see References 118 and 211.

Addition of larger amounts of surfactant, particularly the anionic sodium dodecyl benzene sulfonate, greatly enhances foam stability (211). Also, unlike other synthetic surfactants, the addition of urea and other foam boosters does not decrease the detergent power of sucrose esters [Nobile, *Ann. Chim. (Rome)*, **53**, 1299 (1963)].

OTHER SURFACTANTS
Sucrose-alkylene oxide adducts

Several adducts of sucrose and alkylene oxides have been tested as surfactants. These compounds are anologs of the commercially important nonionic surfactants made from fatty amines, fatty amides, higher alcohols, and other materials with ethylene oxide or propylene oxide.

BUTOXY SUCROSE. The condensation product of sucrose and butylene oxide has poor surface-active properties (290h).

SUCROSE-PROPYLENE OXIDE ADDUCTS show some surface activity (227). The surface tension is 60 dynes/cm for the adduct with eight moles of propylene oxide per mole of sucrose and 45 dynes/cm for the 48:1 adduct. The tests are carried out with selected fractions in 0.5% aqueous solution. The activity is equally good (45–47 dynes/cm) for products of molecular weight ranging from 400 to 1,400.

Alkyleneoxy adducts of sucrose esters

The purpose of preparing alkyleneoxy adducts of sucrose esters is to increase the resistance of the sucrose esters to hydrolysis under the conditions of manufacture and use. The stability of adducts of up to eight moles of ethylene oxide, propylene oxide, or butylene oxide to sucrose stearate and sucrose tallowate has been tested during crutching (220a, c) and in some cases also in bleaching (220a). Their resistance to hydrolysis is increased somewhat over the unmodified product, but not to the desired level (220a, d). The products foam poorly, probably because of some hydrolysis during the addition reaction in an alkaline medium. Hydrolysis also occurs during the bleaching with hydrogen peroxide (220a).

The ethylene oxide adducts were not sufficiently uniform for further studies (220c). The adducts prepared with four moles of epoxide were homogenous.

The detergency of some of these derivatives is poorer in general than that of the sucrose esters (219). However, in low concentrations (under 0.1% of the total detergent formulation) they have higher soil removal efficiency than many other products tested. Tests on the deposition of residues on the fabric show that propoxylated sucrose tallowate is similar to the unmodified ester (220b).

Cetyloxyethyl sucrose

Cetyloxyethyl sucrose (degree of substitution 3.25) is insoluble in water, and has no detergent properties. Monocetyloxyethyl sucrose is probably a water-soluble compound, with the possibility of good surface activity. However, the monoacetal cannot be prepared (55).

Sucrose-fatty acid carbamates

Sucrose fatty acid monocarbamates with C_{12}–C_{18} chains are prepared by reacting sucrose monocarbamate with the appropriate acyl chloride (290d). Preliminary evaluation indicates that the products are more soluble in water than the corresponding fatty esters of sucrose, and possess similar surface activity. In 0.1% solution they have surface tensions of about 30 dynes/cm, and interfacial tension of 7.2–8.4 dynes/cm.

Fatty acid derivatives of sucrose di- and higher carbamates are prepared similarly. Their water solubility, surfactant foaming and emulsification properties have been determined (290e).

These carbamates are probably not pure compounds, as discussed under sucrose carbamate resins.

Dodecylbenzene sulfonyl sucrose

Dodecylbenzene sulfonyl sucrose can be prepared in yields up to 47% (290h). The material shows good stability in acids and alkalies, low surface tension (31 dynes/cm in 0.1% aqueous solution), low interfacial tension (6 dynes/cm in 0.1% aqueous solution), good foam stability in the absence of soil, and rapid wetting of canvas duck. Detergency, foam stability in the presence of soil, and emulsification properties are fair to poor.

Sulfated dodecylbenzene sulfonyl sucrose

This product has surfactant properties similar to those of the neutral alkylaryl sulfonyl ester, except that the sulfonate gives slightly better foam stability in the presence of soil, and shows slightly greater emulsification power (290h).

Lauryl sulfonyl sucrose

The surface-active properties of monolauryl (dodecyl) sulfonyl sucrose are quite favorable (292). In aqueous solution the product has good surface tension (30–31 dynes/cm in 0.1%–0.01% solution), good wetting action, moderate foaming, and inadequate detergency on cotton in built formulations. For details, see Reference 292.

A material with excellent foaming power has also been isolated from the reaction of sucrose with a commercial acylating agent, Alkanol TL® of duPont (199). The agent contained 50% lauryl sulfonyl chloride, free sulfonic acid, and unreacted hydrocarbons. Some inversion of sucrose occurs during the reaction.

Glucose sulfates and other surfactants from glucose

Several surfactants from glucose have been prepared by methods described in the literature and tested for their surfactant properties (129g, h). Among these are lauryl, cetyl, stearyl, and nonyl phenyl glucoside sulfates, and condensation products of nonyl phenol and glucose.

Monolauryl sucrose and other long-chain alkyl ethers of sucrose

Monoalkyl sucroses with fatty alcohol chains of C_8 to C_{18} have been prepared and tested for surface activity (196a). As Table 15-9 shows, the surface tensions of the 0.1% aqueous solutions of octyl and decyl sucrose are lower than those obtained with the majority of commercial surface-active agents. However, the problem of low solubility in water must be overcome by modifying these ethers to obtain more hydrophilic products.

α-Hydroxy-δ-nonyl benzyl sucrose

This derivative of benzyl sucrose is a condensation product of nonyl phenol, formaldehyde, and sucrose:

$$C_9H_{19}-\!\!\bigcirc\!\!-OH + HCHO \longrightarrow C_9H_{19}-\!\!\bigcirc\!\!-OH$$
$$\qquad\qquad\qquad\qquad\qquad\qquad\qquad\qquad | $$
$$\qquad\qquad\qquad\qquad\qquad\qquad\qquad CH_2OH$$

$$ROH + C_9H_{19}-\!\!\bigcirc\!\!-OH \longrightarrow C_9H_{19}-\!\!\bigcirc\!\!-OH$$
$$\qquad\qquad | \qquad\qquad\qquad\qquad\qquad\qquad\qquad | $$
$$\qquad\quad CH_2OH \qquad\qquad\qquad\qquad\qquad CH_2OR$$

The product, obtained in up to 30% yield, shows good foaming. However, no quantitative tests have been carried out.

Alkanolamines

The high boiling amine fraction from the reductive aminolysis of sucrose contains alkanolamines, which can be reacted with fatty acids to give salts or amides. These products show good stabilizing properties for oil-in-water emulsions (244). They have also been suggested for cutting oil bases, corrosion inhibitors, and asphalt wetting agents. Other well known uses of commercial alkanolamines are in shampoos, household and industrial detergents, and waving lotions.

Piperazines

Di-N-substituted piperazines (U. S. Patent 2,508,652) and ethylene oxide derivatives of piperazines (U. S. Patent 2,574,407) are claimed as good dispersants and emulsifiers by the Colgate Palmolive Co.

Table 15-1
Applications of sucrose ester surfactants

Application	Properties
Food uses	– Not toxic
Instant food	Good foamers in drying process for instant food
Bread and cake	Good antistaling on low dosage
	High volumes, excellent grain and texture
Frozen desserts	Excellent emulsifier, with good balance in rate of development of overrun and dryness
Solid flavor concentrates, fats, margarine	Emulsifier
Confectionary coating	Excellent gloss retention
Washing fruits, vegetables	Good detergents for dirt removal
Poultry feed	
Nonfood uses	
Household and industrial detergents	Good detergency
	Easy biodegradability
	Good lime-soap dispersion
	Foaming poor, but can be improved with foam boosters
Cosmetics and toiletries	Good emulsifier
	Good solubilizer
	Good emollient
	Non-irritating
	Non-toxic
	No loss of activity of preservatives
	No tackiness, soft feel
	Gelling
Pharmaceuticals	Improves absorption of drug without accumulation of cholesterol in blood
	See also, Cosmetics and Toiletries
Pesticide emulsions	Good emulsifier
Lubricants	Thickening
	Detergency
Fuel oil	Antisludging
Paint	Good emulsification in small concentrations
	Good integration into the sucrose oil-based paint or other system
	No toxicity

Table 15-2
Composition of sucrose ester surfactants (130)

	Coco ester	Tallow ester	Tall oil ester	Stearate ester	Laurate ester
1. % Alcohol soluble	47.1	97.6	93.3	92.5	83.3
2. % Moisture and volatiles	49.7	0.6	0.3	0.3	2.0
3. % Non-volatile and insoluble in alcohol (100-line 1-line 2)	3.2	1.8	6.4	7.2	14.7
4. % Free fatty acid	1.2	0.5	0.5	0.3	1.5
5. % Soap	1.8	0.6	5.5	0.4	3.4
6. % Ester (line 1 − line 4 − line 5)	44.1	96.5	87.3	91.8	78.4
7. % Total fatty acid isolated	20.3	42.3	46.2	52.5	42.7
8. % Fatty acid combined as ester (line 7- line 4- acid equivalent of line 5)	17.5	41.2	40.6	51.8	38.1
9. M.W. of fatty acid	227	278	276	276	196
10. % Fatty acid in ester (100 × line 8/line 6)	39.6	42.7	46.5	56.5	48.6
11. Mono ester/diester ratio–a	100/0	100/0	98/2	43/57	41/59
12. Found saponification equivalent of alcohol soluble material (line 1), corrected for free acid (line 4) = sap. equiv. of ester (line 6)	518	598	569	492	408
13. Mono ester/diester ratio–b	85/15	98/2	86/14	45/55	45/55

a–Calculated using the found % fatty acid (line 10) and the theoretical values for % fatty acid in sucrose mono ester and diester (based on the experimentally determined MW of the fatty acid).

b–Calculated using the found saponification equivalent (line 12) and the theoretical values of saponification equivalents for sucrose mono ester and diester (based on the experimentally determined MW of the fatty acid).

The esters were analyzed with standard methods recommended by the Foundation (143).

Table 15-3
Soil accumulation tests of sucrose ester *v.* other detergents (130)

Detergent	Reflectance at end of 5 cycles 95% confidence level	
	Soil removal	Redeposition
Series 1. Sucrose tallow and coco esters		
Committee LAS	714.3 ± 2.0	765.9 ± 1.4
Fatty alcohol sulfate, 25	736.3 ± 2.6	782.1 ± 2.5
Sucrose tallow ester, 25	731.2 ± 2.5	798.7 ± 0.7
Sucrose coco ester, 25	725.1 ± 2.4	790.2 ± 0.9
Series 2. Sucrose tall oil and laurate esters		
Committee LAS	685.4 ± 3.1	744.8 ± 1.4
Sodium alpha-sulfo myristate, 25	690.0 ± 2.3	761.6 ± 1.6
Sucrose tall oil ester, 25	691.6 ± 3.9	771.6 ± 2.5
Sucrose laurate ester, 25	689.6 ± 3.5	767.7 ± 1.4
Series 3. Effect of lowered concentration		
Committee LAS	734.9 ± 3.1	768.1 ± 0.7
Fatty alcohol sulfate, 10	743.4 ± 2.9	771.0 ± 4.6
Sucrose stearate ester, 25	748.4 ± 2.4	788.2 ± 2.0
Sucrose stearate ester, 10	737.5 ± 1.6	786.5 ± 1.1
Sucrose tallow ester, 10	737.0 ± 2.7	781.2 ± 2.3
Sucrose tallow ester, 5	742.8 ± 2.6	780.7 ± 0.9
Sucrose tall oil ester, 10	731.6 ± 4.4	781.6 ± 2.0
Series 4. Sucrose stearate and tallow esters and various alkyl benzene sulfonates		
Committee LAS	704.6 ± 3.1	770.8 ± 2.9
LAS-C, 20	703.2 ± 3.3	787.6 ± 2.0
LAS-B, 20	726.2 ± 3.7	793.8 ± 1.9
ABS, 20	714.8 ± 4.2	791.8 ± 2.9
Commercial detergent	705.8 ± 2.1	766.4 ± 1.3
Sucrose stearate ester, 20	712.0 ± 2.2	803.0 ± 1.7
Sucrose stearate ester, 20 crutched	710.5 ± 3.3	801.3 ± 2.0
Sucrose tallow ester, 5	714.9 ± 3.3	791.6 ± 2.0

Except for Committee LAS and Commercial detergent, all others were formulated with 40 parts sodium tripolyphosphate, 6 parts sodium silicate, 1 part carboxymethyl cellulose, and 5 to 25 parts surfactant and filled to 100 parts with sodium sulfate (28 to 48 parts). Committee LAS of the American Association of Textile Chemists and Colorists and the Commercial detergent branched dodecyl benzene sulfonate) both contain about 19% anionic surfactant and the above ingredients.

The analyses of sucrose esters are given in Table 15-2.

The tests were conducted on soiled cloths as described by Schwartz and Berch (*Soap Chem. Spec.* **39** (5), 78 (1963)]. All were run in 150 ppm synthetic hard water, using five washing soiling cycles; each washing was run at 60°C for 10 minutes. The concentration of total formulations in all runs was 0.4%. The results are presented as actual reflectance readings on the Reflectometer at the end of the fifth washing. For more details, see reference.

Table 15-4

Comparative dishwashing tests of sucrose esters and other detergents (273)

Detergent	Suds end point (no. of plates washed)	Soil removed end point (no. of plates washed)
10% Active sucrose tallowate	0 to 1	16
Commercial detergent – a	4 to 5	12
Committee LAS – a	6 to 7	12
10% active fatty alcohol sulfate	0 to 1	12

a – Contains 19% anionic surfactant (branched chain alkylbenzene sulfonate in commercial product, linear chain in LAS).

Plates soiled with a mixture of 50% flour, 48% Crisco ®, 2% oleic acid, and 0.5% Oildag ® (colloidal graphite). Washed by hand in 4 liters of bath at 0.1% concentration of total formulation, at a water hardness of 150 ppm and temperature of 155°F (46°C). The detergents were also used in pollution studies (see Text).

Table 15-5

Foam behavior of sucrose esters *v.* a commercial detergent (130)

Wt. of soiled towels added and elapsed time after addition	Commercial detergent			Sucrose tallow ester			Sucrose laurate ester		
	Height of suds cm	Coverage	Suds consistency	Height of suds cm	Coverage	Suds consistency	Height of suds cm	Coverage	Suds consistency
Initial mixing with									
no fabric	14-15 – a	Full	Lacy	15	0.75	Lacy	15	Full	Lacy
1 lb—1 min	5.5	Full	Creamy	3-3.5	0.75	Creamy	6.5-7	0.9	Creamy
2	5.5	Full	Creamy	3-3.5	0.875	Creamy	6.5-7	0.9	Creamy
2 lb—1 min	4	0.875	Creamy	1	0.9	Creamy	5-6	0.875	Creamy
2	4	0.875	Creamy	1	0.9	Creamy	5-6	0.875	Creamy
3 lb—1 min	4	0.875	Creamy	0.5—1	0.9	Creamy	4	0.875	Creamy
2	3	0.66	Creamy	0.5-1	0.9	Creamy	3	0.75	Creamy
4 lb—1 min	2.5	0.66	Creamy	0.5-1	0.75	Creamy	1.5	0.75	Creamy
2	2.5	0.66	Creamy	0.5-1	0.875	Creamy	1.5	0.75	Creamy
5 lb—1 min	2.5	0.66	Creamy	0.5	0.875	More lacy	0.5	0.625	Creamy
2	1.5	0.5	Creamy	0.5	0.875	More lacy	0.25	0.875	Creamy
6 lb—1 min	1.5	0.5	Creamy	0.5	0.5	More lacy	0.25	0.333	Creamy
2	1.5	0.5	Creamy	0.5	0.5	More lacy	0.25	0.5	Creamy

a – 15 cm is the distance to top of machine.

The sucrose ester formulations for this test contain 20 parts surfactant, similar to the Commercial detergent (see Table 15-3 for detergent composition). 150 g of total detergent formulation was dissolved in about 12 gallons of water, the "high level" on the washing machine. The approximate concentration of detergent formulation in the wash liquor was 0.33%. Six pound loads of soiled towels were laundered at 126°F. For more details, see reference.

The analysis of sucrose esters is given in Table 15-2.

Table 15-6
Lime soap dispersion properties of sucrose esters (130)

Detergent	Dispersion number – a	Dispersion value, in % – b	
		At 0.1% conc.	At 0.02% conc.
Sucrose tallowate	10 to 20	Less than 10	Less than 10
ABS – c	50	30	40
Nonionic – d	10 – e	Less than 10	Less than 10

a – According to Harris, J. C., "Detergency Evaluation and Testing", Interscience, N.Y., 1954.
b – According to Knowles, et al. [*J. Am. Oil Chemists' Soc.* **29**, 158 (1952)].
c – Low salt content. Relatively poor lime soap dispenser.
d – Nonylphenol-10 ethylene oxide. Good lime soap dispenser.
e – Lowest value tested.

Table 15-7
Comparative data on surface and interfacial tension values of sucrose esters of fatty acids and other surfactants (123)

Sucrose monoester and other surfactant	Surface tension at 0.1% conc., dynes per cm	Interfacial tension at 0.1% conc., dynes per cm – a
Sucrose laurate	33.7	7.9
Sucrose myristate	34.8	7.0
Sucrose palmitate	33.7	6.2
Sucrose stearate	34.0	7.7
Sucrose oleate	31.5	5.0
Tall oil-polyoxyethylene condensate	41.0	7.2
Polyoxyethylene-polyoxypropylene condensate	48.0	16.1
Tween 20 ®	37.0	7.5
Tween 40 ®	41.0	10.5
Tween 60 ®	44.0	11.5
Tween 80 ®	42.0	11.0
Sodium dodecylbenzene sulfonate – b	29.4	2.0

a – Against Nujol ®. b – Reference 124

NOTE: Tests were conducted with aqueous solution at room temperature in a duNouy tensiometer. The monoesters were claimed to be of high purity, but probably contain diesters and possibly other esters also. Tweens ® are nonionic polyoxyethylene derivatives of fatty acid-sorbitol condensates.

Table 15-8
Stability of oil-in-water emulsions of sucrose ester emulsifiers (124)

Emulsifying agent, %		10% Silicone oil in water – a		10% Mineral oil in water – a	
Sucrose monopalmitate	Glyceryl monostearate	2 hours	3 days	2 hours	3 days
1.0	0.0	4	4	3	4
0.75	0.25	1	2	3	4
0.50	0.50	1	2	3	4
0.25	0.75	3	3	1	1
0.0	1.0	3	4	3	4
Sodium dodecylbenzene-sulfonate, 1.0%		4	4	4	4
Tall oil-polyoxyethylene condensate, 1.0%		4	4	4	4

a – 1 = Complete emulsification, no creaming; 2 = Creaming, no coalescence; 3 = Partial coalescence; 4 = Emulsion completely broken.

Table 15-9
Surface tension of monoalkyl sucroses at 25°C (196a)

Compound	Concentration in water, %	Surface tension, dynes/cm
Water	—	71.4
Octyl sucrose	0.1	27.4
Decyl sucrose	0.1	28.2
Lauryl sucrose	0.3	37.1
	0.2	37.6
	0.1	38.6 – a
	0.05	38.9
	0.025	39.7
	0.0125	43.8

a – 42.0 at 0°C.
NOTE: Palmityl and stearyl sucrose were insoluble in water even at very low concentrations. They formed white emulsions with a surface tension of 37 to 45 dynes/cm.

16

Surface coatings

SUCROSE esters of unsaturated fatty acids and allyl sucrose ethers are film-forming materials for potential use in coatings. In addition, sucrose and other sugars can be used as modifiers in carbamate-formaldehyde and melamine-formaldehyde coating resins.

SUCROSE FATTY ESTERS

Sucrose esters of unsaturated fatty acids, also called sucrose oils, are promising vehicles for surface coatings with many desirable properties, for both oleoresinous and water systems. Among these are:

In oleoresinous coatings
—Faster drying rate than conventional drying oils
—Low oxygen absorption
—Good tensile strength, adhesion, and humidity resistance
—Ready compatibility with common coating resins
—Good pigment wetting
—High pigment loading
—Good gloss and hardness (at the level of commercial modified alkyds)

In latex coatings
—Ease of preparation of stable emulsions
—Good film properties of selected copolymers
—Homogeneous latex structure

Coatings based on sucrose oils should prove competitive if evaluation and economic studies continue to be promising. Additional work is also necessary to standardize the transesterification process for the manufacture of the desired sucrose ester. Styrene-modified sucrose esters are especially promising. They combine the durability, hardness, water resistance, and fast air-drying of styrene with the good vehicle properties of sucrose oils.

As shown in Table 16-1, unmodified sucrose linoleates and linseedates are useful in sur-

192

face coatings of both the oleoresinous and latex types. Of particular importance is their high compatibility with commercially important resin vehicles, as demonstrated in Table 16-2.

The degree of substitution can be tailored to the requirements of the particular application. Ideally, the octaester would probably perform best either in unmodified form as a drying oil or in copolymers with styrene. However, the octaesters are difficult to prepare economically on a commercial scale, and less highly substituted esters must be used.

Unmodified sucrose drying oils

FILM DRYING. Tack-free air-dried films are formed from products with an average degree of esterification exceeding three (142). Films of sucrose oils with an ester content of 5.6 to 7.1 dry tack-free in 2.0 to 3.5 hours (141). As figure 16-1 shows, all sucrose linoleates and linseedates with a degree of substitution of 4.0 to 6.1 dry more quickly than linseed oil.

In general, the drying rate is enhanced more by increasing degree of substitution than by iodine value. Esters with the same iodine value, but different fatty acid composition may have different rates. Oils with a high content of stearate dry slowly (141). For details on drying tests, see Reference 43.

OXIDATION. The rate of drying is directly proportional to the oxygen absorption of a compound. The oxygen uptake of thin films of sucrose oils has been studied both by volumetric measurement of absorbed oxygen and by weight gain (Figure 16-2). The sucrose oil (Curve 4), unlike bodied linseed oil (Curve 3), shows almost no gain in weight after the sudden initial rise after exposure to the atmosphere. This quick drying is only on the surface.

This "case-hardening" in thick films can be prevented by bodying the sucrose esters by blowing them with oxygen or by raising the iodine value of the fatty acids beyond the minimum for good thin film performance (141). Sucrose esters with a degree of esterification lower than six absorb less oxygen than the higher esters (20). Their rate of oxygen absorption during the initial period is also less than that for the higher esters. The amount of absorbed oxygen also depends somewhat on the method of refining.

TENSILE STRENGTH, HARDNESS, AND ADHESION. The tensile strength, hardness, adhesion, and humidity resistance of all sucrose oils are generally superior to those of linseed oil. However, alkyd resins have better tensile strength (141). These properties of the esters are shown in Table 16-3. For details on tests for hardness and adhesion, see Reference 43.

ALKALI RESISTANCE. The alkali resistance of sucrose oil films is tested by immersion in 1% sodium hydroxide solution. The linoleate ester of 7.1 substitition is unattacked for 60 hours. At that point it whitens. It becomes embrittled at 120 hours and blisters after 180 hours. Hexaesters are less resistant. About 50% of the sucrose oil saponifies in seven hours at 58°C with sodium hydroxide (141).

PIGMENT OIL ABSORPTION. The critical oil absorption by pigments is good. A composite sucrose ester gives the following values, expressed in grams of oil per ten grams of pigment (141):

Rutile TiO$_2$	3.4
Phthalocyanine green	11.3
Iron blue, Milori	10.6
Toluidine red	10.2
Lampblack	29.4

N

Figure 16-1
Film hardening rates of sucrose esters and linseed oil (20)

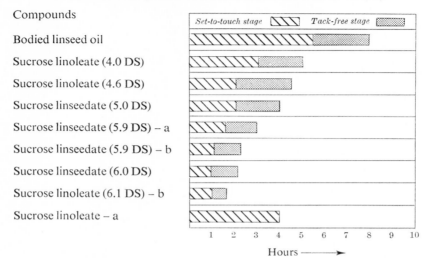

Condition of drying: 2–3 mil oil films, 23°C, 70% relative humidity
DS = Degree of substitution
a – Purified by methyl alcohol extraction.
b – Purified by silica gel absorption.

Figure 16-2
Oxidation rates of films of sucrose hexalinseedate and linseed oil (20)

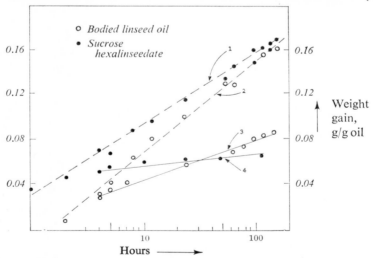

Curves 1 and 2- Absorption measured by volumetric method in pure oxygen, as described by Shelton [*Ind. Eng. Chem.* **36**, 728 (1944)].
Curves 3 and 4- Absorption measured by weight gain in atmospheric drying at 70% relative humidity at 23°C. The lower values in the weight gain method are caused by the loss of volatile matter.

EFFECTS OF PROCESS VARIATIONS. The film properties of sucrose linseedates made by the pyridine-acid chloride process are given in References 198, 257, and 263. In general, their properties are comparable to those of commercial linseed oil but inferior to those of alkyds. However, these sucrose oils have poorer properties, in particular less stable viscosity and a different pattern of oxygen absorption, than those made by transesterification (141).

RELATED PROPERTIES. For such properties as compatibility, solubility, and emulsification, see Fatty Esters, page 52.

Oxidized sucrose oils

Oxidation or "blowing" of sucrose oil is an important step preceding the copolymerization with styrene or other vinyl monomers. It serves to improve the compatibility of the sucrose oil by adjusting the peroxide number and degree of unsaturation.

The oxidation of hexalinoleate has been carefully studied (21, 23). Air is bubbled through the esters at 50°C or 80°C. Temperatures over 100°C decompose the oils and slow the increase in peroxy content. The optimum peroxide value for styrenation is between 400 and 650. Below a value of 400 the styrene interpolymer tends to be cloudy. Above 650 the polymer is clear, but the reaction with styrene is violently exothermic and difficult to control on a large scale.

Addition of an activator such as α, α'-azobisdiisobutyronitrile reduces the time required to get a given peroxide value by more than half. The color of the blown hexalinoleate oil is improved from the initial rating of 9 to a value of 7-8 on the Gardner scale. The viscosity at 77°F increases from 0.5 poise to 2 poise.

The detailed data on the oxidation process, change in viscosity, conversion time, and stability are given in Reference 47.

Films made from blown oils are tougher and more rubbery than those produced from nonoxidized sucrose oils of equal degree of esterification. Blown films dry without a catalyst and give a better "through dry" in thick films. The color of films from blown oils is as good or better as that from unoxidized oils. Data on stability of films of the blown penta-, hexa-, and heptaesters are given in References 21 and 47.

Oleoresinous styrene copolymers

Oxidized sucrose hexalinoleate with a peroxide value of 400 to 650 forms clear and compatible interpolymers when reacted with up to 40 parts of styrene per 100 parts of oil in the presence of organic peroxides at temperatures up to 125°C (23). No solvents, auxiliary initiators or moderators, or other special additives are needed in the process. The resinous vehicle formed in the reaction is not a true copolymer but probably an organosol of polystyrene very finely dispersed in the sucrose ester.

The product can be thinned with mineral spirits. The clear, flexible films obtained by evaporation of the solvent have good gloss and hardness and a rapid drying rate.

For more details on the preparation and properties, see Reference 38.

Styrene copolymer latices

Emulsion polymerization of sucrose oils with styrene gives copolymer latices. The ratio of styrene to sucrose oil is 0.33:1 to 3:1 (21). Potassium persulfate is the catalyst, and sucrose monolinoleate or potassium laurate the emulsifier. The conversion is higher when oxidized sucrose oil is used. The detailed data are given in Reference 47 on the chemistry, quality and quantity of reactants, degree of esterification, peroxide number, choice of emulsifier and catalyst, analysis, control, viscosity, and other properties of the products.

The films formed from these latices are rated poor to good. The good film is obtained by reacting 25 parts of sucrose heptalinoleate (peroxide number 500) with 75 parts of styrene with 58% conversion. The minimum temperature required to form continuous bright films is about 200°F. Most of these films have good water resistance.

STYRENE BUTADIENE copolymers similarly prepared have better film properties. The latex particles in these products are very homogeneous and of excellent texture. These copolymers form clear, bright films of rubbery character even at room temperature. They are the most promising sucrose oil-based coating vehicles of the latex type (21, 47).

Urethane coating oils

Several types of urethane oils can be formed from sucrose tetra-, penta-, or hexaesters (23). One type is made by reacting diisocyanates in stoichiometric proportions with the reactive hydroxyl functions of the sucrose esters. These products form films by oxidative polymerization, similar to drying oils. The second type is produced with excess diisocyanate so that the resulting urethane is capable of further polymerization. The third type uses a two-package system consisting of (a) the sucrose ester and (b) an intermediate with free isocyanate functions. For the preparation of such urethanes, amine catalysts and some metal promoters are preferably used.

In general, sucrose esters can be converted to urethane oils in about the same way as esters of other drying oils. Several compositions show promising properties. For example, sucrose tetralinoleate gives a urethane film which resembles those made with castor oil (47). The best films are preferably made by the two-package system. However, the products are brittle and often yellow and have only fair water-resistance. Further work is necessary to develop a more competitive product by a well-controlled simple process.

For details on the chemistry, process, and film properties, see Reference 47.

Comparison with linseed oil and alkyds

The unmodified synthetic sucrose drying oils are superior to natural drying oils of the same fatty acid content and often equal to alkyd resins with respect to solubility, drying, and film-forming properties. The styrene-modified sucrose oils are competitive in properties with styrenated alkyds.

UNMODIFIED SUCROSE OILS. Comparative properties of (a) sucrose linoleates and linseedates and (b) linseed oil have been studied in considerable detail (20). The coating properties of these esters, linseed oil and alkyd resins are given in Reference 141.

In general, the *drying rate* of thin films of sucrose oils is equivalent or superior to that of alkali-refined natural linseed oil at degrees of esterification over 6 and a total iodine value of 135 or more. If the iodine value is increased to 150, the sucrose esters are equal or better than alkyd resins. However, the subsurface drying rate of sucrose oil films is only average compared to that of natural drying oils (141).

The *solubility* characteristics of sugar hexaesters are approximately the same as those of bodied linseed oil (20). The sucrose esters are *compatible* with all resins which tolerate bodied linseed oil. They also have superior compatibility with urea, phenolic, acrylic, and nonoxidizing alkyd resins (Table 16-2).

Sucrose esters generally show a greater initial rate of *oxygen absorption* than linseed oil (141). The lower uptake in the late oxidative period (Figure 16-2, Curve 3 and 4) shows that sucrose esters case-harden or dry on the surface to produce a more effective diffusion barrier to oxygen than bodied linseed oil. The high drying rate of sucrose oils (Figure 16-1) and their lower oxygen demand than linseed oil is an important practical advantage.

HARDNESS, ADHESION, and TENSILE STRENGTH of sucrose ester films are superior to those of linseed oil (Table 16-3), but alkyds have higher initial gloss and hardness (141). However, the *humidity resistance* of the sucrose esters is equal to that of alkyds (141) and superior to that of linseed oil (Table 16-3).

The *alkali resistance* of highly substituted (7.1) sucrose oil films is equal to that of alkyds. All sucrose oils surpass blown linseed oil in this respect. However, the *rate of saponification* of sucrose oils is higher than that of linseed oil (141).

THE CRITICAL PIGMENT VOLUME CONCENTRATION of a composite ester is equal to that of the best alkyds (141).

MODIFIED OILS. The interpolymer of sucrose oils with up to 40% styrene forms films with gloss and hardness superior to those of unmodified drying oils. The hardness and drying rate of these films resembles those of commercial styrenated alkyds (23, 38).

Commercial development

The status of commercial development and testing of sucrose drying oil esters by such potential users as producers of paints, plastics, plasticizers, and intermediates is summarized in Reference 201.

ALLYL SUCROSE

Highly substituted allyl sucrose ethers and some of their copolymers have been tested as air-drying oleoresinous coating and as additives to up-grade natural drying oils. The preparation and properties of allyl sucrose are discussed under Allyl Ethers, page 23.

Oleoresinous coatings

Allyl sucrose ethers with a degree of substitution between six and seven form coatings with good resistance to organic solvents, oils or heat. The coatings can be applied to wood, metal, glass, paper, fabrics, and other substrates to improve their tensile strength and grease-proofness. Addition of plasticizers or resins to such coatings imparts greater flexibility and thereby minimizes cracking or crazing of films (170).

For the preparation of coating solutions, allyl sucrose is blown with oxygen to obtain a partially polymerized product with a refractive index of 1.4950-1.4955 and a peroxide number over 150. The coating is laid down from solutions of the blown product in toluene, turpentine, or other organic solvents. The film dries tack-free in 60 to 90 minutes at room temperature and completely polymerizes in about a week (170). A drier, such as 0.1% of a cobalt soap, should be included. Curing is more rapid at elevated temperatures without a drier (170) or in the presence of vapors of sulfur chloride or dichloride (114).

Weathering tests show generally good resistance to radiation, but a high degree of water permeability (169).

The coating properties of allyl sucrose prepared by the improved method have also been investigated (248).

Styrene copolymers

Copolymerization of allyl sucrose ethers with styrene yields a product that has better water resistance than allyl sucrose alone (165). A high conversion of styrene is obtained when blown allyl sucrose with a peroxide number of 50-60 is copolymerized with 50% styrene (containing 30% α-methylstyrene) at 125°C in the presence of 0.5-0.65% peroxide catalyst, preferably t-butyl peroxide or cumene peroxide. Films dried in air or baked at 150°C have excellent resistance to boiling water. Films cured for one hour at 100°C have superior overall resistance to solvents.

Upgrading drying oils

Allyl sucrose has been suggested as a possible additive to upgrade linseed, soybean and other drying oils (50, 167). All natural oils except tung and oitica dry more slowly than allyl sucrose. Copolymers of drying oils with 10-50% allyl sucrose have reduced drying time, improved hardness, and greater resistance to solvents. The reaction proceeds at temperatures around 100°C in the presence of oxygen (blowing) and paint driers. The clear copolymers are soluble in organic solvents.

Addition of allyl sucrose also reduces the gelation time of oils (50, 167). As Figure 16-3 shows, it increases considerably the viscosity of soybean and boiled linseed oils as well.

Tests have been carried out to determine whether the addition of drying oils in minor amounts upgrades allyl sucrose, particularly in its film-forming properties (310). The water resistance of films formed in this way is somewhat better than that of the oil-free product. Gelation time, compatibility, viscosity, film formation, and other properties of these mixtures are given in Reference 310.

Commercial evaluation

The evaluation of allyl sucrose by industrial companies in coatings, printing ink, and other related uses is summarized in Reference 310.

SUCROSE CARBAMATE-FORMALDEHYDE RESINS

Films of sugar carbamate-formaldehyde resins laid down on glass or metal surfaces from aqueous solutions show poor water resistance. Films cured at 135°C are transparent and hard. Some dry almost tack-free. All disintegrate completely in water within 90 minutes (249). These resins are made from mono- and dicarbamates by the two-step process.

Resins made in one step show more promising water resistance. Several experiments have been carried out to improve this property (228b). Best results are obtained when the resin is modified with melamine and cured at 150-160°C in the presence of phosphoric acid as accelerator. Films of such resins withstand water for 96 hours.

Figure 16-3
**Change in viscosity of allyl sucrose-oil mixtures during blowing with
oxygen at 100°C (167)**

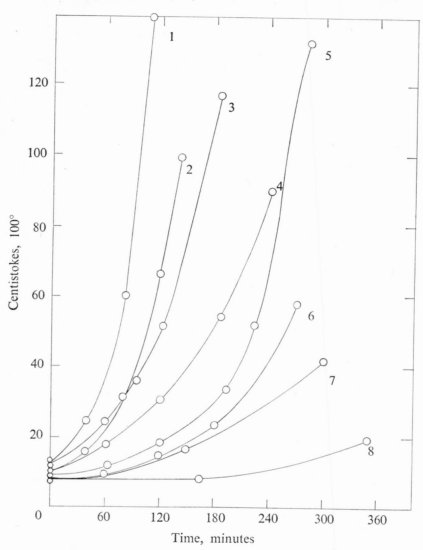

Curve 1 – Allyl sucrose
    2 – 50% Boiled linseed oil, 50% allyl sucrose
    3 – 50% Dehydrated castor oil, 50% allyl sucrose
    4 – Boiled linseed oil
    5 – 60% Soybean oil, 40% allyl sucrose
    6 – 50% Raw linseed oil, 50% allyl sucrose
    7 – 80% Soybean oil, 20% allyl sucrose
    8 – Soybean oil

SUCROSE-MODIFIED MELAMINE-FORMALDEHYDE RESINS

Melamine-formaldehyde resins are important vehicles in enamels for such applications as automobiles, refrigerators, washing machines, metal furniture, toys, kitchen cabinets, and hospital equipment. These resins are often modified with alkyds, which serve as plasticizers. They are also etherified with butyl or ethyl alcohols to reduce the water sensitivity of the resin and to improve its solubility in organic solvents. Etherification occurs on the free hydroxyl (methylol) groups in the melamine-formaldehyde condensate. The etherified resins form very hard, clear coatings after baking at 140-160°C.

Sugars have been tested as modifiers for melamine-formaldehyde resins (307c). The hydroxyl groups of the sugar could either take part in etherification, react with the amino groups, or combine through transesterification. Invert sugar has been thoroughly investigated as a modifier but sucrose, glucose, fructose, corn syrup and other sugars can also be employed. In general, the nature of the sugar has little effect on the performance of the melamine coating.

The performance properties of invert sugar have been evaluated on a variety of melamine-formaldehyde compositions polycondensed by several methods and formulated for different applications. The invert sugar should be added after a short precondensation period, preferably at a level of 20% of the melamine. In clear baking lacquers the finishes modified with invert sugar show no disadvantages in comparison with similar commercial resins. In fact, at low plasticizer levels and high baking temperatures, the sugar-modified clear lacquers have higher hardness and better alkali-resistance than the unmodified control samples.

The properties of the lacquers made from sugar-modified resins are given in Tables 16-4 and 16-5. The melamine-formaldehyde resins are prepared at a constant ratio of one mole of melamine to 47 moles of formaldehyde. The level of sugar is 20% by weight of the melamine. The viscosity of the sugar-modified resin in solution is two to six times greater than that of the control. The modified resin is cloudier, but has less free formaldehyde (0.1-0.4%) than the control (0.7%).

The coating is prepared by adding an alkyd plasticizer to the resin solution at a ratio of 3:1 based on resin solids. For the pigmented lacquers, the ratio of pigment to total solids is 1:1. The lacquers are thinned with xylene and butyl alcohol, sprayed on steel panels, and baked at 145°C for 20 minutes.

Table 16-1
Linoleates and linseedates of sucrose as surface coatings

Degree of substitution of sucrose	Modification	Remarks
Oleoresinous paint		
6-7	None	Coatings are of the drying oil type. Thin film properties generally superior to linseed oil. Thick films have poor drying properties. Pretreatment with oxygen gives tougher film with better through-drying.
4-5	Reaction with iso-cyanate to urethane	Some compositions promising.
5-6	Bulk copolymeriz-ation with styrene	Superior to unmodified drying oils in film quality. Competitive in properties with commercial alkyds.
Latex paint		
5-6	Emulsion poly-merization with styrene	Low to medium grade latex vehicle.
7	Emulsion copoly-merization with sty-rene-butadiene	Promising latex vehicle.

Table 16-2
Compatibility of sucrose hexalinseedate and bodied linseed oil with commercial resin vehicles (20)

| Trade name | Other film forming resin | Compatibility Range (% by weight) of oils with resin in: | | | |
| | | Air dried films | | Baked films | |
		Linseed oil	Sucrose oil	Linseed oil	Sucrose oil
Acryloid ® F-10	Acrylic copolymer	10-20* & 60-100*	0-100*	0-10* & 90-100*	0-10 & 00-000*
Duraplex ® D65A	Oxidizing alkyd-70% oil	0-100	0-100	0-100	0-100
Duraplex ND78	Non-oxid. alkyd-43% oil	0- 20*	0- 10 & 40-100*	0	0- 10 & 00-100*
Dow X ®-2633	Epoxy-novolac	60- 70* & 80-100	0- 20* & 80-100*	60- 70* & 80-100	0- 20* & 30-100
Epon ® 812	Epoxy polyether	0-100	0-100	0-100	0-100
Epon 828	Epoxy polyether	0	0	0	0
Epon 1004	Epoxy polyether	0	0	0	0
Parlon ® S-20	Chlorinated rubber	0	0- 10*	0	90-100*
Parlon S-125	Chlorinated rubber	0	0- 10	0	0
Bakelite ® BR9400	Phenolic	40-100	0-100	40-100	40-100
Pliolite ® S-5A	Cyclized rubber	0	0-100	0	0
Vinylite ® VAGH	Vinyl copolymer	0	10- 20* & 40-100	0	80-000*
Uformite ® F240	Urea resin	70- 90	0-100	70- 90	00-000

*Compatibility in this range is uncertain—film is somewhat hazy.

Table 16-3
Film properties of sucrose esters and linseed oil

Test and reference	Sucrose linoleate – a	Sucrose linseedate – b	Linseed oil
Tensile strength (141)			
Tensile, psi			
Air dried	280	—	110 – c
Air dried and baked	560	—	180 – c
Elongation, %			
Air dried	130	—	100 – c
Air dried and baked	120	—	95 – c
Microknife hardness and Adhesion (20)			
Hardness, gm			
On aluminum	400	325	180
On tin	125	325	100
On bonderized steel	250	250	225
Clearance, mils			
On aluminum	10	9	11
On tin	6	9	10
On bonderized steel	7	7	9
Adhesion, 100/A – d (141)			
On aluminum	200	200	122
On tin	186	201	100
On bonderized steel	223	223	167
Effect of humidity (141)			
Adhesion, 100/A – d			
Before exposure			
Unpigmented	360	—	346 – c
Pigmented to 16% PVC with TiO_2	176	—	—
After 21 day exposure – e			
Unpigmented	332	—	Failed
Pigmented	176	—	—

NOTE: The film thickness in these tests ranges from 0.6 to 1.5 mils. The films are dried in the presence of 0.05% cobalt or 0.5% lead naphthenate.

a – Degree of substitution ranges from 6.1 to 6.5.
b – Degree of substitution is 5.9.
c – Alkali refined linseed oil. All other tests with bodied linseed oil.
d – $A = $ clearance/hardness$^{\frac{1}{2}}$
e – At 35°C, 95% relative humidity.

Table 16-4
Properties of clear baking finishes made from sucrose-modified melamine resins (307c)

Additive	Gloss	Appearance	Pencil hardness	Scratch resistance, g	Alkali resistance – a		
					1	2	3
None	Good	Good	6H	2150	5H	3B	5B
Invert sugar	Good	Slightly yellow	6H	2550	5H	4B	Peeled
Sucrose	Good	Good	6H	2350	5H	5B	Peeled
Glucose	Good	Slightly yellow	6H	2625	5H	4B	Peeled
Fructose	Good	Slightly yellow	6H	2525	5H	4B	Peeled
Corn syrup	Good	Good	6H	2300	5H	3B	6B – b
Commercial butylated resin	Good	Good	6H	2350	5H	2B	6B – b

1 – Initial hardness   a – In 50 % sodium hydroxide solution.
2 – After 96 hours   b – Peeled slightly.
3 – After 144 hours

Table 16-5
Properties of pigmented baking finishes made from sucrose-modified melamine resins (307c)

Additive	None	Invert Sugar	Sucrose	Glucose	Fructose	Corn syrup	Commercial butylated resin
Gloss	Good	Matte	Semi	Matte	Matte	Matte	Good
Appearance	Good	Slightly yellow	Good	Slightly yellow	Slightly yellow	Slightly yellow	Good
Pencil hardness	9H	9H	9H	9H	9H	9H	9H
Scratch resistance, g	3550	3800	3025	3800	3700	3400	3525
Resistance to hot detergent – a							
After 10 min	No effect	No effect	No effect	No effect	No effect	No effect	No effect
After 30 min	No effect	No effect	No effect	No effect	No effect	No effect	No effect
Resistance to overbaking – b							
Initial,							
Yellow	0.25	0.35	0.15	0.35	0.4	0.1	0.1
Red	0	0	0	0	0.35	0	0
After overbaking,							
Yellow	0.5	0.55	0.5	0.55	0.65	0.4	0.45
Red	0	0.35	0	0.3	0.45	0	0
Resistance to UV light – c							
Yellow	0.4	0.35	0.25	0.35	0.35	0.35	0.4
Red	0.2	0.25	0.1	0.2	0.2	0.1	0.1

a – 0.5% "Tide ®" solution at 75°C.
b – Two hours at 160°C. In Lovibond Tintometer readings.
c – After exposure to Std. No. 8 of BS. 1006 Lovibond Tintometer readings.

17

Food and feed additives

INVERT SUGAR

INVERT SUGAR is used in various foods because of its good moisture retention, high degree of sweetness, high solubility of the fructose component, and particularly its retardation of crystallization in mixtures with sucrose. In confectionery, invert sugar is used to restrict the tendency of candy to dry out and crystallize on standing. It is also used in jellies, canned fruits and carbonated beverages, and in bakery products to keep them soft and prevent cracking.

GLUCOSE

Glucose (commercially called dextrose) and corn syrup (the concentrated hydrolysate of corn starch—commercially called glucose) are most often used in combination with sucrose as sweetening agents in the confectionery, canning, baking, dairy, and beverage industries.

FOOD ACIDS
Lactic acid

Lactic acid is used in foods and beverages. Among its desirable properties in these uses are: mild taste, freedom from masking of other flavors, ability to prevent deterioration of food, and ease of application of the liquid form available. Among the products in which it is used are beer, butter, baked goods, cheese, flavoring extracts, jelly, olives, pickles, sauerkraut, and soups.

Citric acid

Citric acid is the most common acidulant for food products. Its use is similar to that of lactic acid, but it is consumed in far greater quantities.

FLAVOR-ENHANCING AGENTS
Sucrose monoacetate

Sucrose monoacetate has a potential use in flavor enhancement (93). This application is based on the well known phenomenon that products have a stronger fragrance when packed with

206

sugar than when packed in water. Because sucrose monoacetate is less sweet than sugar, its use may be extended in food products where lower sweetness is desirable.

BREAD AND DOUGH CONDITIONER

Various sucrose derivatives have been tested as antistaling agents and bread softeners. Sucrose stearates showed the most promising properties.

Sucrose stearates

Sucrose monostearate retards staling and keeps bread soft at the two levels tested of 0.5% and 1.0% (190). As a bread softener, it appears to be as effective as the conventional glycerol monostearates. It shows the same effectiveness as polyoxyethylene stearate in retarding staling in terms of crumb compressibility. However, it is poorer in improving dough quality in respect to larger loaf volume. In comparative tests sucrose distearate shows the poorest qualities in both antistaling and softening (190). Later studies (Pomeranz, Y., Shogren, M. D., and Finnoy, K. F., Cereal chem., **46**(5) 503–518 (1969).) show that sucrose esters have a considerable potential in enhancing the loaf volume of breads made with non-wheat flours and protein supplements.

Later experiments indicate that it is the distearate rather than the monoderivative that shows antistaling activity (195). However, baking tests with British flour show that the overall conditioning properties of the sucrose stearates are inferior to those of commercial glyceryl monostearate (195).

Detailed theoretical studies have been conducted on the interaction of sucrose stearates with starch (28, 29, 30, 276). Like other substances with antistaling activity, these esters form insoluble complexes with starches that are probably significant in conditioning.

Sucrose polyoxypropylene

Sucrose polyoxypropylene is only slightly effective as a bread softener. It is not competitive in properties with the widely used commercial products (189). For these tests, fractions were used of adducts made with 24 and 48 moles of propylene oxide per mole of sugar.

Yeasts

Yeast is an important aerating or leavening agent for a variety of baked products. Fermentation softens and increases the volume of dough, which is more palatable after baking than the unleavened product. Yeast has also been considered in recent years as a food supplement for man and as a feedstuff for animals. Baker's yeast and most of the food yeasts are related to the organism, *Saccharomyces cerevisiae*.

For studies related to sucrose and molasses in the production of yeasts, see Fermentation, page 144.

NUTRIENTS
Fats

Fat is an important nutrient for humans and animals. Its production by fermentation of carbohydrates has been the subject of Foundation research, as discussed under Fermentation, page 144.

Fructose

Pure crystalline fructose is used as a source of calories, primarily for diabetic patients. As a component of invert sugar, fructose is widely used in the baking, candy, and food industries.

ANIMAL AND PLANT FEED ADDITIVES
Ammoniated molasses

The value of molasses itself as a stock feed is well known. Although it possesses very little digestible protein, the nitrogen content can be considerably increased by ammoniation. The nitrogen becomes fixed chemically in the molasses. The product is a good protein extender when used with other feeds containing true protein nitrogen.

Several workers had previously described success in feeding ammoniated molasses to animals (89). Feeding trials have been conducted with cattle, goats, and sheep (78, 89) and pigs, chicks, and rabbits (78) after it was found that trials with water buffalo (89) indicated no toxicity or problems with palatability. Cattle and other ruminants have the power in the rumen to convert non-protein nitrogen into a form that can be assimilated by their digestive systems. Tests with other livestock were carried out mainly to determine the toxicity of the ammoniated molasses.

The feeding trials on ruminants have concluded (89) that:

(a) Some methods of feeding are more favorable than others. In some forms ammoniated molasses is definitely unpalatable, but in others individual animals consume it more readily than molasses.

(b) Although the product has an even higher salt content than molasses itself, it does not cause scouring.

(c) At relatively low concentrations ammoniated molasses can replace some of the natural protein in ruminant feeds without any apparent deleterious effect on the animal.

Further work has been carried out to determine the cause of the toxicity observed in some cases of feeding (78). Pyrazoles and imidazoles of low molecular weight have been found to be toxic and probably are responsible for the hysteria and other toxic reactions. The addition of sufficient quantities of food acids is beneficial in improving palatability. No undesirable toxic symptoms are encountered when they are used. With sheep the digestibility of the dry matter, crude protein and crude fiber are depressed but with goats the digestibility of the crude protein fed is considerably enhanced by the addition of ammoniated molasses.

These experiments were carried out with ammoniated invert molasses from Trinidad with a crude protein equivalent of 30–40%.

Sucrose esters of fatty acids

Sucrose esters of fatty acids have been tested as agents to increase the vitality of transplanted tobacco seedlings (250). Sucrose stearate is poorly soluble in concentrations high enough to provide energy to the seedlings. Sucrose laurate is sufficiently soluble, but toxic to the seedlings.

18

Plastics and polymers

ADHESIVES

Sucrose-modified phenolic resins as plywood glues

THE plywood industry consumes large tonnages of adhesives. Changes in construction have sharply accelerated the demand for exterior plywood by the building industry and also for water-resistant thermosetting adhesives. These adhesives are of the synthetic type, chiefly phenol-formaldehyde resins with a high formaldehyde content.

Sucrose-modified phenol-formaldehyde resins have been developed by the Foundation. Although this work is not complete from the standpoint of standardized commercial adhesive formulations, research results indicate that about one-third of the phenol can be replaced by the lower-priced sucrose without degrading the dry and wet strengths of the plywood adhesive (40, 91, 204).

Table 18-1 shows that the shear strength of the resin is on the level of a good plywood adhesive (200 psi and up) and that the resin is still acceptable after standing for approximately 90 days. The tests are made with plywood strips, according to the standards of the American Society for Testing and Materials and the Douglas Fir Plywood Association. The strips are coated with the resin solution containing 53% resin by weight. The tensile strength measurements are carried out with a Scott Tensile Tester.

Further tests show somewhat lower strength, but still substantially equal to that of unmodified phenolic resin (204). However, additional work to develop commercial adhesive formulations with the resin failed to show any striking improvement or advantage in their use (200).

More details on the adhesive properties are found in References 91, 204, and 259.

Sucrose tritosylate-benzene-1,3-dithiol copolymer

An excellent adhesive for glass is made when this copolymer is plasticized with sucrose octaacetate and thinned with a suitable solvent (264).

Sucrose dimethylolurea resin

This resin has been tested primarily in casting sheets. However, both the unmodified and

o 209

nylon-modified resin show good adhesive properties, particularly for bonding on glass and wood (183j).

2-Tetrahydropyranyl sucrose

The acetal, 2-tetrahydropyranyl sucrose (degree of substitution 6.5), has been tested as an adhesive without success (294a).

Sucrose-modified melamine-formaldehyde resin

Sucrose has been tested as an extender for melamine-formaldehyde adhesives (183a). Although the extended resin cures rapidly, it has poor adhesive properties, and its wet strength is inferior to that of melamine-urea resins.

Urethane resins

The polymer prepared from sucrose and toluene diisocyanate shows promising adhesive properties for wood (306). However, the bonding is very brittle. No attempt has been made to include a plasticizer in the polymer. Attempts to incorporate litharge into the polymer lead to a cement of outstanding quality, but the reaction is somewhat complicated (see below).

Metal compounds of sucrose and its derivatives

Experiments have been carried out to prepare adhesives and cements from the reaction between sucrose or its derivatives and metal compounds, in particular oxides of heavy metals (306). The reaction is based on the well known litharge-glycerol cements. Sucrose reacts under various conditions, but none of the products are comparable to the litharge cement in hardness, strength, and solvent resistance. No useful adhesives have been found. (For details on the reaction, see Metal Derivatives, page 126.)

A number of hard products, some quick-setting, have been prepared, but these lack mechanical strength and are generally disintegrated readily by water. The most resistant products are: (a) the lead salt of the sucrose half-ester of succinic acid, which develops brittleness; (b) the product resulting from the mixture of litharge with molten sucrose octa-acetate, which is readily attacked by organic solvents; and (c) various products from the reaction of litharge with sucrose and toluene diisocyanate. These last are hard and completely water-resistant. They have outstanding adhesion to metal and glass, but are heterogeneous, porous, and extremely difficult to prepare.

Any of the products which appear to have possibilities as adhesives are considerably inferior in water resistance and bond strength to those in use.

FIBERS

PIPERAZINE AND DERIVATIVES. Piperazine or its homologs are promising starting materials in the preparation of synthetic fibers. These compounds are made by reductive aminolysis of sugar. Investigations by duPont have shown that piperazine or 2-methyl piperazine have potential uses in polyamide fibers (British Patent 785,214) and polyurethane fibers (U. S. Patent 2,731,445-6).

Polymerization experiments have also been carried out by the Foundation. These include the unsuccessful preparation of nylon-like products from 2-methyl piperazine adipate, sebacate, terephthalate, and succinate (234 a, c, d) and from the raw reaction mixture containing piperazine, 2-methyl piperazine, and 2,5-dimethyl piperazine (289, 293). However, 2,5-dimethyl piperazine forms a good nylon fiber with dimethyl terephthalate and a urethane fiber with xylylene diisocyanate (183f). The literature indicates that piperazines can be used to modify nylon formulations [*Modern Plastics* **36**, (8), 150 (1959)].

Piperazine fibers are strong, and some have such high melting points that they cannot be spun from melts but require solvents.

2-Tetrahydropyranyl sucrose

The acetal 2-tetrahydropyranyl sucrose (degree of substitution 6.5) has been tested for fiber formation without success (294a).

Sucrose succinate

The half-ester of sucrose with succinic acid reacts with lead acetate to give a white, thermoplastic, water-insoluble material. It can be drawn into fine threads with a metallic luster, but it is brittle (306).

CASTING AND LAMINATING RESINS

Sucrose dimethylolurea resin

Sucrose dimethylolurea resin has been tested as a casting composition. With clay, the best filler, it gives extremely strong and resilient sheets (183i). Addition of up to 10% polyvinyl alcohol greatly increases the thermal stability, tensile strength, and impact strength of the casting resin (183i). The strength of the product increases with the molecular weight of the polyvinyl alcohol, and its compatibility with the rate of hydrolysis of the alcohol (183j).

The strongest resin composition contains nylon and is filled with powdered wood chips (183j). However, the resin has poor water resistance. Boiling in water considerably reduces the strength of the filled, unfilled, or modified resin. Coating with silicone resins improves somewhat the water resistance of the resin sheet. However, addition of nylon to the resin does not improve its water resistance (183g).

Modification with acids and anhydrides decreases the water sensitivity of the resin. For example, a water- and scratch-resistant product is made with phthalic anhydride (183k).

Sucrose-modified melamine-formaldehyde resins

Melamine-formaldehyde resins are widely used in the preparation of decorative laminates. The surface layers of paper sheets are impregnated with a melamine-formaldehyde resin solution and cured during lamination to the core. The core consists of kraft paper impregnated with a phenolic resin.

Melamine laminating resins can be extended with sucrose or invert sugar without detracting from the appearance and properties of the finished laminate (307b). Sucrose can be added in considerably greater quantities than invert sugar, up to 65% by weight of melamine, to give laminates of excellent color, slightly improved stain resistance, and scratch resistance equal to that of laminates made from unmodified resins. The laminates loaded with 65% sucrose have a high gloss, which is not impaired by boiling water for over 30 minutes. At 50% loading, some extraction of sugar occurs under similar conditions. The modified resin is more viscous than the unmodified one, but its viscosity can be reduced by dilution. Addition of invert sugar somewhat reduces the laminating properties. For more details on testing, see Reference 307b.

The slight advantages in performance from the addition of sucrose together with the economic gains may be of interest in this highly price-sensitive market.

Sucrose extended phenolic resins

Although these resins find their main potential application as plywood adhesives, they also show some promise in casting and laminating (259). A casting resin prepared by curing at 120°C for 90 hours is reportedly not attacked by water to any greater extent than an unextended phenolic resin (284, 285-1). The resin contains 25% sucrose by weight. However, in mechanical properties these casting resins are considerably poorer than typical commercial phenolic casting resins (Table 18-2). For additional data, see Reference 285-1.

MOLDING RESINS
Sucrose-modified melamine-formaldehyde resins

A series of tests have been carried out on modifying melamine molding compositions with invert sugar, sucrose, and other sugars (307a). The level of sucrose addition is 20 to 40%, preferably up to 30%, by weight of melamine. The composition contains 35-40% cellulose filler, based on total solids. The powder molded at 142-147°C shows better water-absorption properties than that modified with invert sugar, but only slightly higher values than one modified with corn syrup. The sucrose-modified compositions do not exhibit the temperature sensitivity of invert sugar-modified resins.

The properties of invert-sugar-modified molding compositions have been thoroughly tested, for tensile strength, electrical properties, and temperature-sensitivity. Their properties are not reduced by the incorporation of the sugar, which may be economically attractive as a low-cost extender for such molding powders. Calculations show that, although the effect of sugar addition on the price of the molding material is not substantial, it could be significant in this highly price-conscious market.

Sucrose-acrolein resins

Sucrose-acrolein resins are claimed to make good molding powders (183f). The best molding composition is obtained by mixing 50 parts of acrolein-sucrose resin with 10 parts of methyl cellulose and 10 parts of phloroglucinol.

Sucrose-modified phenolic resins

Sucrose-modified phenolic resins are primarily interesting as adhesives for plywood. However, preliminary tests indicate that they can also be employed as molding resins (259).

Sucrose polycarbonate resins

The resin made by the polymerization of triethoxycarbonyl sucrose has been tested as a molding powder. The resin itself is hard and brittle, and can be broken down to a powder. Hard, tough molded discs are produced under pressure from a mixture of partly polymerized triethoxycarbonyl sucrose with an equal weight of asbestos fiber (148). The discs are cured at 160°C. They are unaffected by chloroform during 24 hours of immersion. Unsuccessful attempts to prepare filled molding powders are reported in Reference 294b.

Cellulosic fillers (cellulose powder, cotton cloth, paper) can be similarly used as fillers, but only after thorough drying or pretreatment with very dilute aqueous sodium bicarbonate (148). This treatment prevents the adsorption on the cellulose of the catalyst required for the final cure.

PLASTIC FOAMS

Urethane foams

Sucrose esters of unsaturated fatty acids can be used as polyol intermediates in the preparation of rigid urethane foams (23). Tetra- and pentalinoleates have both been used in the exploratory experiments, the tetraesters generally with better results than the pentaesters. The foams are prepared by the conventional technique. Although the quality of the foams does not surpass that of commercial products, sucrose esters may be of interest because of their lower price (less than 30¢ a pound), according to preliminary calculations (142) than the presently used synthetic polyol intermediates. Also, the very rapid reaction rate and high degree of crosslinking may be desirable for foamed-in-place plastics or in mix-and-use coating techniques.

For more details on the preparation and chemistry, see Reference 47.

PLASTICIZERS AND MODIFIERS

Some sucrose derivatives are already used as plasticizers. Many others with promising properties are in the developmental stage.

SUCROSE OCTAACETATE is a product of commerce, used primarily as an alcohol denaturant but also as an additive for adhesives.

SUCROSE ACETATE ISOBUTYRATE, also known as SAIB®, made by Eastman Chemical Products, is recommended as an additive for polymers, particularly hot-melt adhesive formulations.

Cyanoethyl sucrose

Heptacyanoethyl sucrose (degree of substitution 7.3) is a clear, viscous liquid with a very high dielectric constant (36.0 at 25°C, 100 cycles) and good volume resistivity (5×10^{11} ohm-cm at 25°C). Its compatibility with other dielectric film-forming polymers suggests the use of this material as a modifying plasticizer in phosphor carriers for electroluminescent components. Cyanoethyl sucrose is made and marketed by Eastman Chemical Products, Inc.

Saturated fatty esters of sucrose

Nine octaesters of sucrose with saturated fatty acids (C_4-C_{18}) have been tested as plasticizers for polyvinyl chloride-acetate copolymers (171). Only the propionyl sucrose is compatible with the resin, but it is less efficient than the widely used dioctyl phthalate.

SUCROSE DISTEARATE has been tested unsuccessfully as a plasticizer for phenolic casting resins (285m). The ester is incompatible with the resin under the conditions tested.

Unsaturated fatty esters of sucrose

The successful modification of sucrose esters of unsaturated fatty acids with styrene suggests the possibility of using these sucrose oils as internal thermosetting plasticizers to modify styrene or other brittle polymers in surface coatings. The hydroxyl functions of the ester may be further utilized for a variety of possible manipulations in formulating vehicles for paints, inks, and adhesives (38).

PRINTING INKS. Sucrose polyesters appear made to order for application as a fast-drying, low-cost, high pigment capacity printing ink vehicle. Further, there is evidence that the important rheological properties of ink can be varied favorably (141).

SEALERS. Sucrose esters can economically replace various alkyd and latex sealers. The oil appears to coat wood surfaces without penetrating excessively, and the low permeability of the dried film should be advantageous (141).

EXTENDERS OR BLENDS FOR ALKYDS. Sucrose ester oils, particularly the lower esters, can serve as extenders for alkyd resins. Incorporation of sucrose oils into typical alkyd resin formulations depends on the heat stability of those oils that permit high-temperature processing. There are indications that this can be accomplished by incorporation of phthalic or maleic acids into the molecule or by the use of sucrose octaester (141).

Ethoxycarbonyl sucrose

Ethoxycarbonyl sucrose has been tested as a modifying agent for polymethyl methacrylate (294b). A 1:1 mixture of monomers gives a transparent colorless resin that decomposes at 160°C.

Lactic acid esters

Lactic esters are efficient plasticizers for vinyl resins. Lactic acid is made by fermentation or alkali degradation from carbohydrates. Butyl lactate adipate is prepared from crude lactic acid, made from molasses by degradation (111, 266). Its plasticizing properties are comparable to those of the pure compound and commercial dioctyl phthalate.

Ethylene diamine

Ethylene diamine, a product of the reductive aminolysis of sucrose, is a well known additive for nonsagging, thixotropic paints. Such paints are thick and gel-like on standing. They become much less viscous on agitation or application, and thicken immediately thereafter.

MONOMERS

Acrylic monomers for plastics

Acrylic monomers can possibly be prepared by the pyrolysis of lactic acid or its derivatives. Lactic acid can be made from sucrose or other carbohydrates by alkaline degradation or fermentation. The conversion of lactic acid and related compounds to the corresponding acrylic ester or acrylonitrile has recently been studied (125, 253). The most promising results are obtained by pyrolyzing lactonitrile in the vapor phase over a phosphoric acid catalyst at elevated temperatures.

Table 18-1
Adhesive properties and shelf life of sucrose-modified phenolic resins (91)

Days	0	60	120
Viscosity, mps	71.7	104.6	197.9
Cure time, sec	88	75	64
Dry strip-shear strength, psi	223	—	225
Wet strip-shear strength, psi	221	205	195

Table 18-2
Properties of sucrose-extended phenolic casting resins (285 1)

Sucrose %	Tensile strength, psi	Compression, psi	Elongation, %	Modulus of elasticity, 10^5 psi
25	165- 335	1,300- 2,200	0.04-0.13	2.7
15	2,400- 2,090	6,300- 7,300	0.23-0.35	7.6-9.3
0	3,000-12,000	13,000-33,600	1.5-2.0	1.3-15

19

Textile Chemicals

SEVERAL sucrose derivatives have been tested as textile processing and finishing chemicals. They have been investigated chiefly in finishing for crushproofing (easy-care) and, more importantly, in modifying the structure of the cellulose fiber by cross-linking.

CRUSHPROOFING

Sucrose carbamate-formaldehyde resin

Sugar carbamate-formaldehyde resins can be applied as easy-care finishes similar to the widely used urea and melamine-formaldehyde resins (218). They impart good dimensional stability to rayon fabrics, and the finish is relatively wash-fast. However, the sugar resins lower wrinkle recovery and increase the stiffness of the treated fabric. They also tend to become yellow under curing conditions, particularly at a high level of add-on.

Oxysucrose-urea resin

The resin can be applied in concentrations of 6% by weight to a cellulosic fabric to produce a wash-fast finish (197). Application is carried out with solutions containing urea and oxysucrose in molar ratios of 2:1 and ammonium chloride as catalyst. The treatment imparts some crease-resistance, but the tensile strength of the fabric is adversely affected, and the color is poor. On the whole, the performance of the resin is poorer than that of the conventional types.

Sucrose-modified melamine resins

Sucrose-modified melamine-formaldehyde resins of varying types have been produced and tested in comparison with unmodified resins in crush-proofing (274). Rayon, cotton and wool fabrics were treated, and their crease and shrink resistance were determined as made, after washing, and in some cases after ironing or prolonged boiling. The resin retained in the fabric was measured and extraction losses compared.

In general, the sugar-modified resins are no more susceptible to loss from the fabric on washing than the unmodified type. In some cases the modified resins are more resistant to leaching than the unmodified. Sucrose-modified resins are no more likely to develop color on

216

ironing than conventional resins. Also, modification with sugar does not affect the chlorine retention of the basic resin.

Of the trimethylol resins produced at a formaldehyde-melamine ratio of 3:1, the best properties are obtained when a relatively short condensation time is employed in the absence of an acid curing catalyst. When sucrose is added before reaction at 10 to 20% by weight of melamine, the modified resin imparts better shrink and crease resistance to rayon fabric after washing than the unmodified resin. The crease resistance of cotton is substantially higher with the modified resin.

By incorporation of 20% sucrose into the methylated hexamethylol melamine resin, the shrink and crease resistance of both cotton and rayon are improved above the level given by unmodified resins.

Details on the preparation of the resins, baths, treatment and evaluation procedures are given in Reference 274.

CROSS-LINKING
Oxysucrose
Oxysucrose has been investigated as a potential cross-linking agent for cellulose (197). The treatment is carried out by the standard method of impregnating cellulose fabric with oxysucrose and an acid catalyst and then heat curing for 15-30 minutes at 130°C. The oxysucrose is decomposed by acid at this temperature to glyoxal.

Methoxymethyl sucrose
When cellulose fibers are impregnated with methoxymethyl sucrose and an acid catalyst and then cured at 130°C, the cellulose is rendered insoluble in cuprammonium solution (197). The product gives a positive test with aldehyde reagent (2,4-dinitrophenylhydrazine). Hydrolysis of the treated cellulose indicates that aldehyde cross-links have been formed between cellulose chains by acetal exchange and that the cross-linking group contains sucrose.

A large number of experiments have led to the following general conclusions: (a) the efficiency of cross-linking increases with increasing degree of substitution of methoxymethyl sucrose. (b) Sulfosalicylic acid is the best catalyst tried. (c) The reaction proceeds best in high concentration. (d) Cotton, mercerized cotton, and viscose rayon all have the same order of reactivity towards the reagent. (e) Fibers are more reactive than fabrics.

The crease resistance of treated samples is increased less than with commercial resins. Treatment is accompanied by a loss of tensile strength 50% higher than with conventional resins. Further research could lead to cross-linked products with desirable mechanical properties, such as rayon fibers for carpeting.

PIGMENTS
Pyromellitic ester of sucrose
The half ester of sucrose with pyromellitic acid gives a brilliant blue pigment when mixed with cupric acetate in pyridine (306). The pigment is insoluble in water, but has considerably lower pigmenting power than Monastral Blue.

Diphenylformazan of invert sugar
Invert sugar reacted with phenylhydrazine can be diazotised to a deep red powder of possible value as a pigment (306).

20

Pharmaceuticals

A FEW derivatives of sucrose have been tested in the field of medicine. Of particular interest is the use of sucrose ester emulsifiers in nutrition to increase absorption of drugs by the body.

Emulsifiers

SUCROSE ESTERS OF FATTY ACIDS. As discussed under Surfactants (page 173), sucrose esters of fats have good properties as detergents and emulsifiers. By lengthening or shortening the hydrophobic moiety, the HLB value can be modified to obtain an ester tailored for wetting, emulsification or other desired use. Sucrose monostearate has been employed as an emulsifier for fats and oils in studies on the absorption of fats and calcium by dogs and humans (152, 301). [See also Turner, *Am. J. Digestive Dis.* **3**, 594, 682 (1958).] Its administration in aqueous solution together with fats increases absorption of the fat and also of calcium.

These experiments indicate that the esters, particularly those of unsaturated fatty acids, could be used as a therapeutic agent in patients suffering from hyperlipemia. Emulsification can be employed similarly in the oral administration of other nutrients and such drugs as antibiotics, hormones and vitamins (301). The higher absorption of these agents in the presence of sucrose esters could reduce the amount of the drug required for the same therapeutical effect [Nobile, *Ann. Chem.* (*Rome*) **53**, 1299 (1963)].

For additional physiological properties and toxicity tests of sucrose esters, see Surfactants, page 173.

Antihistamines

IMIDAZOLE DERIVATIVES. Several ethers of 4(5) hydroxymethylimidazole (see Oxidation Products, page 106) have been tested for antihistamine activity. Of these the two following benzylethers showed promising activity (282). [See also Ruoff and Scott, *J. Am. Chem. Soc.* **72**, 4950 (1950).]

o-Benzylphenoxymethylimidazole, R = I
o-Benzyl-p-chlorophenoxymethylimidazole, R = II

Vasodilator

Mannitol hexanitrate is used as a vasodilator in the treatment of coronary insufficiency and some cases of hypertension.

Vermifuge

Piperazine and its homologs are obtained by reductive aminolysis of sucrose. Piperazine and its derivatives are excellent anthelmintics that are widely used primarily in the veterinary field.

Antitumor agent

Tetramesyl sucrose and *tetramesyltetraacetyl sucrose* have been tested as anticancer agents with negative results (264). (Mesyl esters have been reported in the literature to cause regression of cancerous tumors.)

Suppository base

Because of its favorable melting point (around 35°C), *sucrose hexaacetate distearate* can be used as a substitution for cocoa butter in suppositories. Several such compositions have been prepared (247a).

Germicides

Trichlorodichlorosulfonyl sucrose gives off small quantities of chlorine in a moist atmosphere. It also reacts with sodium iodide in nonaqueous solutions to give sulfur dioxide and iodine, both of which have antiseptic properties (272e).

PHTHALIDYLPIPERAZINES, such as the one made from 2,5-dimethylpiperazine with phthalaldehyde, are claimed to possess good antimicrobial activity. They can be used in germicidal compounds (U. S. Patent 2,834,780).

Manufacture of tablets

MANNITOL is widely used in the preparation of tablets. It is employed as a base in chewable, multilayer, and press-coated tablets of vitamins, antacids, aspirin and other pharmaceuticals. It provides a sweet taste and masks such unpleasant flavors as that of aspirin. Tablets containing mannitol retain little moisture because of its low affinity for water.

Intermediate

ARABONIC ACID. Arabonic acid, an intermediate of vitamin B_2 (riboflavin), has been successfully prepared from invert sugar or molasses (116, 268).

21

Pesticides

A systematic study has been made of the activity of almost 100 sucrose derivatives as herbicides, miticides, insecticides, rodenticides, fungicides, and mold inhibitors (31). Many of these derivatives were made by reacting sucrose with a compound of known biological activity. For example, esters were made of such acids as 2,4-dichlorophenoxyacetic acid (2,4-D), trichlorobenzoic acid, or 2,2-dichloropropionic acid, all of which have herbicidal activity. Several esters of phosphates were also made to obtain analogs of the important insecticide, Parathion®.

In general, these compounds show the types of activity associated with the toxicant moieties. In most cases, the activity of the sucrochemical is much lower than that of the sucrose-free standard. A few are almost equal to the standard inactivity. Special techniques for formulations are required because of the solubility problems of the sucrose derivatives.

Table 21-1 briefly tabulates the sucrose derivatives prepared and tested.

Other carbohydrates

Derivatives of several other sugars have also been tested as insecticides (299a) and fungicides (107; 299b, c, d). These include dithioacetals and other sulfur derivatives of glucose and other sugars and their esters and ethers. None is as effective as the present commercial products.

Table 21-1
Sucrose derivatives as Pesticides (31)

Two general methods have been used for the preparation:
(A) reacting the acyl halide or organic halide with sucrose in pyridine; and
(B) preparation of sodium sucrate, which is then reacted with the halogen compound in ether, benzene, or other inert solvent. In some cases mixtures of

pyridine with other solvents such as chloroform are used, or solvents other than pyridine are employed in procedure A.

The products are solids, some crystalline, or oils. They are analyzed for saponification value, Fehling's test, and elemental analyses of a specific introduced element, such as phosphorus or halogen. However, none of the products has been purified by chromatography or tested by physico-chemical methods. The claimed composition or degree of substitution should thus be accepted with some caution. The products have been screened for some or all of the types of activity listed below, but only positive results are shown in the table. (For more details, see Reference 31.)

SF – Systemic fungicide   M   – Miticide
CF – Contact fungicide   PrH – Preemergence herbicide
R   – Rodenticide   PtH – Postemergence herbicide
I   – Insecticide   MI – Mold inhibitor

Reactant with sugar – a	Preparation	Activity
Esters		
Phosphate and other phosphor esters		
Ethyldichlorophosphate	A, B	
Diethylchlorophosphate (8) – b	A, B	
Dianilinochlorophosphate (8)	A	
Diphenylchlorophosphate – c	A	
Ethyldichlorothionophosphate	B	
bis-Dimethylamidochlorophosphate (8)	A	
p-Nitrophenyldichlorothionophosphate (8)	B	
Dimethylamidodichlorophosphate (8)	A	
Dimethylamidodichlorophosphate + triethyl-phosphate to sucrose pyrophosphate	A	
Thiophosphoryl chloride (8)	B	M
Thiophosphoryl chloride + p-nitrophenate (4)	B	
p-Nitrophenyldichlorothionophosphate (4)	B	
Phosphorus oxychloride + sodium p-nitrophenate (4)	B	
p-Nitrophenyldichlorophosphate (4)	B	
Benzenephosphorus thiodichloride + sodium p-nitrophenate (4) and (8)	B	
Benzenephosphorus thiodichloride (4) and (8)	B	
Benzene-p-nitrophenylchlorothionophosphate (8)	B	
Thiophosphoryl chloride + sodium ethoxide or ethyl alcohol (4) and (8)	B	
Phosphorus oxychloride + ethylene imine	B	
Fatty ester		
o-Chlorophenoxyacetylchloride (8)	A	PrH, PtH
2,4-Dichlorophenoxyacetylchloride (8) and (3)	A	PrH, PtH

Table 21-1 *continued*

Reactant with sugar – a	Preparation	Activity
Trichloroacetyl chloride (8)	A	PrH
Trichloroacetyl chloride (3)	A	
2,4,5-Trichlorophenoxyacetyl chloride (8) and (4)	B	
Dichloroacetyl chloride (5) – c	A	
α-Naphthylacetyl chloride (8)	A	
Fluoroacetyl chloride (8) and (4)	B	R
Chloroacetic anhydride (8)	A	
4-Chloro-2-methylphenoxyacetyl chloride (4)	B	PrH, PtH
α, α-Dichloropropionyl chloride (4)	B	PrH, PtH
2(2′,4′-Dichlorophenoxy)-propionyl chloride (4)	B	
2,4-Dichlorophenoxyacetyl chloride (1) and (2) – d	B	PtH, PrH
Pentachlorophenoxyacetyl chloride (4)	B	
α-α-Dichloro-2,4,5-trichlorophenoxyacetyl chloride (3)	A	
Sodium chloroacetate (4)		
Sodium chloropropionate		
Undecylenoyl chloride (2) – e	B	
Propionyl chloride	A	
Acetic anhydride – f	A	
Sulfonic acid esters		
Trichloromesyl chloride (8)	A, B	
Mesyl chloride (8) – f	A	
Tosyl chloride (8) – f, g and (3) – h	A	SF or CF
Benzoates		
2,4-Dichlorobenzoyl chloride (8) and (3)	A	
m-Nitrobenzoyl chloride (8)	A	
p-Nitrobenzoyl chloride (8) and (3)	A	
3,4-Dichlorobenzoyl chloride (8) and (3)	A	
2,3,6-Trichlorobenzoyl chloride (1) and (4)	B	
Other esters		
Carbon disulfide to xanthate	(i)	
Diethylthiocarbamyl chloride to thiocarbamate (8)	B	
Diethylcarbamyl chloride to carbamate (8)	B	
Sucrose amine + carbon disulfide to dithiocarbamate	(i)	
Diphenylcarbamyl chloride to carbamate (4)		
Diethylchloroarsenite (4)	B	
Chloroethylchlorosulfinate – j	B	
Dimethyltindichloride (4)	B	
Octaethoxycarbonyl sucrose + ethylamine to carbamate		

Reactant with sugar – a	Preparation	Activity
Sulfuryl chloride to di- and trichlorosulfonyl sucrose – k	A	
Ethers		
2,4-Dinitrochlorobenzene		
Cyanuric chloride	B	
2,4-Dichlorobenzyl chloride (4)	B	
Chloranil (4)		
Sodium α, α-dichloropropionate (4)	B	PrH, PtH
Dichloral urea (4)	B	
Hexachlorobenzene	B	
Tri-β-chloroethylamine	B	
Sodium α, β-dichloro-2-methylpropionate	B	
Allyl bromide – f		
Polymers		
Phosphorus oxychloride	A, B	
Thiophosphoryl chloride	A	
Acetals		
Chloral + propionaldehyde	(1)	PrH
α, β-Dichloro-2-methyl propanol	(1)	
Metal derivatives		
Copper sucrate – m		SF or CF

a – Numbers in parentheses give the claimed degree of substitution.
b – Of the several preparations, one was claimed to be an octaester, and one with poor analysis was prepared from trityl sucrose instead of sucrose.
c – Reacted with trityl sucrose.
d – Only the monoester is active. Octahydroxypropyl sucrose was also reacted with the acid chloride by method A; product had no activity.
e – Made from dipotassium sucrate. One sample also prepared by transesterification of sucrose with the methyl ester.
f – Tested as a rodenticide; had no activity (299a).
g – Showed some activity as a fungicide (299b)
h – Tested as a fungicide; had no activity (299b).
i – Prepared in water in the presence of metal salts.
j – Reaction product unstable; decomposed with SO_2 formation.
k – Tested as an insecticide and herbicide; no activity (272e).
l – Prepared in dioxane in the presence of phenolsulfonic acid catalyst.
m – Particularly those with high copper content showed fair fungicidal values (299c, d). Compounds are made from sucrose with cupric sulfate.

22

Chelating agents

CHELATING AGENTS

M<small>ANY</small> carbohydrates and some of their derivatives are good chelating agents for metallic ions. Sucrose itself has low complexing power, particularly for iron and nickel. Mannitol, sorbitol, glucose and fructose are more powerful chelating agents than many commercial products, and the tetracarboxyalkyl ethers of sucrose are promising sequesterants (Figure 22-1).

Metal chelates are used in many fields, particularly agriculture. In plant and animal nutrition, deficiencies of the essential trace elements cause serious problems—for example, iron chlorosis in plants. The high cost of commercial chelates such as EDTA or closely related compounds greatly restricts their use in agriculture. (See "Symposium On the Use of Metal Chelates in Plant Nutrition", The National Press, Palo Alto, Calif., 1956.)

Other potential uses include the purification of metals by the elimination of the contaminant through the chelate, such as the removal of molybdenum from uranium pitchblende (U. S. Patent 2,840,452, Atomic Energy Commission); removal of harmful catalysts from industrial products; and preparation of detergent compositions. Mannitol has been used as a component of soldering fluxes because it will dissolve metal oxides. The use of chelates in analysis is discussed under Analytical Chemistry, page 229.

Sucrose, mannitol, sorbitol, and other carbohydrates

Polyhydroxy compounds have long been known to form chelates with many polyvalent metallic ions (31). Soluble chelates are obtained chiefly in strongly alkaline media.

The chelating power of mannitol and some other carbohydrates has recently been tested (31). Mannitol forms water-soluble complexes with ions of copper, titanium, zirconium, lead, iron, cobalt, nickel, and other metals. No soluble chelates are obtained with silver, calcium, barium, cadmium, and mercury. As Figure 22-1 shows, mannitol, dulcitol and sorbitol are extremely strong complexing agents for ferric ions. Fructose and glucose chelate copper quite strongly.

The chelation of metal ions with mannitol, glucose and sucrose has also been studied in

224

Figure 22-1
Chelating power of sugars and sugar alcohols (296)

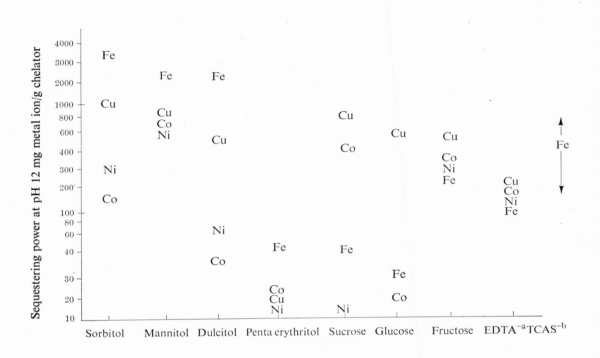

FE = Ferric ion, Cu = Cupric ion, Ni = Nickel, Co = Cobalt
For exact values see Reference 31 and References in footnote b.
a – Ethylene diamine tetraacetic acid.
b – Tetracarboxyalkyl sucrose (237b, c, e; 277). Value based on gram of reacted sucrose.

P

conditions where the metallic ion forms an insoluble salt—namely, in the presence of sulfate, halide, chromate, benzoate, iodate, oxalate, and sulfite ions (279). Except for oxalate, which forms complexes even in the absence of mannitol, no other complexes are formed.

The chelation of ferric ion has been particularly well studied (279). In mannitol solutions of at least 0.5% concentration, iron forms chelates at all pH values above 8. The chelation of iron with tosyl and benzoyl esters and acetals of mannitol and sorbitol has also been studied (279). The esters form complexes only after hydrolysis begins at pH12.

The complexes of sucrose, mannitol, and other carbohydrates with inorganic oxy acids useful in analysis are discussed under Analytical Chemistry, page 229.

Carboxyalkyl sucroses

Sucrose compounds have been synthetized that are structurally analogous to the well-known agents of the polyaminocarboxylic acid type such as ethylenediamine tetraacetic acid, EDTA.

Ferric chelate of EDTA   Ferric chelate of carboxyalkyl sucrose

Carboxyalkyl sucroses should show good chelating properties since a maximum of 16 atoms in the octaderivative are theoretically available for co-ordination, as compared with six in EDTA.

TETRACARBOXYETHYL SUCROSE is a good sequestrant for ferric ion but a poor one for calcium. The chelating value ranges from 275 to 358 mg ferric ion per gram of sucrose at pH7 (237b). Preparation of products with capacities of up to 600–620 mg per gram of reacted sucrose has been also reported (237e, f, g). These products were usually tested without isolating the compound from the aqueous hydrolysis mixture of sucrose and acrylonitrile. The chelating value decreases in acidic media because of lactonization (237b) and in highly alkaline media because of decomposition (237d).

In neutral media the iron chelating value of the tetracarboxyethyl sucrose is equal to or better than that of some commercial iron sequestrants—for example, Permakleer of Refined Products Corp. (237g). However, in basic media, particularly at pH values greater than 11, the sucrose derivative has sharply decreasing values while the commercial sequestrants are only slightly affected (237g). The shelf life of the sucrose product is also poorer, and it can be stored safely only at a pH about 10 (237b).

Similar chelating values are obtained for products made from raffinose and its mixtures with sucrose. Molasses is an economical source for these mixtures (237b). The sequestering values of carboxyethyl sucroses with lower or higher substitution are lower than that of the tetracarboxyethyl sucrose (237f, g).

TETRACARBOXYMETHYL SUCROSE. Tetracarboxymethyl sucrose has a chelating value of up to 430 mg of ferric ion per gram of sucrose (237a). The chelating value appears to be less sensitive to lower pH values than that of the tetracarboxyethyl sucrose (237c). The compound apparently does not easily form lactones.

Additional examination has shown that tetraderivatives prepared through tetrasodium sucrates are not well defined compounds. Fractions purified by adsorption on ion-exchange resin had a chelating power of 160 mg ferric ion per gram of chelating agent (277).

PENTACARBOXYMETHYL SUCROSE. A well defined and carefully analyzed crystalline trimethyl ester derivative has been prepared that has a chelating power of 12 mg iron and 12.6 mg calcium per gram of ester at pH 9.15 (277). The value increases to 20 mg when the ester is heated in alkaline solution (pH 12.5) at 95°C for 40 minutes.

SUCROSE SULFATES. Sucrose sulfates and their barium and sodium salts do not show any promise as chelating agents for iron at pH7 or at pH10 (283a).

OTHER SEQUESTERING AGENTS. The reductive aminolysis of sucrose in diethanolamine yields tetraethanol ethylenediamine and tetraethanol propylenediamine. According to the patent literature, these compounds can be converted into sequestering agents of the ethylene-diamine type (289).

HUMECTANTS

In addition to *sorbitol* and *invert sugar*, the industrially important humectants in the candy, tobacco, textile, and paper industries, other sucrose derivatives also show promising properties.

Sucrose monoacetate

Sucrose monoacetate is a very hygroscopic material. Its water sorption is higher than that of sorbitol and lower than that of ethylene glycol and glycerol. The comparative water absorption and desorption data are given in References 93 and 242. Sucrose monoacetate has been recommended as a humectant to replace sorbitol (93). It absorbs almost 60% more water by weight than sorbitol and does not lose all the water absorbed even after being kept over sulfuric acid for two months. It picks up and loses moisture slowly, which is important for products that should not change much in weight under different atmospheric conditions.

Sucrose-ethylene oxide adducts

Compounds obtained by reacting sucrose with up to 11 moles of ethylene oxide show a high water absorption on the level of glycerol (94). For detailed comparative data, see Reference 288.

INDUSTRIAL ETHYL ALCOHOL

The major part of the industrial alcohol produced in the United States has been made until recent years by fermentation of black-strap molasses. This material consists of the residues after the extraction of the crystallizable sugar from evaporated sugar cane juice. It contains from 50 to 60% sucrose, partly in inverted form. Industrial alcohol can also be produced from other starchy and cellulosic materials. Today it is mostly made from ethylene.

GAS ABSORBENTS

Enthanolamines are widely used as acid gas absorbents. Such amines are produced as by-products in the reductive aminolysis of sucrose. Tests have been carried out with the fractions that contain alkanolamines. They show good affinity for carbon dioxide (289). The aqueous solutions of the undistillable residue also show good gas absorption, but their capacity decreases after two or three cycles (293). Both the absorbent and the absorbed gas can be regenerated by heating.

REMOVAL OF STARCH IN SUGAR REFINING
OR IN OTHER INDUSTRIAL PROCESSES

The mono- and distearates of sucrose form water-insoluble complexes with starch (28, 29, 30, 276). A potential use for this reaction is the removal of small amounts of starch in the presence of high concentration of sucrose. For example, exploratory tests show that sugar cane juices containing about 15% sucrose and 0.025% wheat starch can be refined with sucrose stearate (300). Addition of 0.002% sucrose monostearate removes a large portion of the starch. Degraded wheat starch and starches with a very low concentration of amylose, such as waxy maize starch, cannot be removed as successfully.

23

Analytical chemistry

SOME of the important analytical methods developed by the Foundation are summarized below.

Analysis of reducing sugars

REDUCTION WITH SODIUM BOROHYDRIDE. A new method for the quantitative determination of reducing sugars has been developed (137). The method is based on the ability of sodium borohydride to reduce quantitatively the reducing sugars. It is much simpler than the conventional analysis, which involves oxidation with an alkaline reagent under closely controlled conditions of concentration and temperatures.

VOLUMETRIC METHOD WITH COPPER SALT. A very accurate method has been developed for measuring micro and macro quantities of reducing sugars, especially invert sugar, in the presence of sucrose. The method is a modification of that formerly developed by Shaffer, Hartman and Somogyi. It consists of the volumetric determination of cuprous oxide produced by the reduction of cupritartrate by the reducing sugars under carefully selected conditions (13, 62, 63, 64).

Quantitative analysis of traces of sucrose

Sucrose can be converted into a mildly volatile derivative by reaction with trimethylsilyl chloride (41). The resulting *octa(trimethylsilyl) sucrose* is volatile and can be hydrolyzed to sucrose with water at elevated temperature. The silyl derivatives of sucrose and other carbohydrates are used in gas chromatography for the separation and estimation of carbohydrates.

The process has been further developed by Hedgley and Overend (*Chem. Ind.* **1960**, 378) and later by Sweeley and co-workers (*J. Am. Chem. Soc.* **85**, 2497 (1963)) for the separation and determination of almost 100 carbohydrates.

Metal complexes in the analysis of sugar

The studies on complexing sucrose and other carbohydrates with metal ions (see Chelating Agents, page 224) has led to the development of a number of analytical methods. They are

229

based on differences in the complexing ability of carbohydrates with inorganic materials, particularly oxyacids. These differences can be advantageously used in the analysis of sugars by electrophoresis and also by chromatography. The technique can be extended to the analysis of mixtures of the oxyacids, such as tungstates and molybdates (5).

PAPER ELECTROPHORESIS OF SUGAR. Molecules or ions which have a net charge or which can be given one by simply controlling the pH of their environment migrate in an applied electrical field as anions or cations according to the properties of their functional groups. Sugars and related polyhydroxy compounds do not have a charge. However, in electrolytes containing a variety of inorganic oxyacids, anionic complexes can be formed by reaction between the acid ions and the formally neutral compounds. Structurally different carbohydrates have different complexing properties and consequently different charges. The charge also depends on the type of electrolyte solution in which electrophoresis is conducted.

Paper ionophoresis of carbohydrates was carried out in solutions of borate (33), molybdate (4, 5, 6, 27, 32, 33, 34), tungstate (4, 6), arsenite (33), and sodium hydroxide (33). Borate and arsenite complex best in alkaline media while molybdate and tungstate form complexes under acidic conditions.

Electrophoresis in molybdate (34) and tungstate (4) solutions has revealed that only those compounds migrate that have the cis, cis-1,2,3-triol configuration. Thus good separation is achieved in these solutions between glucose, fructose, and mannitol (27, 34); 2-, 5-, or 6-substituted sorbitols, 4-substituted sorbitols, and 3-substituted sorbitols (27, 34); substituted fructoses from one another and from fructose (33); and pentoses and hexoses from the corresponding alcohols (32).

The technique can also be used for the determination of the position of the glycosidic linkage in oligosaccharides (6, 27). The migration rates of sugars and their derivatives and related polyhydroxy compounds are given in the references. Sucrose is a poor complex-former which shows little or no migration compared to other sugars in electrolytes such as molybdate (33, 34), borate, arsenite, and sodium hydroxide (33).

For an excellent recent review, see H. Weigel, "Paper electrophoresis of carbohydrates", in *Advances in Carbohydrate Chemistry*, **18**, Academic Press, New York, 1963.

Electrophoresis and chromatography of carbohydrates

A preliminary investigation has been carried out to separate sucrose, other carbohydrates, and their derivatives by electrophoresis or by adsorption on basic ion-exchange resins (209). The method is based on the difference in the ionization constants of the carbohydrates in alkaline medium.

24

Selected general references on sucrose

There are few publications dealing exclusively with sucrose. These primarily are books on the technology of manufacture and analysis, and several booklets on uses. The chemistry of sucrose is generally discussed with other carbohydrates.

CHEMISTRY

The carbohydrates—chemistry, biochemistry, physiology. Edited by Pigman, W. Academic Press, N.Y., 1957. 902 p. (New edition in preparation.)

A comprehensive treatise on carbohydrates, particularly monosaccharides.

The Oligosaccharides. By Stanek, J., Cerny, M., and Pacak, J. Academic Press, N.Y., 1965, 567 p.

Translation of the Czech work on structure, synthesis, reactions, and analysis of sucrose and other lower polysaccharides. Sucrose, as the most important oligosaccharide, is generously discussed.

Contemporary carbohydrate chemistry. By Davidson, E. A. Holt, Rinehart and Winston, N.Y., 1966.

Introduction to the chemistry of carbohydrates. By Guthrie, R. D. and Honeyman, J. Oxford University Press, N.Y., 1964.

Introduction to carbohydrate chemistry. By Overend, W. G. and Ferrier, R. S., Oldbourne Press, London, in prep.

Reaction mechanisms in carbohydrate chemistry. By Foster, A. B., and others. American Elsevier, N.Y. In prep.

Advances in carbohydrate chemistry, 23 volumes, 1945–1968. Editors of recent volumes, Wolfrom, M. L. and Tipson, R. S. Academic Press, N.Y.

Major publication reviewing important novel research work on carbohydrates. Each volume contains several papers written by well-known authorities.

Methods in carbohydrate chemistry. Whistler, R. S. and Wolfrom, M. L. Five volumes, 1962–1964. Academic Press, N.Y.

A serial publication on the analysis, preparation, and reactions of carbohydrates. Also volumes on major products, cellulose and starch already covered.

231

TECHNOLOGY

Selected recent sources are:

Principles of sugar technology. Edited by Honig, P. Three volumes: Vol. 1, Properties of sugars and non-sugars, 1953; Vol. 2, Crystallization, 1959; Vol. 3, Evaporation, centrifugation, grading and classification of sugars and molasses, 1963. American Elsevier, N.Y.

Introduction to cane sugar technology. By Jenkins, G. H. American Elsevier, N.Y., 1966.

Beet sugar technology. By McGinnis, R. A. Reinhold Publishing Corp., N.Y., 1951. (New edition in prep.)

Spencer-Meade cane sugar handbook. By Meade, G. P. John Wiley, N.Y., 1963. Ninth edition.

USE

Use of sugars and other carbohydrates in the food industry. American Chemical Society, 1954. (ACS Monograph 12.)

The utilization of sucrose. By Wiggins, L. F. Sugar Research Foundation, N.Y., 1950. (Technol. Report 7.)

Sugar and sugar by-products in the plastics industry. By Long, L. Sugar Research Foundation, N.Y., 1949. (Technol. Report 5.)

Sugar and sugar derivatives in pharmacy. By Pittenger, P. S. Sugar Research Foundation, N.Y., 1947. (Scientific Report 5.)

Industrial fermentations. Edited by Underkofler, L. A. and Hickey, R. J. Two volumes. Tudor Publishing Co., N.Y., 1953–1954.

Chemical compounds formed from sugars by mold. By Gould, B. S. Sugar Research Foundation, N.Y., 1947. (Scientific Report 7.)

PERIODICALS

All major periodicals including *Sugar Industry Abstracts* are abstracted by *Chemical Abstracts*. In addition to the selective list below, papers on carbohydrates, particularly those on pure chemistry (synthesis, reactions, analysis, etc.) appear in such general journals as the *Journal of the American Chemical Society*, *J. of the Chemical Society*, *Canadian J. of Chemistry*, and similar publications. *Carbohydrate Research*, an international journal started in 1965, is dedicated to sugar research.

The sugar periodicals primarily report on sugar technology, food uses, and trade news and less frequently on research. Selected journals in English are:

Carbohydrate Research. Elsevier Publishing Co., Amsterdam. Monthly.

International Sugar Journal. Leighton, D., editor. High Wycombe, Bucks., England. Monthly.

Sugar Journal. Flanagan, W., editor. New Orleans, La. Monthly.

La Sucrerie Belge. Sugar Industry Abstracts. Cope, M. E., editor. Published by Tate and Lyle Research Center and Raffinerie Tirlemontoise, Keston, Kent, England and Tirlemont, Belgium. Monthly abstract service.

Journal of the American Society of Sugar Beet Technologists. P.O. Box 538, Fort Collins, Colo. Quarterly.

Sugar News. Philippine Sugar Association, Manila, P.I. Monthly.

Sugar y Azucar. Mascaro, M. A., editor. Palmer Publications, N.Y. Monthly. (In English and Spanish.)

South African Sugar Journal. Official organ of the South African sugar industry, P.O. Box 1209, Durban, S.A. Monthly.

MISCELLANEOUS

Patents on the reactions of sugars. By Hunt, M. Sugar Research Foundation, N.Y., 1961.

Abstract of patents on chemistry issued in the period of 1947 *to* 1961. See Technical Report 1, Sugar Research Foundation, 1947, on patents prior to 1947.

Index of Foundation Publications. International Sugar Research Foundation, Bethesda, Md. In preparation.

Lists all publications in topical arrangement. Also contains indexes on authors, subjects, and project correlations of the publications.

Bibliography

ARTICLES, PUBLICATIONS AND PATENTS

1 Agarwal, P. N., Peterson, W. H., Utilization of nonsugar carbon of molasses by food yeasts, *Arch. Biochem.* **20**(1), 59–74 (1949).

2 Agarwal, P. N., Singh, K., King, P. S., Peterson, W. H., Yields and vitamin content of food yeasts grown on different kinds of molasses, *Arch. Biochem.* **14**(1 & 2), 105–15 (1947).

3 Ames, J. B., B.S. thesis, A test of Van't Hoff's principle of optical superposition by observations upon the optical properties of aldonic acid amides, Massachusetts Institute of Technology, Cambridge, Mass., 1948.

4 Angus, H. J. F., Bourne, E. J., Searle, F., Weigel, H., Complexes between polyhydroxy-compounds and inorganic oxy-acids, III, Tungstate complexes of sugars and other cyclic polyhydroxy-compounds, *Tetrahedron Letters* **1**, 55–60 (1964).

5 Angus, H. J. F., Bourne, E. J., Weigel, H., Complexes between polyhydroxy-compounds and inorganic oxy-acids, IV, Dimolybdate and ditungstate ions as complexing agents and paper electrophoresis of maltodextrinols and isomaltodextrinols in molybdate and tungstate solutions, *J. Chem. Soc.* **1964**, 3994–4000.

6 Angus, H. J. F., Bourne, E. J., Weigel, H., Complexes between polyhydroxy-compounds and inorganic oxy-acids, V, Tungstate complexes of acyclic polyhydroxy-compounds, *J. Chem. Soc.* **1965**, 21–26.

7 Arni, P. C., Black, W. A. P., Dewar, E. T., Paterson, J. C., Rutherford, D., Alkali metal derivatives of sucrose, I, Preparation of sodium sucrates, *J. Appl. Chem.* **9**, 186–92 (1959).

8 Barasch, W., M.S. thesis, The preparation and reactions of some acetals of D-mannitol, Massachusetts Institute of Technology, Cambridge, Mass., 1949.

9 Barker, S. A., Brimacombe, J. S., Harnden, M. R., Stacey, M., Silyl ethers of tetra-hydro-2-hydroxymethylpyran, *J. Chem. Soc.* **1961**, 5256–58.

10 Barker, S. A., Brimacombe, J. S., Jarvis, J. A., Williams, J. M., Sucrose derivatives, Part I, Reaction of sucrose with enol ethers, *J. Chem. Soc.* **1962**, 3158–61.

11 Barker, S. A., Brimacombe, J. S., Harnden, M. R., Jarvis, J. A., Sucrose derivatives, Part II, Some silyl and cyano-ethyl ethers and a hepta-acetal, *J. Chem. Soc.*, **1963**, 3403–06.

12 Barrette, J. P., Ph.D. thesis, *p*-Toluene, sulfonyl and anhydro derivatives of sucrose, University of Ottawa, Ottawa, Ont., 1960.

13 Benedict, J. D., M.S. thesis, The reducing powers of a series of sugars as obtained by analysis with the Shaffer-Hartmann-Somogyi reagent, Massachusetts Institute of Technology, Cambridge, Mass., 1947

14 Bernsten, R. A., Ph.D. thesis, The oxidation of glucose and related compounds with oxides of nitrogen, Purdue University, Lafayette, Ind., 1949.

15 Berry, J. F., Turner, D. A., The enzymatic hydrolysis and tissue oxidation of fatty acid esters of sucrose, *J. Am. Oil Chemists' Soc.* 37, 302–05 (1960).

16 Billy, J. M., M.S. thesis, Preparation and structures of sucrose monoesters, University of Ottawa, Ottawa, Ont., 1957.

17 Black, W. A. P., Dewar, E. T., Paterson, J. C., Rutherford, D., Alkali metal derivatives of sucrose, II, Condensation of sodium sucrates with organic halogen compounds, *J. Appl. Chem.* 9, 256–65 (1959).

18 Black, W. A. P., Dewar, E. T., Rutherford, D., Alkali metal derivatives of sucrose, III, The composition of the mono-O-methyl-sucrose prepared from a trisodium derivative, *J. Chem. Soc.*, **1959**, 3073–77.

19 Black, W. A. P., Dewar, E. T., Alkali metal derivatives of sucrose, IV, The problem of firmly bound ammonia, *J. Appl. Chem.* **10**, 134–38 (1960).

20 Bobalek, E. G., Walsh, T. J., Chiang, H. H., Drying oil esters of sucrose, *Offic. Dig. Federation Soc. Paint Technol.* 33, 453–58 (1961).

21 Bobalek, E. G., De Mendoza, A. P., Exploration of some novel recipes for emulsion co-polymerization of sucrose ester drying oils with styrene and styrene-butadiene, *Offic. Dig. Federation Soc. Paint Technol.* 35, 1013–35 (1963).

22 Bobalek, E. G., De Mendoza, A., Causa, A. G., Collings, W. J., Kapo, G., Preparation and properties of linoleate esters of sucrose, Div. of Org. Coatings Plastics Chem., *Am. Chem. Soc.* 22(1), 58 (1962).

23 Bobalek, E. G., De Mendoza, A. P., Causa, A. G., Collings, W. J., Kapo, G., Preparation and properties of linoleate esters of sucrose, *Ind. Eng. Chem., Prod. Res. & Dev.* 2(1), 9–16 (1963).

24 Bonner, T. G., Bourne, E. J., Lewis, D., But-2-enylidene derivatives of glucitol, *J. Chem. Soc.* **1963**, 3375–81.

25 Bonner, T. G., Bourne, E. J., Harwood, S. E., Lewis, D., Butylidene derivatives of glucitol, *J. Chem. Soc.* **1965**, 121–26.

26 Bonner, T. G., Bourne, E. J., Ruszkiewicz, M., The iodine-catalyzed conversion of sucrose into 5-hydroxy-methyl- furfuraldehyde, *J. Chem. Soc.* **1960**, 787–91.

27 Bourne, E. J., Hutson, D. H., Weigel, H., Complexes between molybdate and acyclic polyhydroxy-compounds, *J. Chem. Soc.* **1961**, 35.

28 Bourne, E. J., Tiffin, A. I., Weigel, H., Interaction of anti-staling agents with starch, *Nature* **184**, 547–48 (1959).

29 Bourne, E. J., Tiffin, A. I., Weigel H., Interaction of starch with sucrose stearates and other anti-staling agents, *J. Sci. Food Agr.* 2(2), 101–09 (1960).

30 Bourne, E. J., Tiffin, A. I., Weigel, H., Interaction of sucrose stearate with starch, *Nature* **184**, 110–11 (1959).

31 Bourne, E. J., Nery, E. J., Weigel, H., Metal chelates of polyhydroxy compounds, *Chem. Ind*, **1959**, 998.

32 Bourne, E. J., Huston, D. H., Weigel, H., Paper ionophoresis of carbohydrates in molybdate solutions, *Chem. Ind.* **1959**, 1047–48.

33 Bourne, E. J., Hutson, D. H., Weigel, H., Paper ionophoresis of glucopyranosylfructoses and other substituted fructoses, *Chem. Ind.* **1960**, 1111–12.

37 Bourne, E. J., Hutson, D. H., Weigel, H., Paper ionophoresis of sugars and other cyclic polyhydroxy compounds in molybdate solution, *J. Chem. Soc.* **1960**, 4252–56.

35 Bragg, P. D., Jones, J. K. N., The characterization of tri-O-tosyl sucrose, *Can. J. Chem.* 37, 575–78 (1959).

36 Bragg, P. D., Jones, J. K. N., Turner, J. C., The reaction of sulfuryl chloride with glucosides and sugar alcohols, Part I, *Can. J. Chem.* 37, 1412–16 (1959).

37 Buch, M. L., Montgomery, R., Porter, W. L., Identification of organic acids on paper chromatograms, *Anal. Chem.* **24**, 489–91 (1952).

38 Causa, A. G., M.S. thesis, Interpolymers of styrene and sucrose linoleate, Case Institute of Technology, Cleveland, Ohio, 1962.

39 Chang, C. D., Kononenko, O. K., Franklin, R. E., Jr., Maximum data through a statistical design, *Ind. Eng. Chem.* **52**, 939–42 (1960).

40 Chang, C. D., Kononenko, O. K., Sucrose-modified phenolic resins as plywood adhesives, *Adhesive Age* **5**, 36–40 (July 1962).

41 Chang, C. D., Hass, H. B., Synthesis of a silicone derivative of sucrose, *J. Org. Chem.* **23**, 773 (1958).

42 Chang, W. S., Peterson, W. H., Factors affecting the biotin content of yeasts, *J. Bacteriol*, **58**(1), 33–44 (1949).

43 Chiang, H. H., M.S. thesis, Unsaturated sucrose esters as paint vehicles, Case Institute of Technology, Cleveland, Ohio, 1959.

44 Collins, D. V., Ph.D. thesis, The preparation and properties of derivatives of D-erythrose, Massachusetts Institute of Technology, Cambridge, Mass., 1948.

45 Connors, W. M., Stotz, E., The purification and properties of a triacetic acid-hydrolyzing enzyme, *J. Biol. Chem.* **178** (2), 881–90 (1949).

46 Crank, G., Some Reactions of Sucrose, M.S. thesis, Queen's University, Kingston, Ont., 1960.

47 De Mendoza, A. P., M.S. thesis, The pilot plant synthesis and properties of sucrose linoleate, Case Institute of Technology, Cleveland, Ohio, 1963.

48 Docal, G. C., B.S. thesis, Isolation of fructose from electrolyzed invert sugar, Massachusetts Institute of Technology, Cambridge, Mass., 1945.

49 Docal, G. C. (to Sugar Research Foundation, Inc.), Sugar separation, U.S. Patent 2,567,060 (Sept. 4, 1951).

50 Fisher, C. H., Zief, M., Hockett, R. C. (to United States of America), Modified drying oils, U.S. Patent 2,594,303 (April 29, 1952).

51 Griffin, E. L., Jr., Willard, M. H., Jr., Sinnamon, H. I., Edwards, P. W., Redfield, C. S., Preparation of allylsucrose, *Ind. Eng. Chem.* **43**, 2629–34 (1951).

52 Hall, D. R., M.S. thesis, Preparation and characterization of unsaturated sucrose esters, Case Institute of Technology, Cleveland, Ohio, 1961.

53 Hall, L. D., Hough, L., Carbohydrate carbonates, III, The transformation of some 1,2-isopropylidene-α-D-glucofuranose 5,6-Carbonates into 3,6-anhydro-derivatives, *J. Chem. Soc.* **1963**, 5301–08.

54 Harnden, M. R., M.S. thesis, Some new derivatives of sucrose and tetrahydropyran-2-methanol, University of Birmingham, Edgbaston, England, 1960.

55 Harnden, M. R., Ph.D., thesis, Some new ethers of sucrose and tetrahydro-2-hydroxy-methylpyran, University of Birmingham, Edgbaston, England, 1962.

56 Hass, H. B., Snell, F. D., Osipow, L. I., York, W. C. (to Sugar Research Foundation, Inc.), Novel detergent compositions, U.S. Patent 2,970,962 (Feb. 7, 1961).

57 Hass, H. B. (to Sugar Research Foundation, Inc.), Process for preparing drying oils from sucrose and raffinose, U.S. Patent 2,970,142 (Jan. 31, 1961).

58 Hass, H. B., Snell, F. D., York, C., Osipow, L. I. (to Sugar Research Foundation, Inc.), Process for producing sugar esters, U.S. Patent 2,893,990 (July 7, 1959).

59 Hass, H. B., Skell, P. S. (to Research Corp.), Process for the preparation of piperazines, U.S. Patent 2,978,451 (April 4, 1961).

60 Heidt, L. J., Colman, C. M., Degradation of D-glucose, D-fructose and invert sugar in carbonate-buffered water solutions, *J. Am. Chem. Soc.* **74**, 4711–12 (1952).

61 Heidt, L. J., Moon, K. A., Evidence for pentavalent uranium as an intermediate in the reaction in water between photoactivated uranyl ions and sucrose and closely related substances, and quantum yields for these reactions, *J. Am. Chem. Soc.* **75**, 5803–09 (1953).

62 Heidt, L. J., Southam, F. W., A method employing a carbonate buffered cupritartrate reagent of low pH for estimating macro quantities of reducing sugars, *J. Am. Chem. Soc.* **72**, 589–94 (1950).

63 Heidt, L. J., Southam, F. W., Benedict, J. D., Smith, M. E., Reducing powers of sugars under equivalent conditions in a carbonate buffered cupric tartrate micro reagent of low pH, *J. Am. Chem. Soc.* **71**, 2190–96 (1949).

64 Heidt, L. J., Moon, K. A., Stability of carbonated buffered cupritartrate reagents of low pH for estimated micro and macro quantities of reducing sugars, *J. Am. Chem. Soc.* **72**, 4130–35 (1950).

65 Hems, R., M.S. thesis, Fluorinated carbohydrates, University of Birmingham, Birmingham, England, 1966.

66 Hockett, R. C., Sheffield, E. L., Hexitol anhydrides, The preparation and proof of structure of 1,5,3,6-dianhydromannitol (neomannide), The structure of isomannide, *J. Am. Chem. Soc.* **68**, 937–39 (1946).

67 Hockett, R. C., Zief, M., Goepp, R. M., Hexitol anhydrides, The structure of the "2,5-Anhydromannitol" of Brigl and Grüner (2,5-anhydrosorbitol), *J. Am. Chem. Soc.* **68**, 935–37 (1946).

68 Hockett, R. C., Zief, M., Lead tetraacetate oxidations in the sugar group, XI, The oxidation of sucrose and preparation of glycerol and glycol, *J. Am. Chem. Soc.* **72**, 2130–32 (1950).

69 Hockett, R. C., Deulofeu, V., Deferrari, J. O., Mechanism of the formation of "aldose acetamides" in the reaction of acetylated aldonic acid nitriles with ammonia, *J. Am. Chem. Soc.* **72**, 1840–42 (1950).

70 Hockett, R. C., Miller, R. E., Scattergood, A., The preparation and proof of structure of 1,2:5,6-dicyclohexylidene-D-glucofuranose, *J. Am. Chem. Soc.* **71**, 3072–76 (1949).

71 Hockett, R. C., Collins, D. V., Scattergood, A., The preparation of 4,6-ethylidene-D-glucopyranose from sucrose and its hydrogenation to 4,6-ethylidene-D-sorbitol, *J. Am. Chem. Soc.* **73**, 599–601 (1951).

72 Hockett, R. C., Zief, M., Sulfonic acid esters of sucrose, *J. Am. Chem. Soc.* **72**, 1839–40 (1950).

73 Hough, L., Priddle, J. E., A bisglycerol tri-carbonate, *J. Chem. Soc.* **1961**, 581–84.

74 Hough, L., Priddle, J. E., Theobald, R. S., Carbohydrate carbonates, II, Their preparation by ester-exchange methods, *J. Chem. Soc.* **1962**, 1934–38.

75 Hough, L., Priddle, J. E., Carbonate derivatives of methyl 2-D-mannopyranoside and of D-mannose, *J. Chem. Soc.* **1961**, 3178–81.

76 Hough, L., Priddle, J. E., Cyclic carbonate derivatives of carbohydrates, *Chem. Ind.* **1959**, 1600–01.

77 Hough, L., Priddle, J. E., Theobald, R. S., Barker, G. R., Douglas, T., Spoors, J. W., The infrared spectra of some carbohydrate carbonates, *Chem. Ind.* **1960**, 148–49.

78 Howes, J. R., Lines, M. G., Wiggins, L. F., Studies on ammoniated molasses, III, Further work on the feeding of ammoniated cane molasses to livestock, *Proc. Brit. West Indies Sugar Technologists* **1955**, 103–08.

79 Isaac, P. C. G., Jenkins, D., Biological oxidations of sugar-based detergents, *Chem. Ind.* **1958**, 976–77.

80 Isaac, P. C. G., Jenkins, D., England, Biological breakdown of some newer synthetic detergents, Paper presented to Manhattan Conference on April 20, 1960.

81 Isaac, P. C. G., Jenkins, D., England, A laboratory investigation of the breakdown of some of the new synthetic detergents in sewage treatment, Paper presented at meeting of the Institute of Sewage Purification, Glasgow (Oct. 1959).

82 Jarvis, J. A., Ph.D. thesis, Some new ethers and acetals of sucrose, University of Birmingham, Edgbaston, England, 1962.

83 Jarvis, J. A., M.S. thesis, Some new sucrose acetals, University of Birmingham, Edgbaston, England, 1960.

84 Jefferies, R., Ph.D. thesis, Aspects of haloformate and cyclic acetal chemistry, University of Birmingham, Birmingham, England, 1964.

85 Jenkins, D., Sugar-based detergents and sewage treatment, University of Durham, England, *Dept. of Civil Eng. Bull.* 16.

86 Jex, V. B., M.A. thesis, The preparation of a cyanoethyl ether of glucose and related compounds, University of Utah, Salt Lake City, Utah, 1947.

87 Jex, V. B., Ph.D. thesis, Reactions of D-fructose, Massachusetts Institute of Technology, Cambridge, Mass., 1950.

88 Joblin, A. D. H., Thompson, A. F., Wiggins, L. F., Studies on ammoniated molasses, I, The production of ammoniated molasses, *Proc. Brit. West Indies Sugar Technologists* **1954**, 208–12.

89 Joblin, A. D. H., Howes, J. R., Wiggins, L. F., Studies on ammoniated molasses, II, Ammoniated inverted cane molasses as feed for ruminants, *Proc. Brit. West Indies Sugar Technologists* **1954**, 212–17.

90 Jones, B. D., Ph.D. thesis, Some new carbohydrate derivatives, University of Birmingham, Edgbaston, England, 1964.

91 Kononenko, O. K., A new adhesive for exterior plywood, Sugar Research Foundation, Inc., New York, 1962.

92 Kononenko, O. K., Herstein, K. M., Non-aqueous solvents for sucrose, *Chem. Eng. Data Ser.* **1**(1), 87–92 (1956).

93 Kononenko, O. K., Kestenbaum, I. L., Sucrose monoacetate, *J. Appl. Chem.* **11**, 7–10 (1961).

94 Le Maistre, J. W., Seymour, R. B., The reaction of sucrose with ethylene oxide, *J. Org. Chem.* **13**(5), 782–85 (1948).

95 Lemieux, R. U., Barrette, J. P., 3,6-Anhydro-2-D-galactopyranosyl 1,4:3,6-dianhydro-β-D-fructoside, A chemical proof of the configuration at the anomeric center of the fructose moiety of sucrose, *J. Am. Chem. Soc.* **80**, 2243–46 (1958).

96 Lemieux, R. U., Barrette, J. P., A chromatographic analysis of the product from the tritosylation of sucrose: crystalline 6,6'-di-O-tosylsucrose, *Can. J. Chem.* **38**, 656–62 (1960).

97 Lemieux, R. U., McInnes, A. G., The composition of the sucrose monomyristate prepared by transesterification, *Can. J. Chem.* **40**, 2394–401 (1962).

98 Lemieux, R. U., Nagarajan, R., The configuration and conformation of "Di-D-fructose anhydride I", *Can. J. Chem.* **42**, 1270–78 (1964).

99 Lemieux, R. U., McInnes, A. G., The preferential tosylation of the endo-5-hydroxyl group of 1,4:3,6-dianhydro-D-glucitol, *Can. J. Chem.* **38**, 136–40 (1960).

100 Lemieux, R. U., McInnes, A. G., The preparation of sucrose monoesters, *Can. J. Chem.* **40**, 2376–93 (1962).

101 Lemieux, R. U., Barrette, J. P., 1',2:3,6: 3'6'-trianhydrosucrose, *Can. J. Chem.* **37**, 1964–69 (1959).

102 Liston, A. J., The platinum-catalyzed oxidation of sucrose by oxygen, M.S. thesis, University of Ottawa, Ottawa, Ont., 1957.

103 McInnes, A. G., Ph.D. thesis, The preparation and structures of sucrose monoesters and the esterification of 1,4:3,6-dianhydro-D-glucitol, University of Ottawa, Ottawa, Ont., 1961.

104 McKeown, G. G., Serenius, R. S. E., Hayward, L. D., Selective substitution in sucrose, I, The synthesis of 1',4,6'-tri-O-methyl sucrose, *Can. J. Chem.* **35**(1), 28–36 (1957).

105 Marcy, W., Ph.D. thesis, Application of neighboring group theory in the chlorination of polyacetates, Massachusetts Institute of Technology, Cambridge, Mass., 1949.

106 Micich, T. J., Ph.D. thesis, The reductive aminolysis of carbohydrates, Pennsylvania State University, University Park, Pa., 1956.

107 Miller, R. E., Ph.D. thesis, Studies of D-glucose derivatives, Massachusetts Institute of Technology, Cambridge, Mass., 1949.

108 Mitra, A. K., Ball, D. H., Long, L., Methyl 2,6-di-O-methylsulfonyl-α-D-glucopyranoside and new syntheses of 3,4-di- and 3,4,6-tri-O-methyl-D-glucose, *J. Org. Chem.* **27**(1), 160–62 (1962).

109 Montgomery, R., Acidic constituents of lactic acid-water systems, *J. Am. Chem. Soc.* **74**, 1466–68 (1952).

110 Montgomery, R., The chemical production of lactic acid from sugars, Sugar Research Foundation, Inc., New York, *Scientific Report* 11, Jan. 1949.

111 Montgomery, R., Ronca, R. A., The chemical production of lactic and other acids from molasses, *Ind. Eng. Chem.* **45**, 1136–47 (1953).

112 Moon, K. A., Ph.D. thesis, Oxidation of carbohydrates by photoactivated uranyl ion in water, Massachusetts Institute of Technology, Cambridge, Mass., 1952.

113 Morris, F. E., Ph.D. thesis, The alcoholysis of sucrose and the synthesis of 3,5,6-tribenzoyl-D-glucofuranose and its oxidation with lead tetraacetate, Massachusetts Institute of Technology, Cambridge, Mass., 1945.

114 Nichols, P. L., Jr., Yanovsky, E., Allyl sucrose: a new industrial product, *Sugar* **42**, 28–29, 38 (Sept. 1947).

115 O'Connell, P. W., Stotz, E., Biological oxidation of phospholipids by rat liver homogenates, *Proc. Soc. Exp. Biol. Med.* **70**, 675–77 (1949).

116 Olson, L. E., M.S. thesis, The preparation of D-arabonic acid by the alkaline oxidation of invert sugar, University of Utah, Salt Lake City, Utah, 1947.

117 Osipow, L., Marra, D., Snell, F. D., Cosmetics containing sucrose esters, *Drug Cosmetic Ind.* **80**, 312–13, 396–97 (March 1957).

118 Osipow, L., Snell, F. D., Hickson, J. L., Interaction of sucrose monolaurate with other surface-active agents, *J. Am. Oil Chemists' Soc.* **35**(3), 127–29 (March 1958).

119 Osipow, L., Snell, F. D., York, W. C., Finchler, A., Methods of preparation of fatty acid esters of sucrose, *Ind. Eng. Chem.* **48**, 1459–62 (1956).

120 Osipow, L., Snell, F. D., The new sugar esters, *Intern. Sugar J.* **59**, 68–70 (March 1957).

121 Osipow, L., Snell, F. D., Ferencz, M., Stability of emulsions containing sucrose esters, *J. Am. Oil. Chemists' Soc.* **35**(3), 65–68 (1958).

122 Osipow, L., Snell, F. D., Finchler, A., Sugar esters, *J. Am. Oil Chemists' Soc.* **34**(4), 185–88 (1957).

123 Osipow, L., The sugar esters in cosmetics, *J. Soc. Cosmetic Chemists* **7**(5), 249–55 (1956).

127 Osipow, L., Snell, F. D., Marra, D., York, W. C., Surface activity of monoesters of fatty acid esters of sucrose, *Ind. Eng. Chem.* **48**, 1462–64 (1956); Sugar based detergents, *Soap Chem. Specialities* **32**, 57–60 (Dec. 1956).

125 Richardson, A. J., Ph.D. thesis, Part I, Behaviour of ketene toward alpha substituted hemiacetal derivatives, Part II, Dehydration of lactic acid derivatives, Northwestern University, Evanston, Ill., 1963.

126 Rohrman, F. A., Large scale production of levulose, *Sugar J.*, **13**(2), 10–11, 18 (July 1950).

127 Scattergood, A., Miller, W. H., Gammon, J., New aliphatic borates, *J. Am. Chem. Soc.* **67**, 2150–52 (1945).

128 Scattergood, A., MacLean, A. L., Some cyclic acetals of tris-(hydroxymethyl)-nitromethane and their derivatives, *J. Am. Chem. Soc.* **71**, 4153 (1949).

129 Scattergood, A., Hershenson, H. M., Some new glycol trichloracetates, *J. Am. Chem. Soc.* **72**, 2808 (1950).

130 Schwartz, A. M., Rader, C. A., Performance characteristics of sucrose ester detergents, *J. Am. Oil Chemists' Soc.* **42**, 800–04 (1965).

131 Schwartz, J. H., Talley, E. A., Zief, M., Fisher, C. H. (to United States of America), Ether-esters of polyhydroxy compounds, U.S. Patent 2,602,789 (July 8, 1952).

132 Sheffield, E. L., Ph.D. thesis, An investigation of the structure of certain dianhydromannitols, Massachusetts Institute of Technology, Cambridge, Mass., 1944.

133 Shu, P., Johnson, M. J., Citric acid production by submerged fermentation with *Aspergillus niger*, *Ind. Eng. Chem.* **40**, 1202–05 (1948).

134 Shu, P., Johnson, M. J., Effect of the composition of the sporulation medium on citric acid production by *Aspergillus niger* in submerged culture, *J. Bacteriol.* **54**(2), 161–67 (1947).

135 Shu, P., Johnson, M. J., The interdependence of medium constituents in citric acid production by submerged fermentation, *J. Bacteriol.* **56**(5), 577–85 (1948).

136 Singh, K., Agarwal, P. N., Peterson, W. H., The influence of aeration and agitation on the yield, protein and vitamin content of food yeasts, *Arch. Biochem.* **18**(1), 181–93 (1948).

137 Skell, P. S., Crist, J. G., A rapid gasometric method of analysis for "reducing" sugars and other carbonyl compounds, *Nature* **173**, 401 (1954).

138 Southam, F. W., M.S. thesis, Hydrolytes of sucrose by hydrochloric acid, Massachusetts Institute of Technology, Cambridge, Mass., 1949.

139 Sowden, J. C., Blair, M. G., Kuenne, D. J., The isomerization of C^{14}-labeled sugars to saccharinic acids, *J. Am. Chem. Soc.* **79**, 6450–54 (1957).

140 Spencer, R. E. E., M.S. thesis, Studies in the chemistry of D- and L-xylonic acids and their salts, Massachusetts Institute of Technology, Cambridge, Mass., 1948.

141 Sugar Research Foundation, Inc., The chemistry of preparation of sucrose esters for the ink, paint, and protective coating industries, New York, 1963.

142 Sugar Research Foundation, Inc., Engineering and pilot plant data for the commercial production of sucrose esters for the ink, paint, and protective coating industries, New York, 1963.

143 Sugar Research Foundation, Inc., Sucrose ester surfactants, Research report, New York, 1961.

144 Sugihara, J. M. (to Sugar Research Foundation, Inc.), Mercaptalation of sugar, U.S. Patent 2,563,884 (Aug. 14, 1951).

145 Sugihara, J. M., Ph.D. thesis, The reactions of mercaptans with sucrose and molasses, University of Utah, Salt Lake City, Utah, 1946.

146 Sullivan, E. A., M.S. thesis, Autocatalyzed hydrolysis of sucrose by acids, Massachusetts Institute of Technology, Cambridge, Mass., 1952.

147 Theobald, R. S., Carbonic esters of sucrose, Part I, The preparation of O-alkyloxycarbonylsucroses, *J. Chem. Soc.* **1961**, 5359–64.

148 Theobald, R. S., Carbonic esters of sucrose, Part II, The polymerization of O-alkyloxy-carbonylsucroses, *J. Chem. Soc.* **1961**, 5365–70.

149 Theobald, R. S., Carbonic esters of sucrose, Part III, The direct preparation of polysucrose carbonates from sucrose, *J. Chem. Soc.* **1961**, 5370–76.

150 Van Tassel, B. F., Ph.D. thesis, Synthesis of some α- and β-L-arabinopyranosides and the measurement of their rates and activation energies of hydrolysis in dilute hydrochloric acid, Massachusetts Institute of Technology, Cambridge, Mass., 1950.

151 Walsh, T. J., Bobalek, E. G., Hall, D. R., Preparation and characterization of unsaturated sucrose esters, *Absts. Div. of Org. Coatings Plastics Chem., Am. Chem. Soc.* **21**, 125 (1961).

152 Wheeler, T. E., Ph.D. thesis, A study of calcium and fat absorption using Ca^{45} and I^{131}-labeled fat, Georgetown University, Washington, D.C., 1958.

153 Wiggins, L. F., The ammoniation of molasses, *Proc. Ninth Congress Intern. Soc., Sugar Cane Technologists* **2**, 525–29 (1956).

154 Wiggins, L. F., Wise, W. S., Some preliminary observations on the nature of ammoniated molasses, *Chem. Ind.* **1955**, 656–57.

155 Wiggins, L. F., Some recent studies on ammoniated molasses, *Sugar J.* **18**, 18–20 (1956).

156 Winslow, A. E., Ph.D. thesis, Lead tetraacetate oxidation of α-D-glucopyranose-3,4,6-triacetate, and observations on the formation and reactions of intermediate compounds, Massachusetts Institute of Technology, Cambridge, Mass., 1947.

157 Witter, R. F., Snyder, J., Stotz, E., Colori-
metric determination of acetylacetone
and related β-diketones, *J. Biol. Chem.*
176, 493–500 (1948).

158 Witter, R. F., Stotz, E., Fat formation in
F. lycoperseci, Arch. Biochem. **9**(3), 331–
39 (1946).

159 Witter, R. F., Stotz, E., The metabolism *in
vitro* of triacetic acid and related diketones, *J. Biol. Chem.* **176**(2), 501–10
(1948).

160 Witter, R. F., Stotz, E., Synthesis and
properties of triacetic acid, *J. Biol. Chem.*
176(2), 485–92 (1948).

161 Wolfrom, M. L., Blair, M. G., Action of
heat on D-fructose, Isolation of dihetero-
levulosan and a new di-D-fructose dianhydride, *J. Am. Chem. Soc.* **70**, 2406–09
(1948).

162 Wolfrom, M. L., Binkley, W. W., Shilling, W. L. Hilton, H. W., Action of heat
on D-fructose II, Structure of dihetero-
levulosan II, *J. Am., Chem. Soc.* **73**, 3553–
57 (1951).

163 Wolfrom, M. L., Shilling, W. L., Action of
heat on D-fructose, III, Interconversion to
D-glucose, *J. Am. Chem. Soc.* **73**, 3557–
58 (1951).

164 Wolfrom, M. L., Hilton, H. W., Binkley,
W. W., A new di-D-fructose dianhydride,
J. Am. Chem. Soc. **74**, 2867–70 (1952).

165 Wrigley, A. N., Zief, M., Styrenation of
allyl-sucrose improves its properties as a
coating material, *Offic. Dig. Federation
Paint Varnish Prod. Clubs,* **1950**(303),
302–08.

166 York, W. C., Finchler, A., Osipow, L.
Snell, F. D., Structural studies on sucrose
monolaurate, *J. Am. Oil Chemists' Soc.*
33, 424–26 (1956).

167 Zief, M., Allylsucrose: a potential up-
grader for drying oils, *Offic. Dig. Federation Paint Varnish Prod. Clubs* **1949**(297),
711–15.

168 Zief, M., Yanovsky, E. (to United States
of America), Polymerization of polyallyl
and polymethallyl ethers of polyhydroxy
compounds, U.S. Patent 2,606,881 (Aug.
12, 1952).

169 Zief, M., Yanovsky, E., Preparation and
properties of allylsucrose, *Ind. Eng. Chem.*
41, 1697–700 (1949).

170 Zief, M., Yanovsky, E., Properties of
allylsucrose and allylsucrose coatings,
*U.S. Dept. Agr., Bur. Agr. Ind. Chem.,
Eastern Reg. Res. Lab.,* AIC-265 (March
1950).

171 Zief, M., Saturated esters of sucrose, *U.S.
Dept. Agr., Bur. Agr. Ind. Chem., Eastern
Reg. Res. Lab.,* AIC-309 (Sept. 1951).

172 Zief, M., Scattergood, A., The structure of
2,4:3,5-dimethylene-D-gluconic acid, *J.
Am. Chem. Soc.* **69**, 2132 (1947).

173 Zief, M., Unsaturated esters of sucrose,
J. Am. Chem. Soc. **72**, 1137–40 (1950).

174 Zief, M., Yanovsky, E. (to United States
of America), Unsaturated ether-esters of
polyhydric alcohols, U.S. Patent
2,541,142 (Feb. 13, 1951).

INTERNAL REPORTS

175 Pinkalla, H. A., American Bio-Synthetics
Corporation, Milwaukee, Wisc., Reports
on project 96, July 9, 1954–April 3, 1956.
(a) Jan. 3, 1955; (b) April 3, 1956.

176 Aries, R. S. and associates, New York,
Fermentation as a source of glycerine
with consideration of the 1948–50 outlook
and present situation, Sugar Research
Foundation, Member report 14, 1949.

(a) Digest of the final report on project 5
by Carl Neuberg of New York University
(in member report).

177 Aries, R. S., Copulsky, W., New York,
The commercial potential of levulinic acid
and related products produced from sucrose including 5-hydroxymethyl-furfural
and formic acid, Sugar Research Foundation, Member report 20, Nov. 1949.

178 Barnebey, H. L., Sucrose carbamates, laboratory and pilot plant preparation, Reports of project 98, 1953.

179 Billy, J. M., Lemieux, R. U., Ottawa University, Ottawa, Ont., Composition of sucrose monacetate, Report of project 88, Oct. 1956.

180 Overend, W. B., Birkbeck College, University of London, England, Reports of project 145. (a) Dec. 31, 1958; (b) Aug. 31, 1959.

181 Brimacombe, J. S., Birmingham University, Birmingham, England, Final research report on project 165, Oct. 15, 1965.

182 Birmingham University, Birmingham, England, Carbohydrate fluorides, Report 7 on project 183, May 1964.

183 Bjorksten Research Laboratories For Industry, Inc., Madison, Wisc., Reports of project 105. (a) Dec. 27, 1957; (b) Oct. 4, 1957; (c) July 10, 1957; (d) April 3, 1957; (e) Jan. 4, 1957; (f) Oct. 1, 1956; (g) July 3, 1956; (h) April 4, 1956; (i) Oct. 4, 1955; (j) Dec. 30, 1955; (k) Report on work from Jan. to June 1955.

184 Bjorksten Research Laboratories For Industry, Inc., Madison, Wisc., The reaction between sucrose, maleic anhydride, and pyridine, Summary report, Project 105, Feb. 1959.

185 Bjorksten Research Laboratories For Industry, Inc., Madison, Wisc., Screening program for utilization of sucrose in phenolic resins, Project 105, Project summary through March 1959. (For more details on application, see Application of JR-223, Section I and II.)

186 Black, W. A. P., A. D. Little Research Institute, Midlothian, Scotland, Quarterly reports on project 132. (a) 3 (Oct. 10, 1957); (b) 4 (Jan. 6, 1958); (c) 5 (April 15, 1958).

187 Blair, M. G., Sowden, J. C., Washington University, St. Louis, Mo., Reports of project 100, The isomerization of D-glucose to D- and L-sorbose by a strong base resin, Dec. 10, 1954; Summary of results Oct. 1, 1953–March 1, 1954 and April 1–June 30, 1954.

188 Boggs, A. D., Kazmaier, H. E., Battelle Memorial Institute, Columbus, Ohio, Synthesis of sucrose derivatives for evaluation as agricultural chemicals, Final report on project 160, June 30, 1958.

189 Bohn Food Research, Inc., Woodside, Long Island, Sucrose propylene oxide as bread softener, project 82, June 22, 1954.

190 Bohn Food Research, Inc., Woodside, Long Island, Letter to Kelly, N., of Sugar Information, Inc., Sucrose stearates as bread softeners, Report on project 83, Dec. 9, 1955.

191 Bourne, E. J., Royal Holloway College, University of London, England, Interim report of project 127, Dec. 9, 1960.

192 Brimacombe, E., Birmingham University, England, Progress reports on project 165, Nov. 1961, Jan. 1962, March 1962.

193 Hough, L., Bristol University, England, Reports of project 121. (a) Progress report 2, March 1957; (b) Progress report 4, Sept. 1957; (c) Progress report 5, Dec. 1957; (d) Progress report 8, Sept. 1958; (e) Progress report 9, Dec. 1958; (f) Quarterly report 11, June 1959; (g) Quarterly report 14, March 1960; (h) Quarterly report 15, June 1960; (i) Progress on plans listed for 1960–61; (j) Quarterly report 18, March 1961; (k) Influence of various factors upon alkali-stability of polymerized O-ethoxycarbonyl sucroses, May 8, 1961; (l) The preparation and polymerization of O-ethoxycarbonyl sucrose, June 16, 1961; (m) Interim report, July 1961; (n) Interim report, Aug. 1961; (o) Quarterly report 20, Sept. 1961; (p) Quarterly report 21, Dec. 1961; (q) Quarterly report 22, July 1962.

194 Hough, L., Bristol University, England, Quarterly reports of project 192. (a) Dec. 1962; (b) March 1963; (c) June 1963; (d) Oct. 1965; (e) Jan. 1966; (f) May 1966; (g) July 1966; (h) Sept. 1966; (i) Dec. 1966; (j) April 1, 1967; (k) Samples attached to structural formulas of bifunctional derivatives, 1966 (special report on project 192).

195 British Baking Industries Research Association. Baking Industries Research Station, Chorleywood, England, Sugar esters as crumb-softening agents in bread, Project 125, Dec. 18, 1958.

196 Reeder, J. A., British Columbia Research Council, Vancouver, B.C., Studies on the preparation of sodium sucrates, Reports of project 212. (a) 7 (Nov. 3, 1966); (b) 6 (July 6, 1966); (c) 5 (April 18, 1966); (d) 4 (Dec. 31, 1965); (e) 3 (Oct. 8, 1965); (f) 2 (July 7, 1965); (g) 1 (April 7, 1965); (h) Final report (Jan. 20, 1967).

197 Honeyman, J., Manchester, England, British Cotton Industry Research Association, Summary report of project 149, 1957–60, For details, see monthly reports.

198 Cahn, B. S., National Lead Co., New York, N.Y., Annual report, Project 85, Feb. 1, 1954.

199 Chang, C. D., Herstein Labs., New York, N.Y., Non-ester surfactants from sucrose, Summary report of project 150, 1959.

200 Silling, C. E., Com–Dev, Inc., Philadelphia, Pa., Report on project 198, March 26, 1963.

201 Silling, C. E., Com–Dev, Inc., Philadelphia, Pa., Drying oil sugar esters, Summary report on project 202, Dec. 12, 1963.

202 Silling, C. E., Com–Dev, Inc., Philadelphia, Pa., Sugar ester detergents, Summary reports on project 203, Jan. 17, 1964.

203 Crank, G. and co-workers, Queen's University, Kingston, Ont., Reports of project 143. (a) Oct.–Dec. 1959; (b) April–June 1960; (c) Aug. 1960; (d) Final monthly report, Jan. 6, 1961.

204 De Bell & Richardson, Inc. to Com–Dev, Inc., Hazardsville, Conn., Sucrose modified plywood resin, Project 198, April 29, 1963.

205 Degering, E. F., Purdue University, Lafayette, Ind., Carbohydrate oxidation studies, Sugar Research Foundation, Oct. 1950, Member report 23.

206 De Mendoza, A., Polymer Lab., Eng. Div., Case Institute of Technology, Cleveland, Ohio, A pilot plant process for manufacture of sucrose ester drying oils, Report of project 147, Oct. 10, 1961.

207 Dewar, E. T., A. D. Little Research Institute, Midlothian, Scotland, Review of literature on the preparation and reactions of alkali metal derivatives of carbohydrates, with particular reference to sucrose, Project 132, Dec. 1956.

208 Eades, E. D. M., Birmingham University, England, Reports on project 165, June–July 1963.

209 Schwarz, J. C. P., Edinburgh University, Scotland, Steric and electronic effects in carbohydrate chemistry, Summary of aims, Progress report for the first 18 months and future plans of project 185, May 1964. (See additional monthly and quarterly reports through May 1965.)

210 Evans Research and Development Corp., New York, N.Y., Investigation of possible eutectic mixtures of sucrose with other organic or inorganic materials, Progress report on project 189, April 30, 1963.

211 Finchler, A., Osipow, L., Foster D. Snell, Inc., New York, N.Y., Twenty-first quarterly report on synthetic detergents from sugar, Project 83, Jan. 31, 1958.

212 Flavell, W., Yarsley Research Laboratories, Ltd., Chessington, England, Letter to Jones, B. D., March 3, 1965, Attached to final research report on project 165 (165–10).

213 Foster, A. B., Birmingham University, Carbohydrate fluorides, Reports of project 183. (a) 4 Part I (Dec. 1962), 5 Part I (March 1963); (b) 6 Part I (July 1963).

214 Fox, A. L., Greenwood, Va., Reports on project 205. (a) Letters to Hickson, J. L., Nov. 9 and Nov. 27, 1964 (in report file); (b) Letter to Schwartz, A. M., of Harris Research Laboratories, Inc., Dec. 20, 1964 (in report file).

215 Guisley, K., Ruoff, P. M., Syracuse University, New York, Sulfation of sucrose, Report of project 130, July 1, 1957.

216 Hall, D. R., Case Institute of Technology, Cleveland, Ohio, Ninth monthly progress report, Project 147, April 1, 1960.

217 Harnden, M. R., Birmingham University, England, Progress reports on project 165. (a) July 1960; (b) Dec. 1960; (c) July 1961.

218 Harris Research Laboratories, Inc., Washington, D.C., Evaluation of sugar carbamate resins for textile applications, Final report, Reports of project 98, Mar. 30, 1954.

219 Schwartz, A. M., Rader, C. A., Harris Research Laboratories, Inc., Washington, D.C., Summary of detergency tests on sucrose esters and related compounds, Special report on project 205, Dec. 1, 1964.

220 Schwartz, A. M., Rader, C. A., Harris Research Laboratories, Inc., Washington, D.C., Progress reports on project 205. (a) 5 (Feb. 5, 1965); (b) 4 (Dec. 23, 1964); (c) 3 (Nov. 23, 1964); (d) 2 (Sept. 18, 1964); (e) 1 (July 27, 1964).

221 Hayward, L. D. and co-workers, University of British Columbia, Vancouver, Final report of project 101, Sept. 30, 1955. (a) The vinylation of D-mannitol; (b) Vinylation of sucrose.

222 Heggie, R. M., Lemieux, R. U., Ottawa University, Ottawa, Ont., The preparation of sulfur derivatives of sucrose, Progress reports of project 88, Third quarter 1954, Fourth quarter 1954, First quarter 1955. (See also previous reports.)

223 Herndon, L. K., Ohio State University, Columbus, Ohio, Engineering study of preparation of levulinic acid from sucrose, Sugar Research Foundation, Member report 21, Sept. 1950.

224 Herstein Laboratories, Inc., New York, N.Y., Reaction of sucrose with ethylene oxide, Project 82, Progress reports 14 and 15, April 3 and 17, 1953.

225 Herstein Laboratories, Inc., New York, N.Y., Reaction of ammonia with sugars, Project 82, Summary report on Project III, April 24, 1953.

226 Herstein Laboratories, Inc., New York, N.Y., Condensation of phenols with sugars, Project 82, Progress reports 1–4, Dec. 19, 1952–Jan. 16, 1953; 15–18, April 17–May 29, 1953.

227 Herstein Laboratories, Inc., New York, N.Y., Reaction of sucrose with alkylene oxide, Project 82, Progress reports 28–33, Dec. 31, 1953–March 26, 1954.

228 Herstein Laboratories, Inc., New York, N.Y., Sucrose carbamates, Progress reports on project 82. (a) 11–20 (March 6–Sept. 11, 1953); (b) 21–26 (Sept. 25–Dec. 4, 1953), (c) 28–39 (Dec. 31, 1953–June 18, 1954).

229 Herstein Laboratories, Inc., New York, N.Y., Miscellaneous reactions, Project 82, Progress report 43, Aug. 13, 1954.

230 Herstein Laboratories, Inc., New York, N.Y., Sucrose-linseed ester, Project 82, Progress report 42–46, July 30–Sept. 24, 1954.

231 Herstein Laboratories, Inc., New York, N.Y., Preparation of 2-methyl piperazine, Project 82, Nov. 8, 1954.

232 Herstein Laboratories, Inc., New York, N.Y., Cyanoethylation of sucrose, Project 82, Progress reports 43–51, Aug. 13–Dec. 3, 1954.

233 Herstein Laboratories, Inc., New York, N.Y., Di-trichloro-methyl-thiol sucrate, Project 82, Progress report 51, Dec. 3, 1954.

234 Herstein Laboratories, Inc., New York, N.Y., Polyamides from mixed piperazines, Project 82, Progress report (a) 58 (June 17, 1955); (b) 42 (July 30, 1954); (c) 35 (April 23, 1954); (d) 34 (April 9, 1954).

235 Herstein Laboratories, Inc., New York, N.Y., Condensation of sucrose with acrolein derivatives, Project 82, Progress report 60, Aug. 17, 1955.

236 Herstein Laboratories, Inc., New York, N.Y., *p*-Dodecylbenzyl sucrose, Project 82, Progress reports 60–65, Aug. 17, 1955–Jan. 17, 1956.

237 Herstein Laboratories, Inc., New York, N.Y., Carboxyalkylation and cyanoethylation of sucrose, Progress reports on Project 82. (a) 70 (June 15, 1956); (b) 67–68 (March 19–April 16, 1956); (c) 63 (Nov. 17, 1955); (d) 57 (May 18, 1955); (e) 56 (April 18, 1955); (f) 55 (March 17, 1955); (g) 54 (Feb. 17, 1955); (h) 52 (Dec. 17, 1954).

238 Herstein Laboratories, Inc., New York, N.Y., Trimethylsilyl derivatives of sucrose, Project 82, Progress report (a) 80 (July 31, 1957); (b) 79 (June 28, 1957).

239 Herstein Laboratories, Inc., New York, N.Y., Reductive aminolysis of levulinic acid, Project 82, Progress report 84–86 Jan. 31–March 31, 1958.

240 Herstein Laboratories, Inc., New York, N.Y., Reductive aminolysis of sucrose, Project 82, Progress report 86–87, March 31–May 1, 1958.

241 Herstein Laboratories, Inc., New York, N.Y., Polymerization of reductive aminolysis products, Project 82, Progress report (a) 91 (Aug. 29, 1958); (b) 86–87 (March 31–May 1, 1958).

242 Herstein Laboratories, Inc., New York, N.Y., Preparation of sucrose monoacetate, Project 82, April 17, 1959.

243 Herstein Laboratories, Inc., New York, N.Y., Sodium sucrates, Project 82, Progress report (a) 101–03 (June 30–Aug. 31, 1959); (c) 98–100 (March 31–May 29, 1959); (d) 48–52 (Oct. 22–Dec. 17, 1954); (e) 53 (Jan. 17, 1955).

244 Herstein Laboratories, Inc., New York, N.Y., Utilization of high boiling amines from reductive aminolysis of sucrose, Project 82, Progress report 104–106, Sept. 30–Nov. 30, 1959.

245 Herstein Laboratories, Inc., New York, N.Y., Reports on project 82, Monthly progress reports on sucrose esters 1955–60; Preparation of sucrose esters, Nov. 29, 1958; Special progress report on sucrose esters 1958; Selected references in monthly progress reports (a) 116 (Sept. 30, 1960), 118 (Nov. 30, 1960); (b) 115 (Aug. 31, 1960); (c) 114 (July 30, 1960); (d) 113 (June 30, 1960); (e) 112 (May 31, 1960); (f) 106 (Nov. 30, 1959); (g) 105 (Oct. 30, 1959); (h) 104 (Sept. 30, 1959); (i) 110–111 (March 31, April 29, 1960); (j) 98 (March 31, 1959); (k) 97 (Feb. 28, 1959); (l) 70 (June 15, 1956).

246 Herstein Laboratories, Inc., New York, N.Y., Reaction of sucrose with epoxides, Project 82, Progress reports (a) 113–14 (June 30–July 30, 1960), 116 (Sept. 30, 1960), 118–21 (Nov. 30, 1960–Feb. 28, 1961); (b) 91 (Aug. 29, 1958).

247 Herstein Laboratories, Inc., New York, N.Y., Mixed esters of sucrose, Project 82, Progress report (a) 71–74 (Nov. 1, 1956– Jan. 31, 1957); 122 (March 31, 1961), 130 (Nov. 31, 1961); (b) 79 (June 28, 1957); (c) 77 (April 30, 1957).

248 Herstein Laboratories, Inc., New York, N.Y., Allylsucrose, Project 82, Progress reports 119-140, Dec. 29, 1960–Sept. 28, 1962. (a) 137 (June 29, 1962).

249 Herstein Laboratories, Inc., New York, N.Y., Evaluation of Sharples sucrose carbamate resins, Reports of project 98, Aug. 27, 1953.

250 Hickson, J. L., Sugar Research Foundation, Inc., New York, N.Y., memorandum to Hass, H. B., Visit to North Carolina State College, Report on project 83, June 22, 1956.

251 Hickson, J. L., Sugar Research Foundation, Inc., New York, N.Y., Memorandum on visit to Food & Drug Administration, Report on project 83, March 27, 1957.

252 Hockett, R. C., and co-workers, Lead tetraacetate as a tool for sugar research (a collection of fourteen research papers), New York, Sugar Research Foundation, March 1948, Member report 1.

253 Hurd, C. D., Richardson, A. J., Northwestern University, Evanston, Ill., Final report on project 90, Jan. 28, 1963.

254 Isaac, P. C. G., Jenkins, D., University of Durham, Newcastle, England, An investigation of the biological breakdown of sucrose esters, Final report on project 134, Oct. 1959.

255 Jones, J. K. N., Queen's University, Kingston, Ont., Reports of project 143. (a) Sucrose sulfates, Received July 7, 1958; (b) Sucrose sulfates, Oct. 1, 1958 and Jan. 6, 1959; (c) Ionic replaceable groups of sucrose, March 26, 1959 and report on work ending June 30, 1959; (d) Feb. 1960; (e) April 1960.

256 Jones, B. D., Birmingham University, England, Reports on project 165. (a) Summary of work carried out since Oct. 15, Jan. 15, 1965; (b) Feb. 1965.

257 Kollman, R. C., Schlauch, W. C., National Lead Co., New York, N.Y., Evaluation of sucrose linseed oil fatty acid octaester, Final report, Project 85 (no date).

258 Kononenko, O. K., Herstein Labs., Inc., Boontown, N.J., Reductive aminolysis of sucrose, Final report of project 155, 1967.

259 Kononenko, O. K., Herstein Labs., Inc., Boontown, N.J., Sucrose phenolic resin adhesives for plywood, Project 170, 2 reports, 1962. (For additional tests on uses, see project 82, progress reports 108–10, Jan. 29–March 31, 1960.)

260 Lemieux, R. U. and co-workers, Ottawa University, Ottawa, Ont., Progress reports of project 88. (a) Esterification and oxidation of sucrose, Sept. 30–Dec. 30. 1955; (b) Esterification and oxidation of sucrose, Jan. 9, April 9, July 6, and Oct. 1957, (see also former progress reports); (c) Esterification and oxidation of sucrose, Oct. 1957; (d) Esterification of sucrose, March–July, 1959; (e) Preparation of sucrose monoesters, Special report, May 31, 1961.

261 Lemieux, R. U., Nagarjan, N., University of Alberta, Edmonton, Progress report on project 180. (a) July 1–Sept. 30, 1961; (b) Jan. 1–June 30, 1962.

262 Little Research Institute, Arthur D., Quarterly report 1 of project 132, March 5, 1957.

263 Lominska, C. A., National Lead Co., New York, N.Y., Sucrose linseed octaester, Project 85, Progress reports (a) 1 (Aug. 19, 1955); (b) 2 (April 4, 1956); (c) 3 (Aug. 30, 1957).

264 Long, L., Jr., Quartermaster Research and Engineering Command, U.S. Army, Natick, Mass., Bifunctional derivatives of sugar, Final report of project 141, July 31, 1959.

265 Micich, T. J., Pennsylvania State University, University Park, Pa., Research report of project 86. (a) Feb. 2, 1956; (b) Nov. 1, 1955.

266 Montgomery, R., Eastern Regional Research Development Lab., U.S.D.A., Philadelphia, Pa., The chemical production of lactic and other acids from molasses, Sugar Research Foundation, Member reports 26 (1951) and 31 (1952).

267 Needle, H. C., Aries, R. S., New York, N.Y., Lactic acid and lactates, Sugar Research Foundation, Member report 7, Aug. 1948.

268 Olson, L. E., University of Utah, Salt Lake City, Utah, The preparation of D-arabonic acid by alkaline oxidation of invert sugar and molasses, Sugar Research Foundation, Member report 33, Dec. 1952.

269 Overberger, C. G., Takekoshi, T., Polytechnic Institute of Brooklyn, N.Y., Quarterly reports of project 193. (a) Sept. 1965; (b) June 1965; (c) March 1965; (d) Dec. 1964; (e) Sept. 1964; (f) June 1964; (g) March 1964; (h) Dec. 1963.

270 Skell, P. S., Pennsylvania State University, University Park, Pa., Annual report summary for project 86, 1954–55.

271 Price, H. A., Degering, E. F., Purdue University, Lafayette, Ind., Progress reports on project 34. (a) 7 (March 15–April 15, 1947); (b) 1–6 (Sept. 15, 1946–March 15, 1947).

272 Jones, J. K. N., Queen's University, Kingston, Ontario, Reports of project 143. (a) Sugar sulfates, Jan. 16, 1958; (b) Oct. 1960; (c) March 13, 1961; (d) Structural studies on the product of sucrose-sulfuryl chloride reaction, Sept. 18, 1961; (e) Hydroxyl replacement reactions of sucrose, Final report Aug. 1962.

273 Rader, C. A., Harris Research Laboratories, Washington, D.C., Correspondence on project 206, Aug. 20, 1965.

274 Redfern, G. L., Yarsley Research Laboratories, Ltd., Chessington, England, Sugar-modified melamine resins for textile applications, Final report on project 209, May 27, 1966.

275 Rohrman, F. A., Woodward, R. E., Stuewe, D. A., University of Colorado, Boulder, Colo., The pilot plant production of levulose (D-fructose), Sugar Research Foundation, Member report 29, Dec. 1951.

276 Bourne, E. J., Royal Holloway College, University of London, Englefield Green, England, A study of the effects of sucrose esters and other antistaling agents on starch, Final report on project 125.

277 Bourne, E. J., Royal Holloway College, University of London, Englefield Green, England, Preparation and proof of structures of carboxymethyl sucroses and their chelating power for metallic ions in solution, Final report of project 126, 1958.

278 Bourne, E. J., Royal Holloway College, University of London, Englefield Green, England, Reports to project 127 (a) Quarterly, June 30, 1961; (b) Quarterly, Dec. 31, 1961; (c) Monthly, May 31, 1962.

279 Bourne, E. J., Royal Holloway College, University of London, Englefield Green, England, Final report of project 160, 1961.

280 Bourne, E. J., Royal Holloway College, University of London, Englefield Green, England, Cyclic acetals of sucrose, Final report on project 159 and part of 161, Nov. 1959.

281 Bourne, E. J., Royal Holloway College, University of London, Englefield Green, England, Final report to project 161, June 1960.

282 Ruoff, P. M., Syracuse University, New York, N.Y., Letter to Phillips, R. F., Correspondence on project 63, Dec. 22, 1950.

283 Ruoff, P. M., Syracuse University, Syracuse, N.Y., Reports of project 130. (a) June 22, 1957; (b) June 16, 1958.

284 Schneider, P., New York University, New York, N.Y., Letter to Hickson, J. L., Report file of project 196, Feb. 8, 1963.

285 Schneider, P., New York University, New York, N.Y., Progress reports on project 196. (a) 15 (Jan. 1–Feb. 29, 1964); (b) 14 (Dec. 1963); (c) 13 (Nov. 1963); (d) 12 (Oct. 1963); (e) 11 (Sept. 1963); (f) 10 (Aug. 1963); (g) 9 (July 1963); (h) 8 (June 1963); (i) 7 (May 1963); (j) 6 (April 1963); (k) 5 (March 1963); (l) 4 (Feb. 1963); (m) 3 (Jan. 1963); (n) 2 (Dec. 1962); (o) 1 (Nov. 1962).

286 Schnitzer, H. S., De Bell & Richardson, Inc., Hazardville, Conn., to Silling, C. E., Com–Dev, Inc., Correspondence Nov. 4, 1964 (attached to letter from Silling, C. E. to Hickson, J. L., Nov. 10, 1964), Modification of product and production of sucrose linoleate, Project 202.

287 Serenius, R. S. E., Hayward, L. D., University of British Columbia, Vancouver, B.C., Vinylation of sucrose, Quarterly report 3 of project 101, June 30, 1954.

288 Seymour, R. B., LeMaistre, J. W., University of Chattanooga, Chattanooga, Tenn., Reaction of sucrose with ethylene oxide, Sugar Research Foundation, Member report 10, 1948.

289 Skell, P. S., Pennsylvania State University, University Park, Pa., Summary report on reductive aminolysis, Project 86, Dec. 6, 1958.

290 Snell, Foster D., Inc., New York, N.Y., Quarterly reports on synthetic detergents from sugar on project 83. (a) Thirteenth report, Jan. 18, 1956; (b) Fourteenth report, April 26, 1956; (c) Fifteenth report, July 16, 1956; (d) Sixth report, April 19, 1954; (e) Seventh report, July 21, 1954; (f) Eighth report, Oct. 7, 1954; (g) First quarterly report, Jan. 9, 1953; (h) Second report, April 28, 1953; (k) Third report, July 13, 1953; (m) Fourth report, Oct. 7, 1953; (n) Fifth report, Jan. 22, 1954.

291 Snell, Foster D., Inc., New York, N.Y., Reports on project 83. (a) Results of the preliminary rat feeding program with sucrose monostearate, June 9, 1955; (b) Chronic toxicity testing with sucrose stearate, Feb. 14, 1957.

292 Snell, Foster D., Inc., New York, N.Y., Evaluation of monododecyl sulfonyl sucrose, Report of project 151, June 8, 1959.

293 Chambers, H. H., Sondes Place Research Laboratories, Ltd., Sondes Place, England, Summary report on pilot plant development of reductive aminolysis of sugar, Project 131, July 29, 1959.

294 Chambers, H. H., Sondes Place Research Laboratories, Ltd., Sondes Place, England, Evaluation tests on sucrose polymers, Project 171, Progress report (a) 1 (March 3, 1961); (b) 2 (May 12, 1961); (c) 3 (Oct. 19, 1961); (d) 4 (Jan. 26, 1962); (e) Report (May 8, 1961).

295 Flynn, J. M., Suffolk County Department of Health, Riverhead, N.Y., Preliminary conclusions, site 2 of the Long Island ground water pollution study, Report on project 206, April 20, 1966.

296 Bourne, E. J., Royal Holloway College, Englefield Green, England, Research proposal to project 160, Jan. 15, 1959.

297 Swenson, A. D., University of Utah, Salt Lake City, Utah, Sucrose esters, Report on project 25, (no date).

298 Szmant, H. H., University of Puerto Rico, San Juan, Puerto Rico, Deoxychloro-sucroses, Quarterly reports on project 157. (a) Jan. 12, 1959; (b) May 18, 1959; (c) July 15 and Sept. 15, 1959; (d) Jan. 1, 1960; (e) April 15, 1960.

299 Tischler, N., Massachusetts Institute of Technology, Cambridge, Mass., Reports of project 42. (a) Jan. 27, 1947; (b) June 29, 1947; (c) July 5, 1947; (d) July 20, 1947.

300 Tongaat Sugar Co., Ltd., Maidstone, Natal, South Africa, Precipitation of low concentrations of wheat starch with sucrose monostearate in the presence of a high concentration of sucrose, Project 125, March 13, 1959.

301 Turner, D. A., Sinai Hospital, Baltimore, Md., The use and effect of sucrose fatty acid esters in dogs and men, Report on project 109, March 25, 1957.

302 Wiggins, L. F., Birmingham University, England, The preparation of levulinic acid from sugar, Sugar Research Foundation, Member report 2, 1948.

303 Derse, P. H., Wisconsin Alumni Research Foundation, Madison, Wisc., Assay reports, Project 136. (a) Jan. 17, 1958; (b) Feb. 10, 1958.

304 Wrigley, A. N., Mast, W. C., Eastern Regional Research and Development Laboratory, U.S.D.A., Philadelphia, Pa., Joint project report for August 1948 (Sept. 31, 1948), Report on project 40.

305 Yanovsky, E., Eastern Regional Research and Development Laboratory, U.S.D.A., Philadelphia, Pa., Unsaturated derivatives of carbohydrates, Reports on Project 40, Sept. 7, 1949.

306 Flavell, W., Yarsley Research Laboratories, Ltd., Chessington, England, The reaction of sucrose with heavy metal oxides and related compounds, Abbreviated final report on project 181, July 19, 1962.

307 Flavell, W., Yarsley Research Laboratories, Ltd., Chessington, England, Invert and other sugars as extenders in melamine-formaldehyde resins, Final report on project 182, Oct. 8, 1963. (a) Part 1. Invert sugar in molding materials; (b) Part 2. Invert sugar and sucrose in decorative laminates; (c) Part 3. Invert sugar in surface coatings.

308 Zief, M., Eastern Regional Research and Development Laboratory, U.S.D.A., Philadelphia, Pa., Report on project 40, March 13, 1947.

309 Zief, M., Eastern Regional Research and Development Laboratory, U.S.D.A., Philadelphia, Pa., Preparation and properties of allyl-sucrose, Sugar Research Foundation, Member report 5, 1948.

310 Zief, M., Eastern Regional Research and Development Laboratory, U.S.D.A., Philadelphia, Pa., Preparation, properties and applications of allylsucrose, Sugar Research Foundation (with supplement), Member report 30, April 1952.

311 Zemplen, G., Georgetown University, Washington, D.C., Reports on project 46, (a) June 1947; (b) Letter to Hockett, R. C., Aug. 6, 1947 (in report file).

Author Index

Numbers refer to references under Bibliography

Agarwal, P. N., 1, 2, 136
Ames, J. B., 3
Angus, H. J. F., 4, 5, 6
Aries, R. S., 176, 177, 267
Arni, P. C., 7

Ball, D. H., 108
Barasch, W., 8
Barker, G. R., 77
Barker, S. A., 9, 10, 11
Barnebey, H. L., 178
Barrette, J. P., 12, 95, 96, 101
Benedict, J. D., 13, 63
Bernsten, R. A., 14
Berry, J. F., 15
Billy, J. M., 16, 179
Binkley, W. W., 162, 164
Black, W. A. P., 7, 17, 18, 19, 186
Blair, M. G., 139, 161, 187
Bobalek, E. G., 20, 21, 22, 23, 151
Boggs, A. D., 188
Bohn Food Research, Inc., 189, 190
Bonner, T. G., 24, 25, 26
Bourne, E. J., 4, 6, 24, 25, 26, 27, 28, 29, 30, 31, 32, 33, 34, 191, 276, 277, 278, 279, 280, 281, 296
Bragg, P. D., 35, 36
Brimacombe, E., 192
Brimacombe, J. S., 9, 10, 11, 181
British Baking Industries, 195
Brown, A. E., 218
Buch, M. L., 37

Cahn, B. S., 198
Causa, A. G., 22, 23, 38
Chambers, H. H., 293, 294
Chang, C. D., 39, 40, 41, 199
Chang, W. S., 42
Chiang, H. H., 20, 43
Collins, D. V., 44, 71
Collings, W. J., 23
Colman, C. M., 60
Connors, W. M., 45
Copulsky, W., 177
Cox, R. P., 183, 184, 185
Crank, G., 46, 203
Crist, J. G., 137

De Bell & Richardson, 204
Deferrari, J. O., 69
Degering, E. F., 205, 271
De Mendoza, A. P., 21, 22, 23, 47, 206
Derse, P. H., 303
Deulofeu, V., 69
Dewar, E. T., 7, 17, 18, 19, 207
Docal, G. C., 48, 49
Douglas, T., 77

Eades, E. D. M., 208
Edwards, P. W., 51
Evans Research & Development, 210

Ferencz, M., 121
Finchler, A., 119, 122, 166, 211
Fisher, C. H., 50, 131
Flavell, W., 212, 306, 307

Flynn, J. M., 295
Foster, A. B., 182, 213
Fox, A. L., 214
Franklin, R. E., Jr., 39

Gammon, J., 127
Goepp, R. M., 67
Griffin, E. L., Jr., 51
Guisley, K., 215

Hall, D. R., 151, 216
Hall, L. D., 53
Harnden, M. R., 9, 11, 54, 55, 217
Harwood, S. E., 25
Hass, H. B., 41, 56, 57, 58, 59
Hayward, L. D., 104, 221, 287
Heggie, R. M., 222
Heidt L. J. 60, 61, 62, 63, 64
Hems, R., 65
Herndon, L. K., 223
Hershenson, H. M., 129
Herstein, K. M., 92
Herstein Laboratories, Inc., 224, 225, 226, 227,
    228, 229, 230, 231, 232, 233, 234, 235, 236,
    237, 238, 239, 240, 241, 242, 243, 244, 245,
    246, 247, 248, 249
Hickson, J. L., 118, 250, 251
Hilton, H. W., 164
Hockett, R. C., 50, 66, 67, 68, 69, 70, 71, 72,
    252
Honeyman, J., 199
Hough, L., 53, 73, 74, 75, 76, 77, 193, 194
Howes, J. R., 78, 89
Hurd, C. D., 253
Hutson. D. H., 27, 32, 33, 34

Issac, P. C. G., 79, 80, 81, 254

Jarvis, J. A., 10, 11, 82, 83
Jefferies, R., 84
Jenkins, D., 79, 80, 81, 85, 254
Jex, V. B., 86, 87
Joblin, A. D. H., 88, 89
Jones, B. D., 90, 256
Jones, J. K. N., 35, 36, 255, 272
Johnson, M. J., 133, 134, 135

Kapo, G., 23
Kazmaier, H. E., 188
Kestenbaum, I. L., 93
Kollman, R. C., 257

Kononenko, O. K., 39, 40, 91, 92, 93, 258, 259
Kuenne, D. J., 139

Le Maistre, J. W., 94, 288
Lemieux, R. U., 95, 96, 97, 98, 99, 100, 101,
    179, 222, 260, 261
Lewis, D., 24, 25
Lines, M. G., 78
Liston, A. J., 102
Little Research Institute, Arthur D., 262
Lominska, C. A., 263
Long, L., Jr., 108, 264

MacLean, A. L., 128
Marcy, W., 105
Marra, D., 117, 124
Mast, W. C., 304
McInnes, A. G., 97, 99, 100, 103
McKeown, G. G., 104
Micich, T. J., 106, 265
Miller, R. E., 70, 107
Miller, W. H., 127
Mitra, A. K., 108
Montgomery, R., 37, 109, 110, 111, 266
Moon, K. A., 61, 64, 112
Morris, F. E., 113

Nagarajan, R., 98, 261
Needle, H. C., 267
Nery, E. J., 31
Nichols, P. L., Jr., 114

O'Connell, P. W., 115
Olson, L. E., 116, 268
Osipow, L. I., 56, 58, 117, 118, 119, 120, 121,
    122, 123, 124, 166, 211
Overberger, C. G., 269
Overend, W. G., 180

Paterson, J. C., 17
Peterson, W. H., 1, 2, 42, 136
Pinkalla, H. A., 175
Porter, W. L., 37
Price, H. A., 271
Priddle, J. E., 73, 74, 75, 76, 77

Rader, C. A., 130, 219, 220, 273
Redfearn, G. L., 274
Redfield, C. S., 51
Reeder, J. A., 196
Richardson, A. J., 125, 253

Rohrman, F. A., 126, 275
Ronca, R. A., 111
Ruoff, P. M., 215, 282, 283
Ruszkiewicz, M., 26
Rutherford, D., 17, 18

Scattergood, A., 70, 71, 127, 128, 129, 172
Schlauch, W. C., 257
Schneider, P., 284, 285
Schnitzer, H. S., 286
Schwartz, A. M., 130, 219, 220
Schwartz, J. H., 131
Schwarz, J. C. P., 209
Searle, F., 4
Serenius, R. S. E., 104, 287
Seymour, R. B., 94, 288
Sheffield, E. L., 66, 132
Shilling, W. L., 162, 163
Shu, P., 133, 134, 135
Silling, C. E., 200, 201, 202
Singh, K., 2, 136
Sinnamon, H. I., 51
Skell, P. S., 59, 137, 270, 289
Smith, M. E., 63
Snell, F. D., 56, 58, 117, 118, 119, 120, 121, 122, 124, 166
Snell, Foster D., Inc., 290, 291, 292
Snyder, J., 157
Southam, F. W., 62, 63, 138
Sowden, J. C., 139, 187
Spencer, R. E. E., 140
Spoors, J. W., 77
Stotz, E., 45, 115, 157, 158, 159, 160
Stuewe, D. A., 275
Sugar Research Foundation, Inc., 141, 142, 143

Sugihara, J. M., 144, 145
Sullivan, E. A., 146
Swenson, A. D., 297
Szmant, H. H., 298

Takekoshi, T., 269
Talley, E. A., 131
Theobald, R. S., 74, 77, 147, 148, 149
Thompson, A. F., 88
Tiffin, A. I., 28, 29, 30
Tischler, N., 299
Tongaat Sugar Co., Ltd., 300
Turner, D. A., 15, 301
Turner, J. C., 36

Van Tassel, B. F., 150

Walsh, T. J., 20, 151
Weigel, H., 4, 5, 6, 27, 30, 31, 32, 33, 34
Wheeler, T. E., 152
Wiggins, L. F., 78, 88, 89, 153, 154, 155, 302
Willard, M. H., Jr., 51
Williams, J. M., 10
Winslow, A. E., 156
Wise, W. S., 154
Witter, R. F., 157, 158, 159, 160
Wolfrom, M. L., 161, 162, 163, 164
Woodward, R. E., 275
Wrigley, A. N., 165, 304

Yanovsky, E., 114, 168, 169, 170, 174, 305
York, W. C., 56, 58, 119, 124, 166

Zemplen, G., 311
Zief, M., 50, 67, 68, 72, 131, 165, 167, 168, 169, 170, 171, 172, 173, 174, 308, 309, 310